METHUEN'S MONOGRAPHS ON BIOLOGICAL SUBJECTS

General Editor: KENNETH MELLANBY

THE PHYSIOLOGY OF INSECT SENSES

The Physiology of Insect Senses

V. G. DETHIER
Professor of Zoology and Psychology
University of Pennsylvania

London: METHUEN & CO. LTD
New York: JOHN WILEY & SONS INC

First published in 1963

Printed in Great Britain by
Richard Clay & Company, Limited
Bungay, Suffolk
Catalogue No. 2/4125/11

Contents

Preface

Thirty years have elapsed since the appearance of Eltringham's *The Senses of Insects* (first published 1933 in this series). In the intervening time our knowledge of sensory physiology has advanced further than during any previous period of study. The augmented and accelerated advance may be attributed to new technological developments and a notable increase in the number of research workers interested in insects for their own sake or as material uniquely suited to the solution of one or another basic biological problem.

The two most powerful modern tools placed at the disposal of the sensory physiologist are electronic apparatus for detecting electrical events in nerve tissue and the electron-microscope. The first has been responsible for removing from the realm of mystery the function of so-called Type II neurons in insects, for confirming the facts that campaniform sensilla are mechano- rather than olfactory receptors, and for initiating the unravelling of the multitude of events that occur as a part of vision. Electric recording from neural tissue has greatly expanded our rather conservative estimation of sense organs in general.

Developments in the field of electronics has not, however, rendered the behavioural approach to sensory physiology obsolete. In fact, experiments in behaviour not infrequently point the direction that electrophysiological research should follow. Two cases in point are the studies of the tympanic organ of moths and of the chemoreceptors of flies. Without behavioural correlates the electrophysiological findings are of small value.

Just as behavioural studies have engendered electrophysiological experiments, these in turn have driven the physiologist back to structure. Whereas in many instances conventional histology has been extended to its limit, in others it has barely scratched the surface, and large areas of the nervous system are still empty areas whose only detail is the notation 'unexplored'. Where light microscopy has reached the limit of resolution, the electron-microscope has opened up vast new areas of investigation and stimulated additional electrophysiological studies, which in turn have posed new behavioural questions to bring the endeavour full turn.

We are in the midst, therefore, of a revolution in sensory physiology. There is no better evidence for this than the high element of controversy that flourishes in many areas indicating that exploration is still in its early stages. This state of affairs is best illustrated by the controversies in photoreception. The final verdict is by no means rendered. In many cases our knowledge is still in a state of flux. While every effort has been made in this book to present both sides of questions, a personal bias has been applied. This bias is fashioned by an appraisal of how well the antagonists have presented their cases in the literature.

Recent advances in the physiology of the insect sensory system have proceeded at such a pace that it is impossible to refer to every published report. In the field of sound reception alone there are over 2,000 articles. For all phases of this book, about 2,000 references *in toto* have been examined. Of these, about 700 have been selected for listing, but the accumulated knowledge of others has been built upon freely. For the reader interested in the older literature, the works of Demoll and von Buddenbrock should be consulted. For all purposes, the works of Wigglesworth and Roeder are invaluable. Where possible, references have been made to reviews rather than to the multitudes of individual papers. Where an investigator has published a series of papers on a given subject, only the most recent has been quoted unless an earlier paper is germane to some particular point. During the period of preparation of this book insect physiologists have not been idle. The most recent papers have probably been treated somewhat cavalierly, since a running revision is hardly feasible, but at the very least they are included in the references to assist the reader in pursuing the matter himself.

The segment of knowledge represented by this book has been rather narrowly circumscribed, a circumstance dictated by the enormous volume of literature but ameliorated by the fact that other excellent volumes exist to fill the lacunae. The subject matter has been 'sensory physiology'; behaviour, as such, has been neglected. It is well represented, however, by Carthy's fine book, by Roeder, by Wigglesworth, and by von Buddenbrock. Also, I have not ventured farther into the central nervous system than the lamina ganglionaris of the optic lobes, partly because I have been interested primarily in sensory input and the interaction of sense organs and their environment and possibly because one naturally hesitates to venture far into an unexplored jungle. And finally, the temperature sense has been completely neglected. This, in part, merely reflects the neglect that it has received at the hands of research investigators. There is considerable literature on the behavioural aspects of temperature sensitivity, little of value on the physiological aspects.

The co-operation and courtesy of a number of persons and organizations has been invaluable in the preparation of this book. Paul B. Hoeber, Inc. has granted permission to reprint sections of Chapter II which formerly appeared in *Roots of Behavior*, edited by E. L. Bliss. Similarly, the Society for Experimental Biology has granted permission to reprint sections of Chapter V which appeared in Symposium No. 16 of the Society for Experimental Biology. Figs. 17, 18, 21, and 25 were supplied through the courtesy of M. L. Wolbarsht; Figs. 40 and 41, through the courtesy of O. Lowenstein and L. H. Finlayson; Figs. 56, 65, 66, and Pl. I, through the courtesy of K. D. Roeder and A. E. Treat; Pl. III, through the courtesy of J. R. Adams. Peter G. Walsh has assisted in the preparation of illustrations. To all of these I express my sincere gratitude.

V. G. DETHIER

E. Blue Hill, Maine
June 1962

CHAPTER I

Introduction

The gross characteristics of the planet earth are the same for all living things inhabiting it. It has a characteristic gravitational field; it receives radiant energy from outer space to the extent determined by the filtering properties of its atmosphere; it is built of specific kinds of chemical compounds in certain quantitative relationships. The details of these properties differ from place to place on the planet. Some are more conducive to animal life than others, and the uneven distribution of animals in the biosphere is a measure of this and of the adjustments that various forms of life have made to the details. To regulate their relations with the earth's environment, animals have evolved sensing devices for detecting such details as are of direct adaptive value.

Since we 'see' the world with our own particular sensing devices, it is difficult to understand fully how other animals 'see' it. What picture of the details of the world is perceived by the bee that sees in the ultraviolet, the snake that is deaf to air-borne sounds but detects infra-red, the shrew that cannot see colour, the electric fish that detects changes in the electric field about it? To appreciate these points of view, let alone understand the manner in which all biological sensing devices work, it is helpful to look first at the world, not at the level of detail perceived by us but at a level that we cannot perceive directly, the elementary particles whose interactions and combinations form the universe.

Of the thirty or so kinds of particles that make up earth or come to it from outer space, the only stable ones are protons, neutrons, neutrinos, electrons, and photons (Ruderman and Rosenfeld, 1960). Some of these (e.g., photons, neutrinos) occur free; others, usually combined into atoms and molecules. Some, such as electrons and photons with certain energy, have profound effects on living material; others, such as neutrinos, pass through organisms undetected and without effect. All have different kinds of energy. In the final analysis it is to these particles that animals must make adjustments. Organisms living in other parts of the universe would be exposed to other kinds of particles and would have to evolve differently, each in its own milieu.

Pertinent details of an animal's environment are detected first by utilizing the energy of particles to perform work in the biological system. Thus, light is detected by virtue of an absorber which transforms the energy of photons of certain specific energy. There is no absorber to transform the energy of photons which, for example, make up X-rays and gamma-rays. Heat is detected by absorbing the energy of photons of a different energy level. Electricity is detected by utilizing the energy of electrons. Tastes and smells are detected by utilizing the potential energy existing in the mutual attraction and repulsion of the particles making up atoms. Sound is detected by using the energy of moving particles of molecular size.

A sense organ is a part of an organism specialized to receive a small amount of energy from certain of the sources mentioned above and to utilize it to set off a train of events culminating in a nerve impulse. Many cells and parts of cells do work with energy derived from the sources mentioned. Many cells use the potential energy in carbohydrates to do work, yet they are not sense organs. Certain of the cells of green plants absorb photons of certain energies and perform work much as the pigment rhodopsin of the eye absorbs protons and does work. A sense cell differs from these in at least three major respects: first, the work which is done by the sense cell is done at the expense of its own potential energy, the energy of the environment is merely a trigger; second, all sense organs, as far as we know, transform their potential energy into electrical energy; third, they transmit this electrical energy to another cell. And this energy, in turn, is transmitted by an element which by itself could not have detected the original environmental energy.

A sense organ implies another element that will receive the change. In this sense our attitude towards sense organs is teleological, but there seems to be no escape from this attitude. As Granit (1955) has concluded: 'For many purposes, e.g. physiochemical studies of primary events, we can neglect the teleological aspects of the sensory message and the general problem of central decoding of the code of spikes, but I want to emphasize that research into special senses differs from many other recognized branches of physiology in presupposing and accepting the fact that understanding of biological purpose is part of its aim, be it movement or perception. To close one's eyes to this aspect of sensory physiology is to neglect the biological, psychological, and philosophical implications of a branch of natural science which actually is capable of giving some meaning to "meaning".'

Receptors change reversibly when energy is applied to them (i.e., they are sensitive, they detect), they do work (i.e., they are responsive), they generate a message to be transmitted beyond their boundaries. Thus, there are three levels at which the physiology of receptors may be considered.

Considered first as detectors, receptors would not make much information available to an organism if they were so imperfect as to be insensitive to any but the greatest energy changes or so perfect as to be sensitive to every single elementary particle. Furthermore, their usefulness would be limited if they were so indiscriminate as to detect equally all kinds of particles and so simple as to detect only the presence or absence of a stimulus. From the point of view of an animal's survival, there must be an optimum sensitivity, a capacity for discriminating different kinds of stimuli, and a capacity for measuring not only on–off, but rate of change, magnitude of change, absolute change, and direction of change.

It is characteristic of protoplasm that it has moderate sensitivity to many forms of stimuli and may be sensitive to more than one parameter of the stimulus. But receptors have become specialized in that they possess enhanced sensitivity to some particular form of energy and to some particular parameter. First, there is development of special characteristics at the molecular level. The presence of a pigment to absorb radiant energy in some particular wavelength (rhodopsin in the rods and cones of the vertebrate eye) or the presence of molecules to uncouple the potential energy in sugar molecules (sweet taste receptors) are more well-known examples.

In addition to specialized sensitivity *per se*, receptors have also become surrounded with accessory structures whose presence modifies in various fashions the incident energy. A striking example is the complicated accessory structures of the auditory labyrinth of the vertebrate ear. These accessory structures may not only affect the sensitivity of the combined system but may also determine which parameter (magnitude, rate of change, etc.) of a stimulus may be used. Thus, refinement of the receptor from a generalized non-discriminating sensing element with many imperfections has come about through evolutionary specialization of the sensing part of the receptor itself and the structures with which it has become associated.

In addition to looking at the sensitivity of a receptor, one must also look at its responsiveness. In transforming the energy that comes to it to do some form of work, the receptor does not maintain a one-to-one ratio between input and output. A great deal of integration

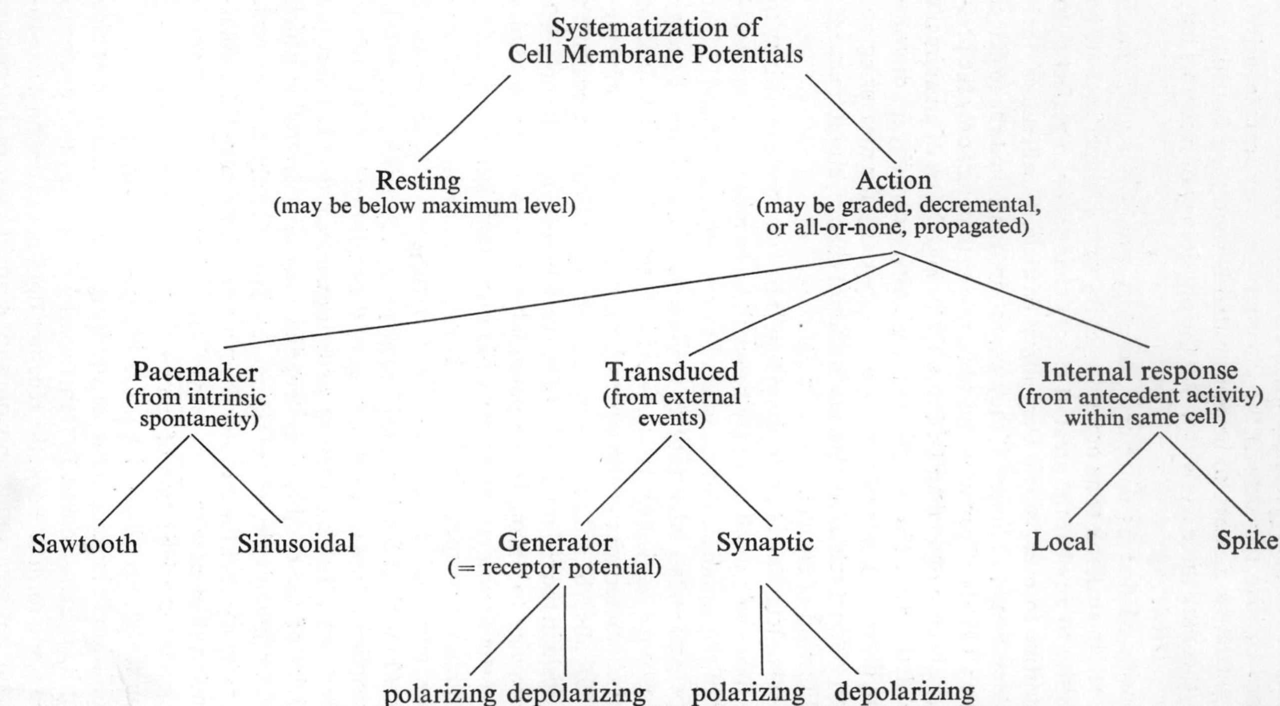

FIG. 1. The types of nerve-cell membrane potentials. (From Bullock, 1959.)

(putting parts together into a whole) takes place in the receptor, so it is probably desirable to anticipate a bit and to present a general picture of events as they occur in a receptor cell.

Energy impinging upon the cell initiates changes that ultimately generate a propagated all-or-none nerve impulse. As Bullock (1958, 1959) has pointed out, '*The determination of firing is not merely the build-up of an adequate stimulus* or its transduced and amplified resultant to a critical level, but rather it is a sequence of labile couplings between graded events, each occurring in a limited fraction of the neuron.' A series of separate steps with alternate pathways lead to firing. Some are reflected in changes in the cell membrane potential (Fig. 1). Others are excitability cycles and the presence or absence of after-effects not reflected in the membrane potential. Between the advent of the physical stimulus from outside the receptor, therefore, and the final production of a nerve impulse, there is a long complicated series of events. The importance of these is that the receptor, a highly complex, physiologically non-uniform cell, not only detects energy and transduces it but also carries out a considerable amount of integration.

When it comes to the transmission of information from the receptor, one begins the long and difficult intellectual trek into the central nervous system. This is beyond the scope of our endeavour here; however, it is worth pointing out that much additional integration is possible long before the central nervous system is reached. Different channels (nerves) from the receptor may have very different transmitting characteristics – different gain, time constants, and maximum output (cf. Bullock, 1953).

Thus, the sensory physiologist is interested in the way in which accessory structures filter or direct the energy going to a receptor, the way in which the receptor transduces this energy into another form, and how there is generated a propagated nerve impulse which is a code relating to the central nervous system or to special effectors the nature and parameters of a stimulus. And in seeking answers to these questions, it is of no import to the sensory physiologist whether the stimulus originates outside of the animal or from within or whether or not it is ever perceived at a conscious level.

CHAPTER II

General Characteristics of the Sensory System

One of the biggest challenges that animals faced in their evolutionary history occurred when they essayed terrestrial life. By all counts the sea is a more permissive environment than land. It is above all a more stable and uniform environment. It exhibits no profound temperature changes; humidity is no problem; osmotic relations are constant. Consequently, the need to develop sense organs to detect changes in these realms is minimal. The physical properties of water obviate the necessity of differentiating between olfaction and taste in the sense that terrestrial organisms do. Density precludes distant vision as well as limiting wavelength discrimination. Since water is a medium of transport, food procurement does not present all the problems that confront the terrestrial animal. By the same token water serves as a medium of dispersal of eggs and sperm and as a cradle for the young so that the complex sensory discrimination and behaviour patterns which have evolved among land animals for reproduction and parental care are largely absent in the sea.

One of the more fundamental problems that confronted animals on emergence to land was that of support, since air does not lend the helping hand that water does. Before emerging on land, animals had already set out on two paths of skeletal development. The arthropods cast the die for an exoskeleton; the chordates, for an internal skeleton. The choice of skeleton had profound effects upon the direction that the development of the nervous system followed. The skeleton is a major limiting factor; all other organs accommodate to it. The arthropod exoskeleton determined the method of growth – the only way to increase size is by moulting – and it also limited the overall size of the animal. Once free of the support of the sea, the animal was limited in size by the engineering principles of a frame dwelling (cf. Thompson, 1943). This may be one of the reasons why insects in general are small animals (although during the Carboniferous one dragonfly attained a wingspread of more than 2 ft.). The largest living species are somewhat larger than the smallest mammals, while the smallest are smaller than many protozoa (Folsom and Wardle, 1943). The range extends from about 166 mm. (the Venezuelan grasshopper *Tropidacris latreillei* and some East Indian walking sticks which are even larger) down to a fraction of a millimetre (some springtails, ceratopogonine midges, and beetles of the family Trichopterygidae).

An exoskeleton and small size are therefore two of the outstanding characteristics of insects. Clearly they must impose upon the nervous system certain restrictions which will be reflected in behaviour. For example, smallness reduces the distance over which conduction of impulses is required. This would imply, other things being equal, more rapid response and movement. At the same time, however, size limitations compel a reduction in the number of neurons possible in the system. A reduction in number of units implies a reduction in the informational capacity of the system. Reduction is carried further by the development of so-called giant fibres. Thus, in the abdominal nerve cord of the cockroach *Periplaneta americana* the giant fibres occupy about 12 per cent of its cross-sectional area (Roeder, 1948). The largest of these fibres measure 30 microns in diameter, exceeding in this respect the largest (alpha) fibres in the mammalian system.

Roeder (1959) argues persuasively that the relative merits of a nervous system composed of a few large units versus one consisting of many small units can be appreciated if one concluded that detail of information has been sacrificed for speed. It is noteworthy that large insects tend to react more slowly than smaller ones and that one at least, the giant Australian cockroach (*Macropanesthia rhinocerus* Suass.), lacks giant fibres (Day, 1950). A large fibre cannot carry as much information from one point to another as can a number of smaller fibres because of the on–off or all-or-none nature of the nerve impulse, but it can transmit its information more rapidly. The giant fibres are the internuncial units in an alarm reaction. In the detection of, and escape from, predators, speed has greater survival value than detailed information. From the point of view of a predator also, speed is important, since attack must be as rapid as the startle response of a prey. Here, however, the information required is of a much more complex nature, but it, too, must be handled by a small nervous system with relatively (as compared with vertebrates) few units.

Another example of the parsimony of neuronal elements is seen in the motor system of insects. As Hoyle (1957) has pointed out, there are functionally important muscles which are microscopically small and yet move joints with precision and delicacy. In contrast with vertebrate muscles, which are innervated by hundreds of nerve fibres under a complex central control, the insect muscle is supplied with a very small number of motor fibres. Some muscles are supplied by four or more axons; some are mono-axonic. More commonly, a muscle is supplied by two axons. Thus, the entire system of nervous control differs from that in the vertebrates (Hoyle, 1957).

In the sensory system, too, there is a limitation on the number of neurons. This is related not only to the small size of the body but also to the fact of its being encased in a rigid non-living cuticle. Only at certain points do the energies of the external environment filter through to sense cells. As compared with the integument of an echinoderm, which may have as many as 4,000 sense cells per square millimetre of surface, and a mammal, whose skin receptors may run into the millions, the integument of an insect is relatively barren and insensitive. The fourth-stage larva of *Rhodnius*, for example, has only about 420 receptors on the entire ventral surface of each abdominal segment (Wigglesworth, 1953); the sensory complement of the entire leg of a fly is less than 500 (Grabowski and Dethier, 1954; Dethier, 1955 b); the total number of stress receptors on the whole body of the drone honeybee is only about 2,948 (McIndoo, 1914 b, 1916). It is only when one counts the cells in the two most highly developed sensory areas of insects, the eye and the antennae, that the number of receptors becomes large. And even then they fall short, by several orders of magnitude, of equalling the number in vertebrates. The maximum number of receptors in any compound eye is that found in Odonata and is estimated to be approximately 210,000 (Snodgrass, 1935). The number is more usually a few hundred or thousand. The antennal sense cells of the honeybee only number between 30,000 and 500,000 (Vogel, 1923 b; Snodgrass, 1956).

Economy of cells is seen further in the remarkable organization of the nervous system whereby stimulation of a single sense cell may be adequate to set off a whole chain of behaviour. Stimulation of one neuron in the labellar taste organs of flies initiates proboscis extension and the initial steps in the feeding pattern (Grabowski and Dethier, 1954; Dethier, 1955 a; Arab, 1959). Roeder and Treat (1957) have shown that the acoustic response in noctuid moths is mediated by only two receptor cells. Similarly, stimulation of one neuron in tactile receptors can initiate a whole series of behaviour patterns ranging from simple withdrawal of an appendage to running.

The ultimate in parsimony is achieved by all known receptors being primary sense cells, that is to say, they are true neurons rather than modified epithelial cells connected synaptically to a neuron (vom

Rath, 1888, 1895, 1896; Hanström, 1928). Although the sensory system of vertebrates also contains some primary sense cells (e.g., the rods, cones, and olfactory receptors), the taste receptors and auditory receptors are specialized non-neural cells connected with neurons. Possession of primary sense cells means that one cell does the work of

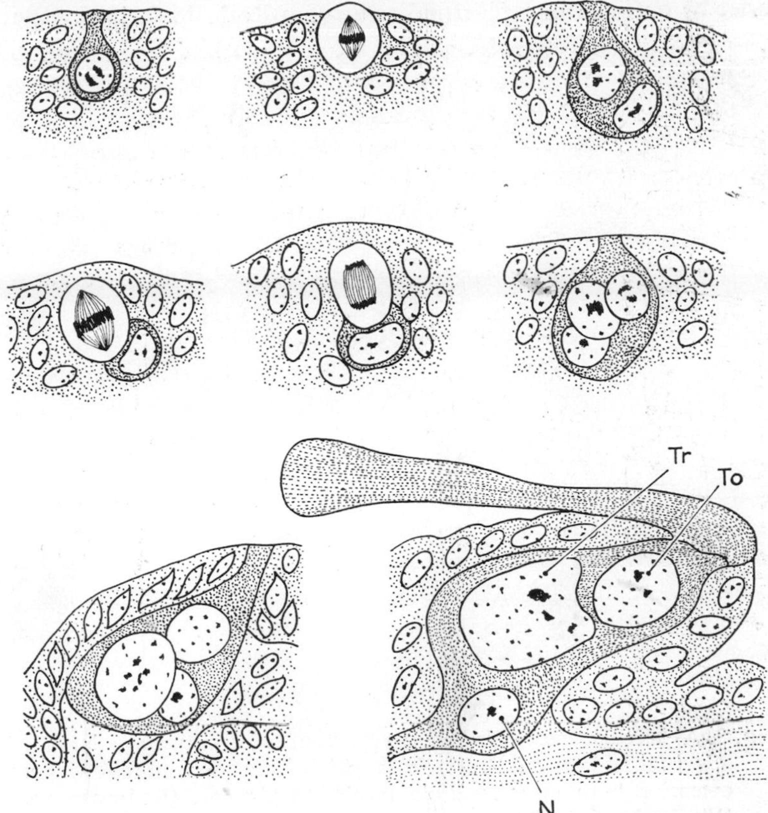

FIG. 2. Stages in the embryonic development of a hair. Tr, trichogen cell; To, tormogen cell; N, bipolar neuron. (Redrawn from Krumiņš, 1952.)

at least two; it performs the multiple function of detecting environmental energy, transducing it, and initiating and transmitting impulses to the appropriate ganglion. From the point of view of the sensory physiologist, the primacy of the insect receptor is a boon to investigations, since all events occur in the one cell. It is generally believed, furthermore, that the primary neurons make their connexions directly with the central nervous system. From time to time peripheral ganglion cells have been described, but these not infrequently turn out to be non-neural cells. On the other hand, one of the more recent reports, that of Peters (1961) describing a multipolar neuron in the labellum of flies, warrants further investigation.

While it has generally been accepted for some time that sense cells arise by mitosis from epidermal cells (vom Rath, 1888, 1895, 1896;

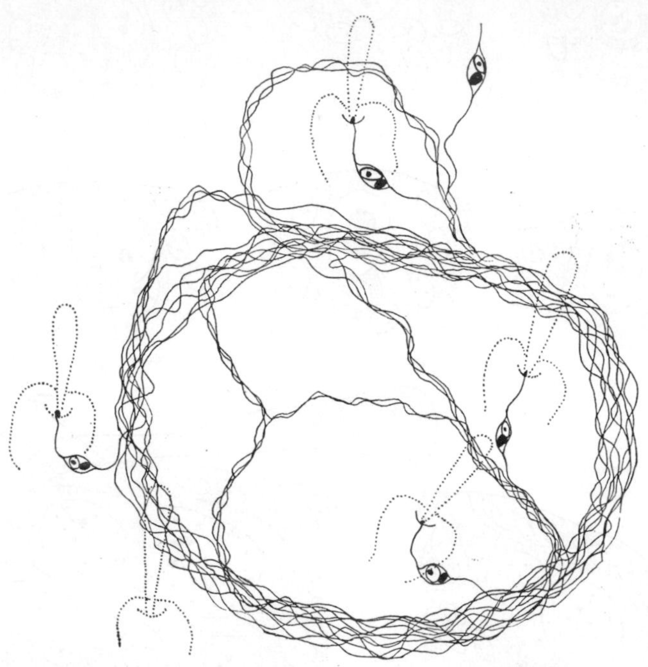

FIG. 3. A 'circular nerve' in the integument of fourth-stage larva of *Rhodnius* and the cell bodies from which it was derived following an extensive burn of the cuticle in the third-stage. (Redrawn from Wigglesworth, 1953.)

Haffer, 1921; Hanström, 1928; Snodgrass, 1935) (Fig. 2), proof that the cells are *primary* sense cells is of relatively recent origin. Vogel (1923 b) claimed that in Hymenoptera the sensory axon grows out from the central nervous system and joins the sense cell. Newton (1931), Henke and Rönsch (1951), and Krumiņš (1952) maintained that the epidermal sense cells differentiate axons which then grow centripetally to join the central nervous system. The matter would seem to have been settled, at least for *Rhodnius prolixus*, by Wigglesworth (1953), who proved by interrupting sensory nerves that axons are regenerated by epidermal cells and grow centripetally until they encounter a nerve. If they do not encounter a nerve or if they become trapped above the basement membrane, which separates the epidermis from the rest of the body space, they grow in loops and circles, apparently indefinitely (Fig. 3).

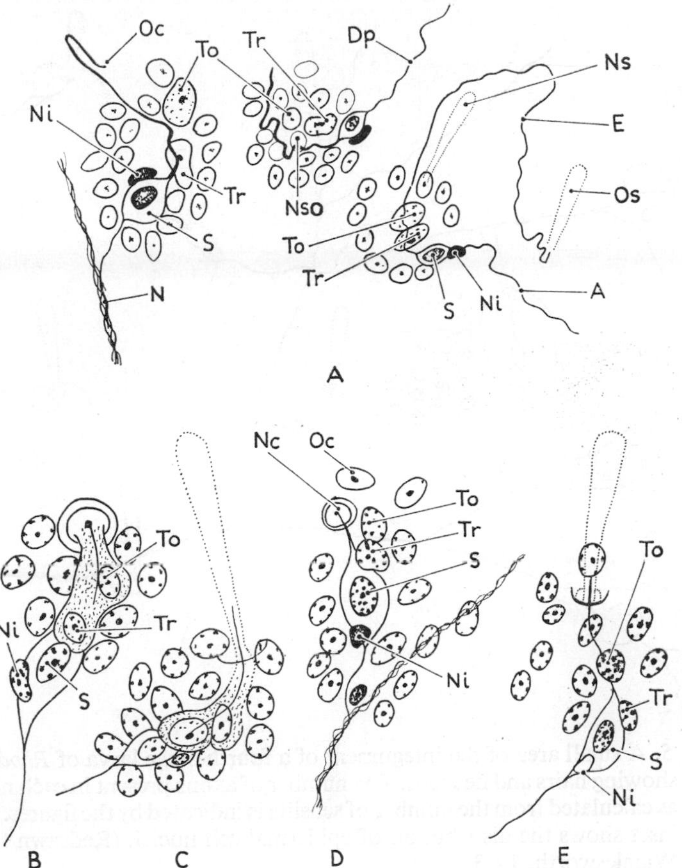

FIG. 4. A. Stages in the moulting of sensilla in a fourth-stage larvae of *Rhodnius*. B. Campaniform organ (haematoxylin). C. Tactile hair (haematoxylin). D. Campaniform organ (Romanes' method). E. Tactile hair (Romanes' method). N, nerve; S, sense cell; Dp, distal process; A, axon; Tr, trichogen; To, tormogen; Nc, new campaniform organ; Oc, old campaniform organ; Ns, new seta; Os, old seta; Ni, neurilemma cell; Nso, new socket; E, extension of distal process from new to old seta. (Redrawn from Wigglesworth, 1953.)

At each moult, when new receptors arise to service the increased body size, they, just like regenerating receptors, send axons centripetally to the central nervous system (Fig. 4). Whether or not the axons fuse when they come together is still in doubt. Pringle (1938 a) was of the opinion that fusion did occur in the cockroach, but Wigglesworth (1953) felt that the matter was in doubt in *Rhodnius*.

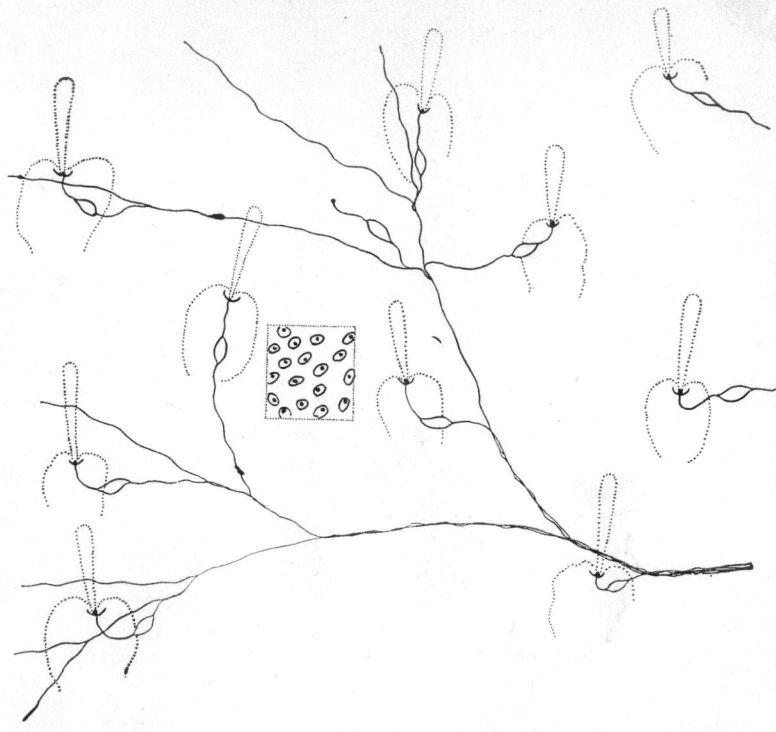

FIG. 5. A small area of the integument of a fourth-stage larva of *Rhodnius* showing hairs and neurons. The number of axons present in each nerve as calculated from the number of sensilla is indicated by the figures. The inset shows the distribution of epidermal cell nuclei. (Redrawn from Wigglesworth, 1953.)

He showed in *Rhodnius* (Wigglesworth, 1959) by making a rough count of the numbers and types of sensilla on the antenna and a count of the axons in the antennal nerve that there must be a fusion of at least fifteen sense cells to one axon. Similar counts in the leg indicated that similar fusion of the tactile fibres here does not occur. He pointed out that a lack of fusion is understandable in view of the need of accurate touch localization. On the other hand, fusion of axons within groups of campaniform sensilla, hair plates, and some chordotonal sensilla does occur in the leg of the cockroach (Pringle, 1938 a; Nijenhuis and Dresden, 1952).

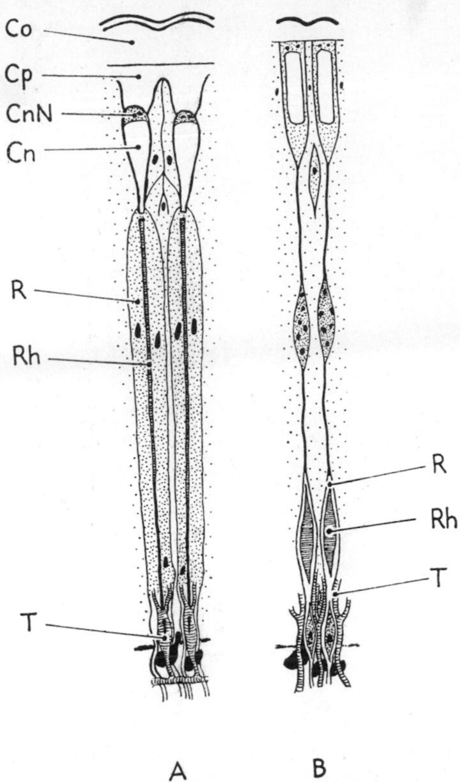

FIG. 6. Diagrammatic representation of two types of ommatidia. A. Appositional type of diurnal Lepidoptera. B. Superpositional type of nocturnal Lepidoptera. Co, cornea; Cp, corneal process; Cn, crystalline cone; CnN, crystalline cone nuclei; R, retinal cell; Rh, rhabdom; T, tracheal tapetum. (Redrawn from Snodgrass, 1935 after Nowikoff.)

The presence or absence of fusion is a matter of considerable importance to the electrophysiologist, who must try to interpret recordings from afferent nerves. Another unsettled question of importance is whether or not the large cells frequently observed at the junction of uniting nerves or axons are multipolar nerve cells. If they are, it means that a synapse is interpolated between the peripheral sensory neuron and the central nervous system. Otherwise,

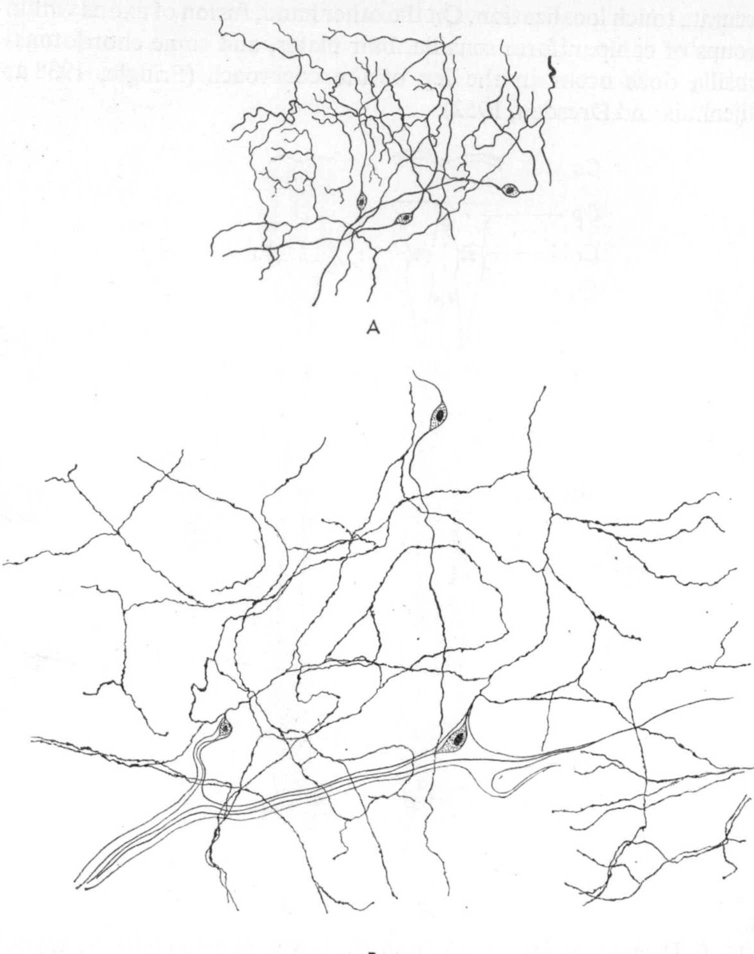

FIG. 7. Examples of Type II neurons. A and B. Subepidermal nerve plexus in the larva of *Melolontha*. (Redrawn from Zawarzin, 1912.)

the path from the primary neuron to the central nervous system is a direct one. According to Snodgrass (1935) there are no cells in sensory nerves, and Wigglesworth (1953) is of the opinion that the cells seen there are actually neurilemma cells.

Morphologically there are two broad categories of sense cells: those whose dendrites are nearly always associated with the cuticle or its invaginations (apodemes, tracheae, and cuticle of preoral and oral cavities) (Type I) (Fig. 5); multipolar neurons never associated with cuticular processes but lying instead on the inner face of the body wall, the walls of the alimentary canal, muscles, and connective tissue (Type II). Only the cells of photoreceptors lack an obvious distal process or dendrite, although even in these cells the distal end is

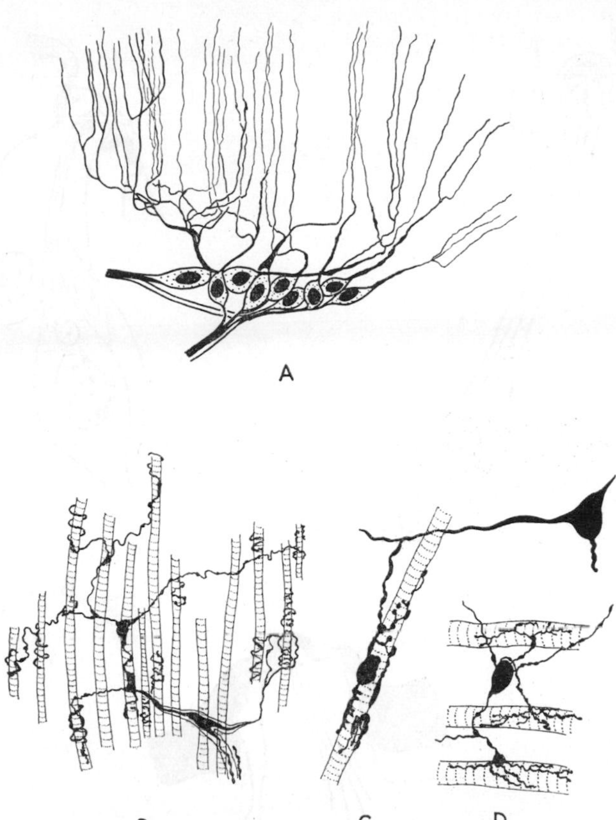

FIG. 8. Type II neurons. A. The hypopharynx of termites. (Redrawn from Richard, 1951.) B. The muscles of the mid-gut of *Melolontha* larvae. C and D. The muscles of the oesophagus of *Oryctes* larvae. (Redrawn from Orlov, 1924.)

structurally modified (Fig. 6). Depending on the position of the neurocyte with respect to the epidermis, Type I neurons are termed intraepidermal or sub-epidermal, but there are certainly all gradations between the two positions.

The ontogenetic origin of Type II neurons from the ectoderm has not yet been determined (Snodgrass, 1935). Numerically they are less common than Type I and are most abundant in soft-skinned larvae. Their branching distal processes may form an elaborate subepidermal net, as in the larva of *Melolontha vulgaris* (Fig. 7) (Zawarzin, 1912 b). They also occur in the walls, muscles, and connective tissue of the

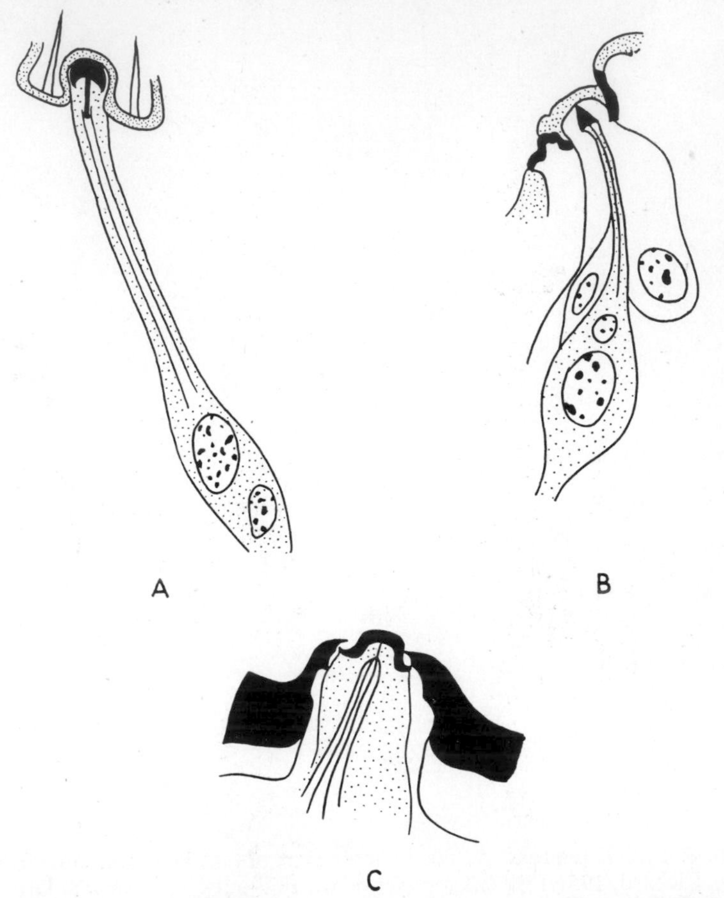

FIG. 9. Types of campaniform sensilla. A. From the haltere of *Calliphora erythrocephala*. B. From the cercus of *Gryllus domesticus*. C. From the cercus of *Blatta orientalis*. (Redrawn from Hsü, 1938.)

alimentary tract of some insects (*Periplaneta americana* [Zawarzin, 1912 a] and larvae of scarabaeid beetles [Orlov, 1924] [Fig. 8]). Richard (1951) has described them in the labium, labrum, and hypopharynx of termites (Fig. 9). Until Finlayson and Lowenstein (1955, 1958) studied some Type II receptors electrophysiologically,

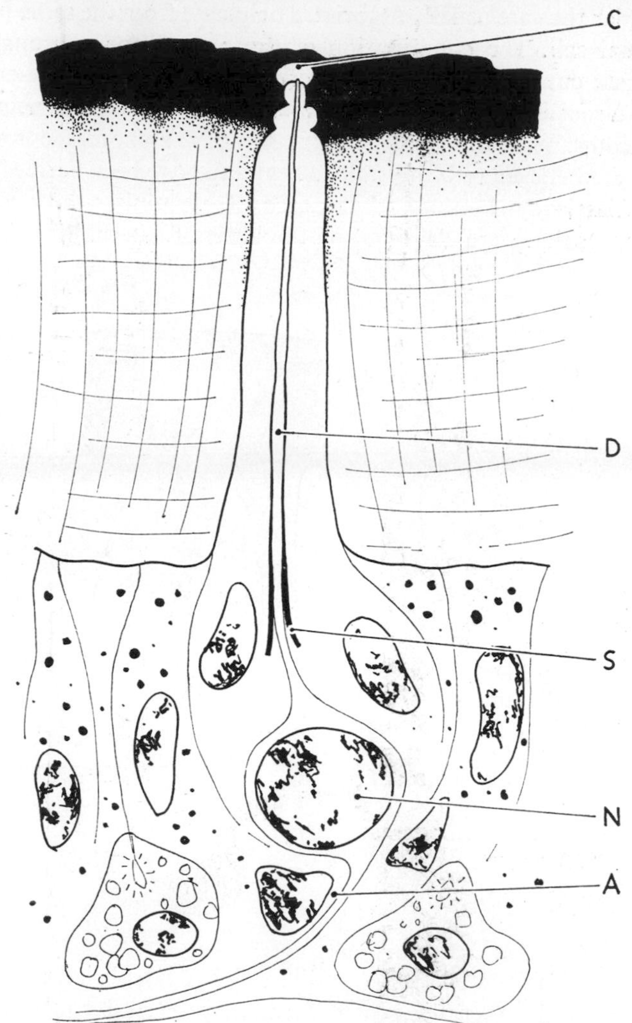

FIG. 10. A campaniform sense organ from the antenna of a grasshopper. N, bipolar neuron; S, scolopoid sheath; A, axon; D, dendrite; C, cuticular dome. (Redrawn from Slifer *et al.*, 1959.)

there was no certain knowledge of the function of any of them. Electrophysiological studies of those associated with muscle and connective tissue have proved them to be proprioceptors. Their structure and function will be described in Chapter III.

Type I neurons and the cells giving rise to the cuticular structures with which they are usually associated originate from the same parent epidermal cell. The combination of the neuron (or neurons), the immediate cuticular area, when present, and its generative cells is termed a sensillum. A sensillum is thus a sense organ; the neuron is the receptor. With the possible exception of the photoreceptors, all sensilla are believed to be homologous and to have been derived from setae. Classically, because of the ease of examining the cuticular portion, sensilla were classified on the basis of external form. They

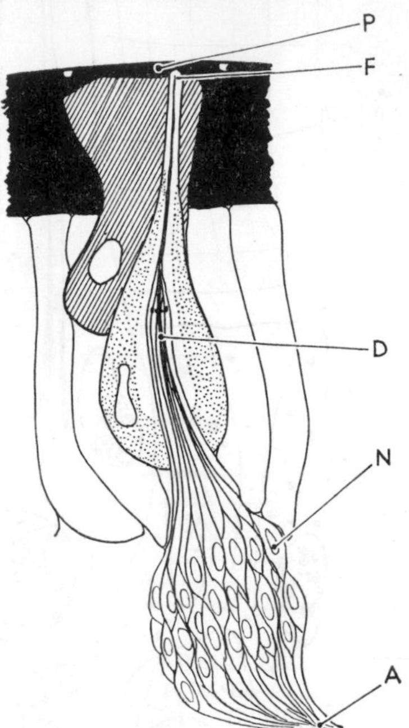

FIG. 11. Sensillum placodeum from the antenna of the honeybee. N, bipolar neuron; A, axon; D, dendrites; P, plate; F, attachment of fibres. (Redrawn from Snodgrass, 1935.)

include setiform varieties (sensilla trichodea), bristles (sensilla chaetica), scales (sensilla squamiformia), pegs and cones (sensilla basiconica), pegs, cones, or bristles sunk in shallow depressions (sensilla coelonconica) or in deep pits (sensilla ampullacea) (Schenk, 1903).

Other sensilla whose external cuticular structures are not seta-like are undoubtedly derived from setae (Snodgrass, 1935; Lees, 1942). The campaniform organs (sensilla campaniformia, sense pores, etc.) are visible externally as minute pits in the cuticle, but in section are seen to possess a bell-shaped cuticular cap (Figs. 10, 30). Each is innervated by a single neuron. Their structure will be discussed in detail in Chapter III. The plate organs (sensilla placodea) are marked externally by an oval or elliptical plate surrounded by a narrow membranous ring. Each is innervated by a number of neurons (Fig. 11).

One type of sensillum (sensillum scolopophorum, scolopoid sensillum, peg organs, chordotonal organs, stiftführender Sinnesor-

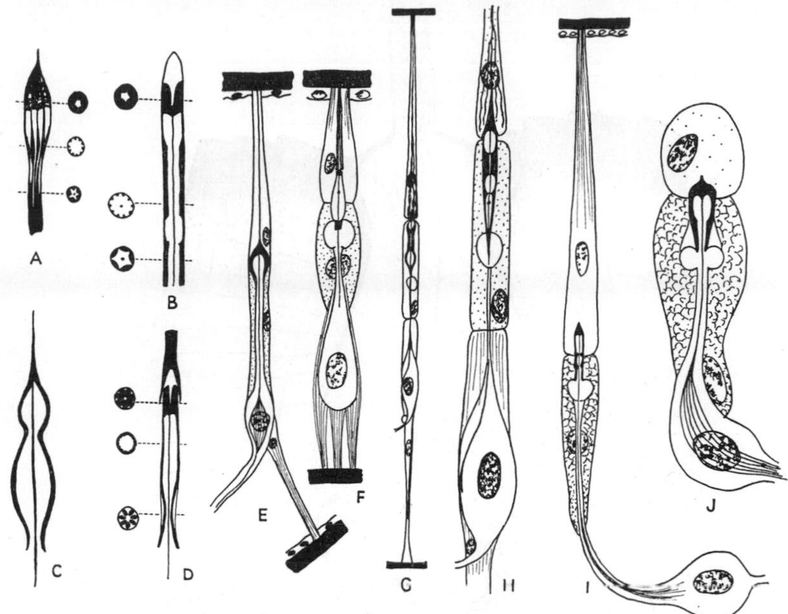

FIG. 12. Different forms of scolopoid sensilla. A. Terminal peg from a grasshopper sensillum. (From Eggers.) B. Terminal peg from the tracheal organ of *Gryllus*. (From Schwabe.) C. Terminal peg from the femoral chordotonal organ of *Pediculus*. (From Graber.) D. Terminal peg from a chordotonal organ in the abdomen of a cerambycid larva. (From Hess.) E. A simple chordotonal organ with one sensillum. (From Eggers.) F. A. chordotonal sensillum from the haltere of a muscid fly. (From Pflugstaedt.) G and H. Scolopoid sensilla from the tympanic organ of *Cicadetta coriaria* ♂. (From Vogel.) I. Sensillum from the tibial organ of *Decticus*. (From Schwabe.) J. Sensillum from the subgenual organ of *Decticus*. (From Schwabe.)

gane) does not fit conveniently into any category. The sense cell is a bipolar neuron, but its dendrite is not always associated with a particular cuticular structure. These sensilla usually do not occur singly. They are generally gathered together in bundles having a common point of attachment to an undifferentiated part of the body wall. Sometimes a small external pit, thickened disk, or nodule marks the point of attachment. In special cases they are associated with a tympanic membrane. They all possess in the region of the dendrite a cuticle-like sheath, usually ribbed, and in the majority of cases capped with a prominent refractile body. Because of the

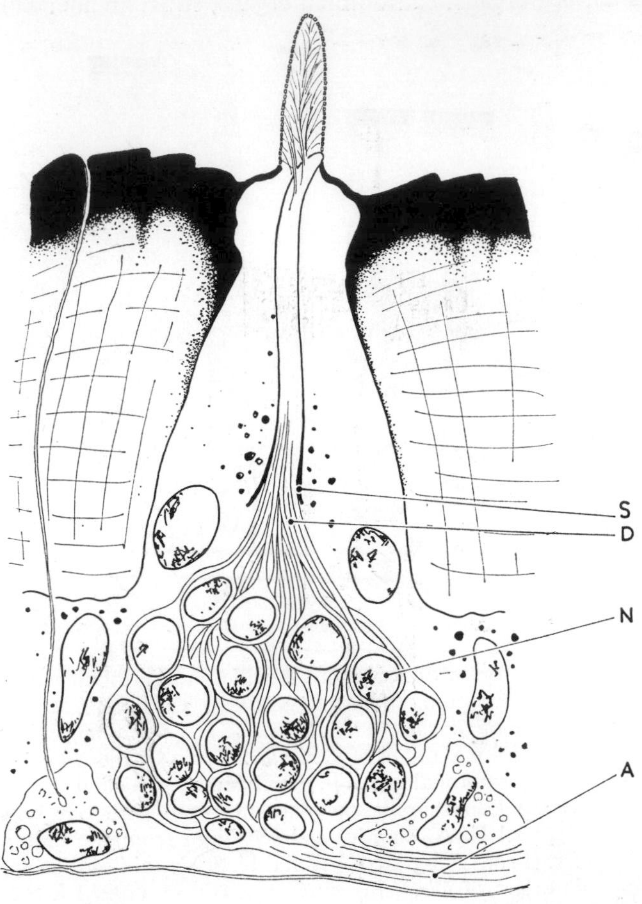

Fig. 13. A sensillum basiconicum from the antenna of a grasshopper. N, bipolar neuron; S, scolopoid sheath; A, axons; D, dendrites. (Redrawn from Slifer *et al.*, 1959.)

resemblance of the combined sheath and cap to a peg-shaped rod, the structure has been termed the scolops (Stift). A terminal strand may or may not extend from the cap distally to the point of attachment on the body wall.

There is no completely satisfactory name to apply to these sensilla.

They were called chordotonal organs by Graber (1882 a) because many of them stretched like taut cords from point to point and were believed to be auditory organs. Those with a terminal strand were termed amphinematic because they appeared to be stretched between two threads; the others were termed mononematic (Graber, 1882 a). It soon became clear that these sensilla were neither exclusively audi-

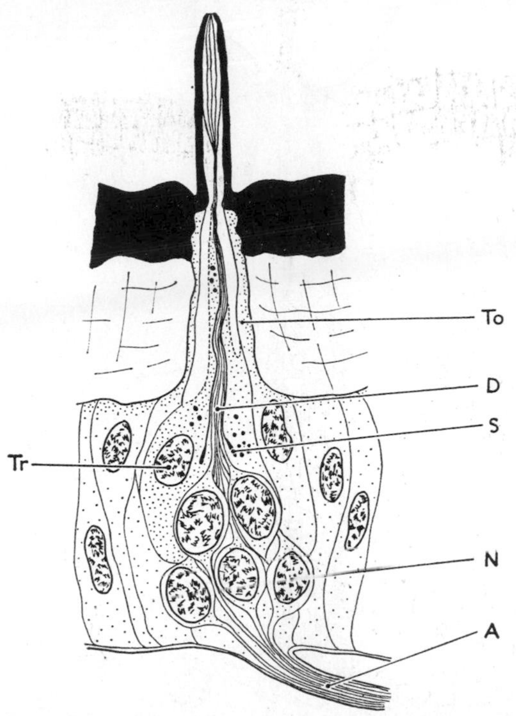

FIG. 14. A thick-walled sensillum basiconicum from the antenna of a grasshopper. N, bipolar neuron; S, scolopoid sheath; A, axons; D, dendrites; Tr, trichogen cell; To, tormogen cell. (Redrawn from Slifer *et al.*, 1957.)

tory nor always cord-like in appearance. In recognition of the universal existence of a peg-like rod within them, Eggers (1923, 1924, 1928) proposed that they be called scolopophorous or scolopal organs. With this terminology one sensillum would be called a scolopidium (by analogy with the ommatidium of the eye) and a group of scolopidia comprising a unit would be termed a scoloparium. Even Eggers admitted, however, that other kinds of sensilla possessed peg-like rods, and it now appears that such structures are a constant feature of insect sensilla. In recognition of this fact Snodgrass (1926) originally preferred the term chordotonal in deference to custom; however, he later (1935) switched to the term scolopophorous sensillum. Neither

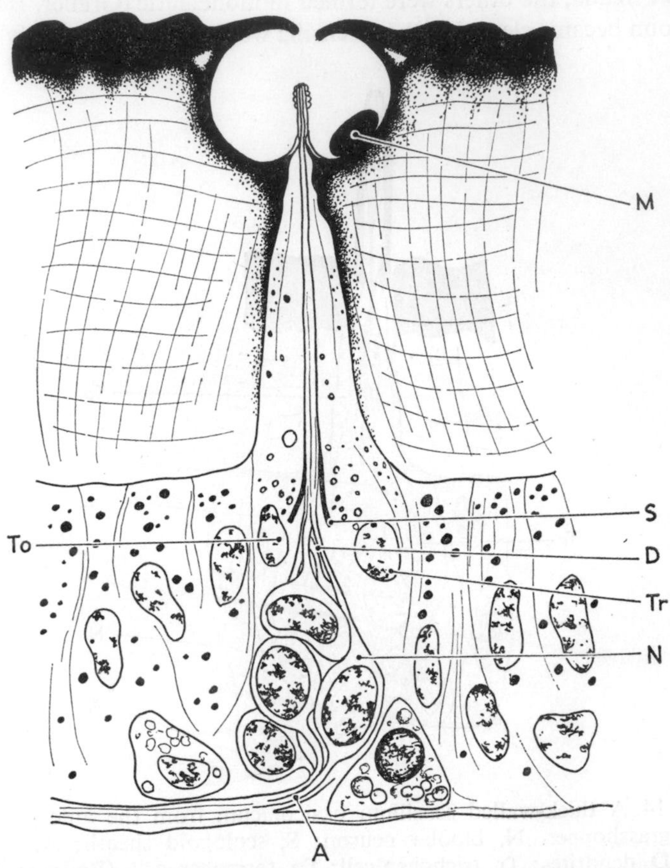

FIG. 15. Sensillum coeloconicum from the antenna of a grasshopper. N, bipolar neuron; S, scolopoid sheath; A, axons; D, dendrites; Tr, trichogen cell; To, tormogen cell; M, dried residue from moulting fluid. (Redrawn from Slifer *et al.*, 1959.)

term seems singularly appropriate, so the choice at the moment is a matter of taste (for a complete discussion of this matter see Eggers, 1923, 1924, 1928; Snodgrass, 1926, 1935).

A typical sensillum consists of a minimum of four cells (Fig. 16): (1) the trichogen or hair-forming cell; (2) the tormogen or socket-

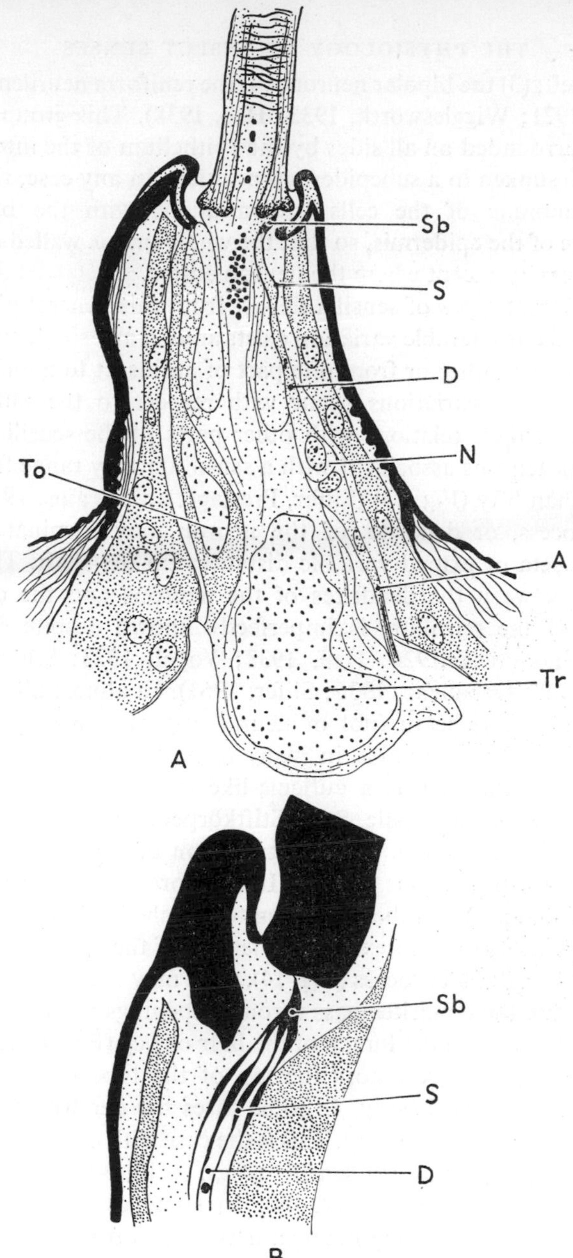

FIG. 16. A. Tactile hair from the larvae of *Vanessa urticae*. B. Scolopoid body in the tactile hair of the larva of *Pieris rapae*. S, scolopoid sheath; Sb, scolopoid peg; D, dendrite; N, bipolar neuron; A, axon; Tr, trichogen cell; To, tormogen cell. (Redrawn from Hsü, 1938.)

C

forming cell; (3) the bipolar neuron; (4) the reniform neurilemma cell (Haffer, 1921; Wigglesworth, 1933; Hsü, 1938). This group of cells may be surrounded on all sides by the epithelium of the integument or may lie sunken in a subepidermal position. In any case, the basement membrane of the cells is continuous with the basement membrane of the epidermis, so that the whole unit is walled off from the body cavity except where the neuron enters.

The different types of sensilla depart from this general picture in details, and considerable variation exists among any single type from one insect to another or from one part of an insect to another. The most significant variations occur with respect to the number of neurons and their relations with other parts of the sensillum. The number of neurons associated with a sensillum may range from one to more than fifty (Fig. 13) (Slifer, Prestage, and Beams, 1959). The distal process, or dendrite, of the neuron may terminate at the base of a seta or extend variable distances up the shaft. The exact relations between the dendrites of the neurons and the cuticular portions of the sensillum is imperfectly known despite extensive studies (Snodgrass, 1926; Hsü, 1938; Vogel, 1923; Sihler, 1924; Eggers, 1928; Debauche, 1935; Slifer, 1961). In almost all cases the dendrite enters a sheath (not of neural origin) whose optical and staining properties resemble in many respects that of cuticle. The sheath, best described as a cuticula-like tube, has been variously termed sense rod, scolopale, Stift, Stiftkörperchen, corps scolopöid, Hülle, Chitineurium, etc. The exact relation of the dendrite to this tube differs in the various sensilla. In chemoreceptors especially the top (distal) end of the tube may open to the shaft of the hair or peg so that the dendrites can extend the length of the tube and into the lumen of the external process (Fig. 14). Or it may open to the outside, in which case the dendrites pass through openings in the side of the tube and continue in the lumen of the hair or peg (Fig. 13).

In many mechanoreceptors the top of the tube is capped with a dark-staining apical body. In some cases the dendrite terminates within or just beneath this cap. This is the case with many tactile hairs (Fig. 16) and campaniform sensilla (Figs. 9, 10, 30) and with most chordotonal sensilla (Figs. 12, 48). In some cases, especially in chordotonal organs, a long filament may extend from the cap to the cuticle (Fig. 12). There are, however, chordotonal organs in which the terminal filament is absent (Figs. 47, 48).

Recent studies with the electron-microscope (Gray and Pumphrey, 1958; Gray, 1960; Slifer, 1961; Adams, 1961; Larsen, 1962; Dethier,

Larsen, and Adams, 1963) have revealed a most extraordinary complexity in the structure of the dendrites and scolopoid bodies of sensilla. Since details appear to differ so much from one sensillum to another, specific cases will be dealt with in later chapters.

While certain generalizations can be made about the function of some types of sensilla (e.g., sensilla campaniformia are mechanoreceptors sensitive to deformation of the cuticle, and chordotonal sensilla are mechanoreceptors sensitive to sound, vibration, and stretching of parts of the body), it is dangerous as well as unprofitable to attempt to link a particular structure with a particular function. This is so because a type of sensillum which may subserve one function in one species may subserve a different function in another. Furthermore, a single sensillum may consist of more than one type of receptor (e.g., the labellar hairs of *Phormia*, which have two chemoreceptors and a mechanoreceptor associated with them). Each is a case unto itself.

CHAPTER III

Mechanoreception

Every insect maintains its body in a particular attitude with respect to gravity. This attitude, its primary orientation, means for most ventral-side down. There are, however, many that habitually live upside down (the backswimmers, praying mantids, many lepidopterous larvae) and a few, such as those living in vertical burrows, whose normal attitude is posterior-end down. For aquatic insects and flying insects, both of whom are freely suspended in a homogeneous medium, there must be sense organs that can give information about the direction of the force of gravity. Vision is of some help in this connexion, especially in flying insects, since the sky is invariably up and the ground down, but that is not the prime service of vision. Insects in contact with a substrate derive some information from sense organs touching the substrate, but this information tells them only which surface of the body is in contact, not what the attitude of their body is with respect to gravity.

In addition to maintaining a primary orientation all insects have characteristic postural relations. To maintain these, to have information concerning the position of one part of the body with respect to another, requires special sense organs. The same sort of information is needed to be able to move one part of the articulated body precisely with respect to another in order to walk, swim, fly, spin cocoons, dig burrows, court, copulate, and feed. Finally, for the proper working of the internal organs there must be information concerning the presence of faeces in the rectum, eggs in the ootheca, and food in the alimentary canal.

Serving all of these needs is a whole spectrum of sense organs responding to energy derived, in the final analysis, from the surface gravitation of the earth. They are organs sensitive to stretch, compression, or torque imparted to cuticle, connective tissue, or muscles by the weight (which is a measure of the force with which the earth attracts it) of parts of the body, the relative movement of parts, the gyroscopic effects of moving parts, and impingement of the substrate or surrounding media. Since there is no neuron directly sensitive to gravitational force, all of the receptors concerned with primary orientation, postural relations, and touch are associated with complicated and highly specific accessory structures whose function is to transduce the energy of the stimulus into mechanical deformation of the protoplasm of the neuron. Many cells are sensitive to mechanical deformation, but the mechanoreceptors are highly specialized in this respect. The different accessory structures and the different response characteristics (e.g., rate of adaptation) of the receptor determine the sensitivity of the sense organ and to which parameter of the stimulus it will respond.

THE TACTILE SENSE–SENSILLA TRICHODEA

A non-living, tough, and most often rigid cuticle effectively insulates tissues from all but the grossest mechanical disturbances of the external environment. To provide the surface sensitivity denied by the exocuticle there are numerous thin, hollow extensions, the sensilla trichodea, on all surfaces of the body. They are most numerous on those areas, such as legs, which come most frequently into contact with the substrate, those, such as the antennae and mouth-parts, which are employed in palpating or manipulating the environment, and on such extended portions of the body as the antennae and cerci which represent perimeter guards of the body. They also occur abundantly on surfaces between joints, segments, and other appressed areas of the body where their function is proprioceptive. Their shape, mechanical properties, and the physiological properties of the neurons associated with them vary considerably, depending upon the service they are designed to perform. Those at the joints are short and slow adapting; those on the cerci, extraordinarily long and delicate, and hence sensitive to the most gossamer disturbance; the thick tibial leg spines, gross and slow adapting.

The sensilla trichodea are set in membraneous sockets. The shaft is so rigidly constructed that any force applied to the structure is transmitted to the socket. It is here that movement takes place and, because of the leverage, is greatly amplified. The simplest sensilla trichodea are those that are innervated by one neuron. These are simple mechanoreceptors. There are others, however, that are innervated by more than one neuron, and these are compound sense organs. In the labellar hairs of the blowfly, for example, one neuron is the mechanoreceptor responding when the hair is moved in its socket; the remaining neurons are chemoreceptors responding when certain chemicals touch the tip of the hair (cf. Chapter V).

The exact manner in which the dendrite of the neuron is associated with mechanoreceptive hairs is not always clear (Fig. 16). It is reported as being inserted on that part of the hair shaft that extends below the socket, on the socket itself, or at some point part way up the shaft of the hair. It is enclosed in a scolopoid sheath, but may or may not be capped with an apical body. The sheath may be ribbed and possess thickened zones. Just below the cap may be seen with the light microscope some darkly staining spots, the sense rods (Snodgrass, 1926) or points sensoriels (Hsü, 1938). Further observation with the electron-microscope may reveal more complicated structural relationships similar to those seen in tympanal chordotonal sensilla (Gray, 1960).

Richard (1952) showed clearly in the case of sensilla trichodea of termites that at moulting the sheath and the neuron process extending

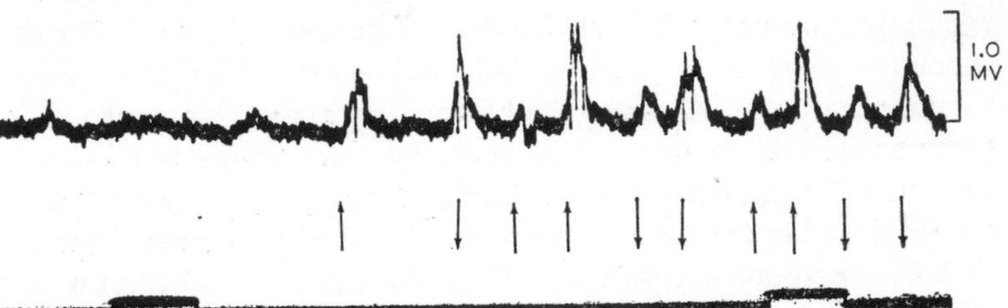

FIG. 17. Response to repetitive mechanical stimulation of a chemosensory hair on the wing of *Sarcophaga*. The arrow indicates the onset of a rapid one-directional displacement, and the direction of the displacement with reference to the preceding stimulus. Positive potential at recording electrode is down. Time marks recur at 0·2-second intervals. (Courtesy of M. L. Wolbarsht.)

through and beyond it are lost. A new sheath and filament are regenerated to supply the new hair. During the period when the new cuticle is forming the distal fibre remains attached to the old hair to provide tactile sensitivity until the last moment. Shortly before the moult the distal fibre ruptures, and at this time there is a loss in tactile sensitivity (Richard, 1952; Wigglesworth, 1953).

From the geometry of these sensilla it is likely that bending of the hair in its socket deforms the terminal region of the distal process of the neuron. The response to angular deflexion varies with direction relative to the long axis of the joint (Pumphrey, 1936; Pringle, 1938 a). Stimulation is followed by an electrical response that can be divided into two components. The work of Wolbarsht (1960) has shown that there is a graded slow potential, the receptor potential, that can be recorded from the distal process. It occurs prior to any impulses, varies smoothly, and must attain some critical level before any impulses are initiated.

All hairs have a steady resting potential until a mechanical stimulus is applied. The potential may be either positive or negative, depending upon the type of hair. When the hair is stimulated an increase in negativity, which varies smoothly as the stimulus is increased or decreased, is seen at the recording electrode. Two types of receptor potentials have been observed. In one kind of hair the potential persists only during the motion of the hair (Fig. 17); in another kind, it lasts as long as the hair is deformed (Fig. 18). In the former the return of the hair to the unstrained position initiates another receptor

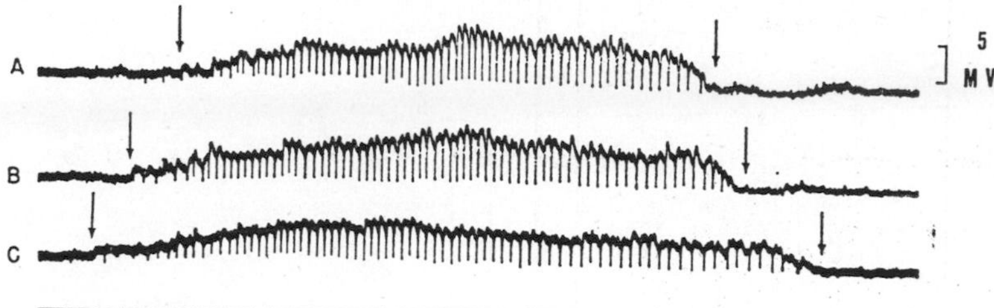

FIG. 18. Response of mechanosensory hair on outer clasper of male *Phormia* to mechanical stimuli. A, B, and C are successive records taken from the same hair, but the stimuli were not the same. Arrows indicate onset and cessation of deformation. The deformation of the hair was approximately proportional to the amplitude of the response for each record. Positive at recording electrode is down. Time marks recur at 0·2-second intervals. (Courtesy of M. L. Wolbarsht.)

potential. This kind of hair adapts very rapidly. The other type adapts very slowly. Sometimes adaptation is still incomplete at the end of twenty minutes.

The impulses always have an initial positive phase in contrast to the negative-going receptor potential. They are usually monophasic. Impulses occur only after some threshold of receptor potential has been reached. The threshold receptor potential for two types of fast-adapting hairs which is accompanied by an impulse is plotted for a series of test stimuli in Figs. 19 and 20. There is also a relation between the frequency of discharge and the magnitude of the receptor potential. Bernhard, Granit, and Skogland (1942) had shown that frequency was determined by the refractory period of the spike-generating mechanism and the magnitude of the generator potential. Up to the point where the increase in generator potential causes no further increase in frequency because the interval between impulses is equal to the refractory period of the neuron there is a direct relation between frequency and the amplitude of the generator potential. These relations hold for the insect mechanoreceptor (Figs. 21, 22).

The most striking feature of insect mechanoreceptors is the change in size of the impulse as the receptor potential changes (Figs. 23, 24,

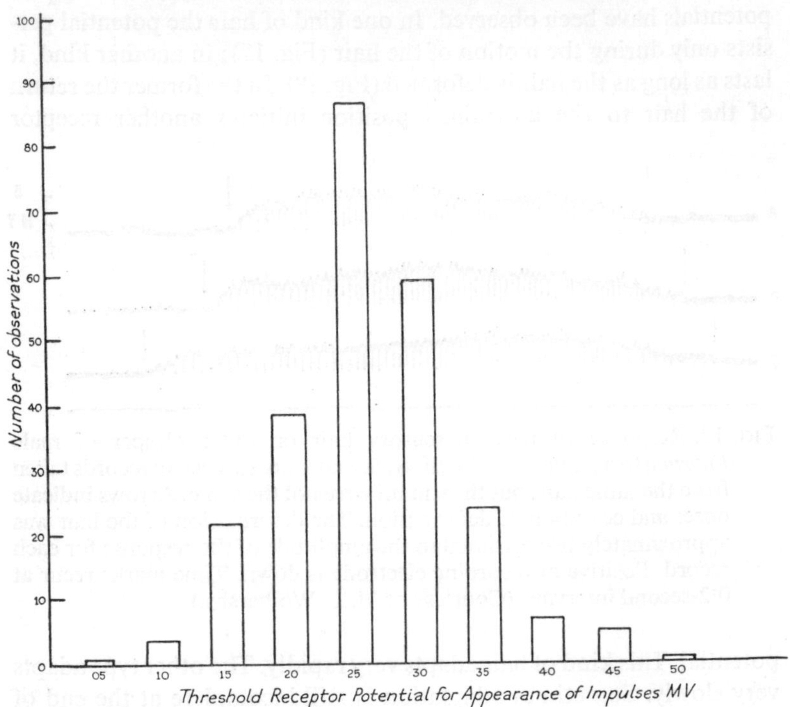

FIG. 19. The threshold receptor potential of a mechanoreceptor on the grasshopper claw which is accompanied by an impulse is plotted for a series of test stimuli. In the largest number of trials the threshold was 2·5 MV with the spread as shown. (Redrawn from Wolbarsht, 1961.)

25) (Wolbarsht and Dethier, 1958; Wolbarsht, 1960). Wolbarsht (1960), after analysing the electrical events occurring in the mechanoreceptor, concluded that: the mechanical stimulus effects a change in the membrane resistance at the receptor site; the receptor potential (which is undoubtedly the generator potential) is the difference between the potential across the membrane at the receptor site and the general polarization of the cell; the impulses are generated proximad

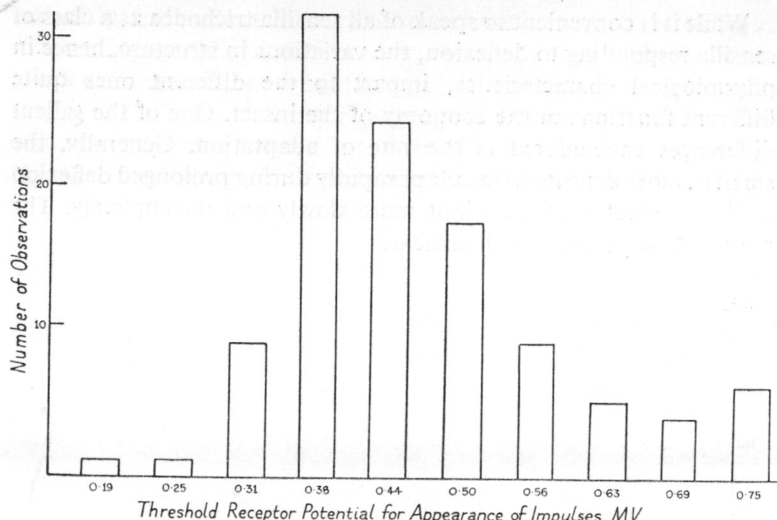

FIG. 20. The threshold receptor potential of the mechanosensory neuron of a chemosensory hair on the wing of *Sarcophaga* which is accompanied by an impulse is plotted for a series of mechanical stimuli. In the largest number of trials the threshold was 0·38 MV with the spread as shown. (Redrawn from Wolbarsht, 1961.)

of the receptor site and do not invade it; changes in impulse size are due to changes in the membrane resistance of the receptor site; there is a high resistance between the fluid-filled centre of the hair and the general body fluid; the value of this resistance is effectively determined by the close anatomical conjunction of the receptor membrane and the lumen of the hair cavity. In most respects the electrical response of the insect mechanoreceptor is similar to that of the Pacinian corpuscle of vertebrates.

FIG. 21. Response of mechanosensory hair on the anal plate of a female *Phormia* to changing mechanical stimulation. The left-hand arrow indicates the approximate beginning of the deformation; the middle arrow, the minimum; and the right-hand arrow, the return to the undeformed position. Positive at the recording electrode is down. Time marks recur at 0·2-second intervals. (Courtesy of M. L. Wolbarsht.)

While it is convenient to speak of all sensilla trichodea as a class of sensilla responding to deflexion, the variations in structure, hence in physiological characteristics, impart to the different ones quite different functions in the economy of the insect. One of the salient differences encountered is the rate of adaptation. Generally, the smaller, more delicate hairs adapt rapidly during prolonged deflexion while the stouter spines adapt more slowly and incompletely. The nature of the process is still unclear.

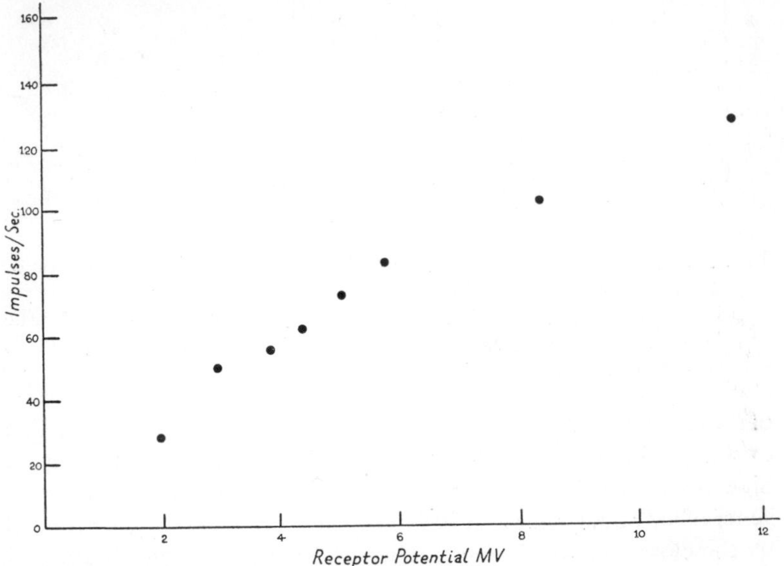

FIG. 22. Receptor potential amplitude plotted against frequency of impulses for a mechanosensory hair on the anal plate of a female *Phormia*. Each point is the average of 2 seconds. (Redrawn from Wolbarsht, 1961.)

Evidence has been presented to show that the generation of impulses follows depolarization of the neuron membrane. The rate of adaptation appears to be closely related to the rate of decay of the depolarization. The generator potential of the rapidly adapting Pacinian corpuscle of the cat (Alvarez-Buylla and de Arellano, 1953; Gray and Sato, 1953), the fast adaptory crustacean muscle receptor (Eyzaguirre and Kuffler, 1955), and the sensory hairs on the wings of flies (Fig. 17) (Wolbarsht, 1960) fall rapidly below threshold. The slowly adapting frog-muscle spindle (Katz, 1950), the slow muscle receptor of Crust-

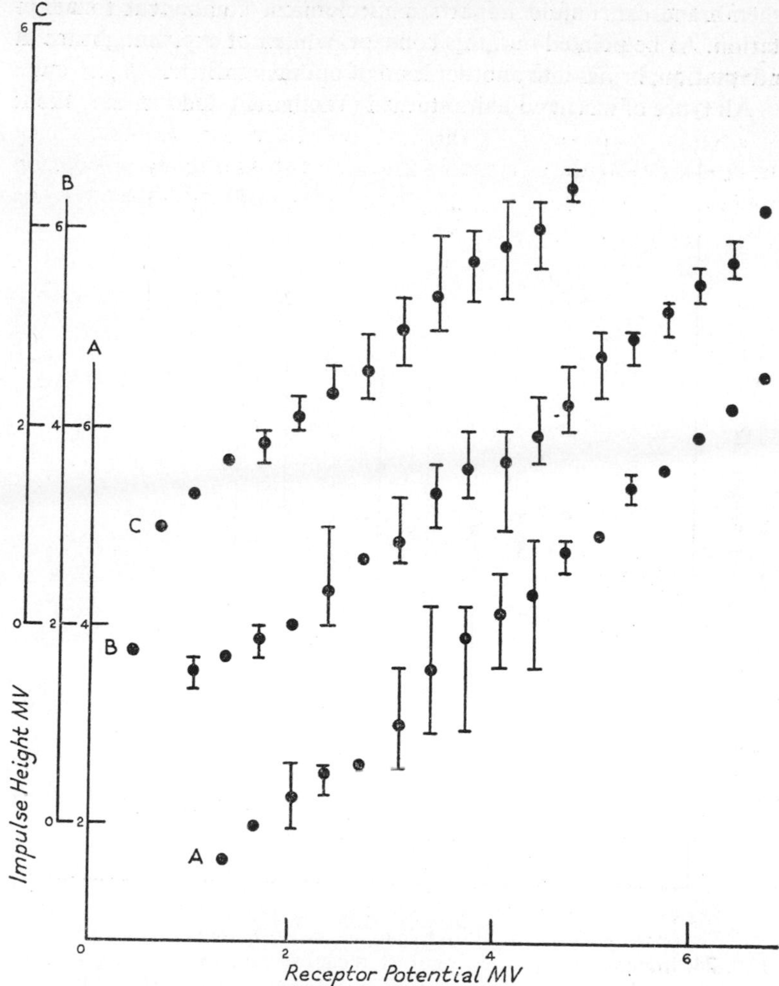

Fig. 23. Impulse size plotted against receptor potential for a mechanosensory hair on the outer clasper of a male *Phormia*. Points are average values; bars denote extreme values. (Redrawn from Wolbarsht, 1961.)

acea, and the mechanosensory hair on the claspers of male flies (Fig. 18) (Wolbarsht, 1960) exhibit slow potentials that are maintained above threshold for a considerable period of time. It has been assumed, at least in some cases, that depolarization is a consequence of the unfolding of the cell membrane (Katz, 1950; Gray and Sato, 1953). Lowenstein (1956) has suggested that the degree to which the membrane can unfold imparts a mechanical component to adaptation. As he pointed out, this concept, while not explaining rates of adaptation, brings it to another level of understanding.

All types of mechano-hairs studied (Wolbarsht and Dethier, 1958;

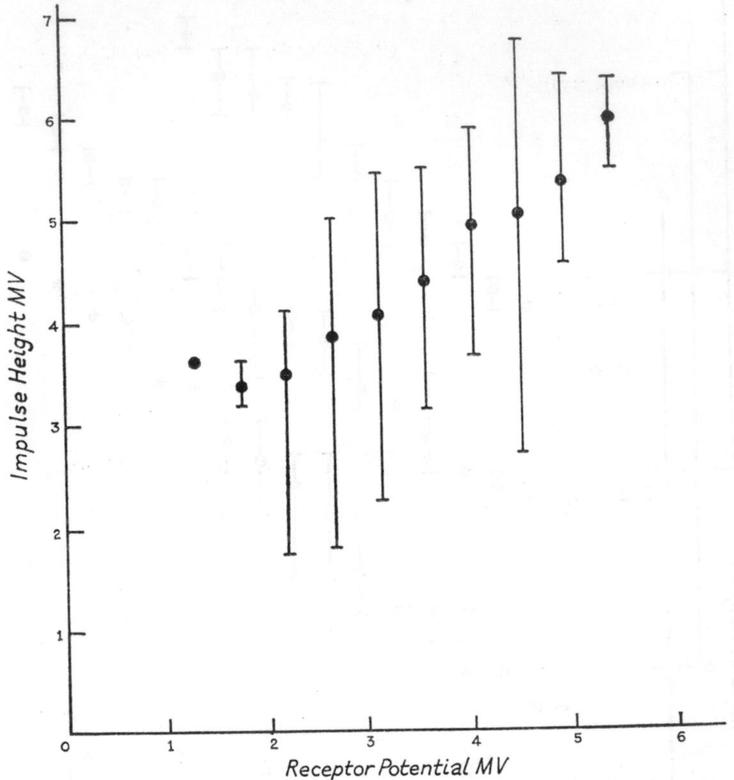

FIG. 24. Impulse size plotted against receptor potential for a mechanosensory hair on the second antennal joint of *Melanoplus*. All points except lowest receptor potential are averages of at least twenty impulses. Lowest value is a single impulse. Bars denote extreme values. (Redrawn from Wolbarsht, 1961.)

Wolbarsht, 1960; Pumphrey, 1936) appear to fall into two classes: velocity sensitive and pressure sensitive. The former fire only while the stimulus is changing. Some, such as the hairs on the leading edge of the wings of flies and other insects (Wolbarsht and Dethier, 1958), may fire at a rate of 600 or more impulses per second. Pressure-sensitive hairs show a repetitive discharge during a static deformation.

Tactile receptors are usually of the velocity-sensitive type and are most common on those portions of the body that encounter the environment as the animal progresses or on those appendages with which the animal explores its environment. Pressure-sensitive receptors are

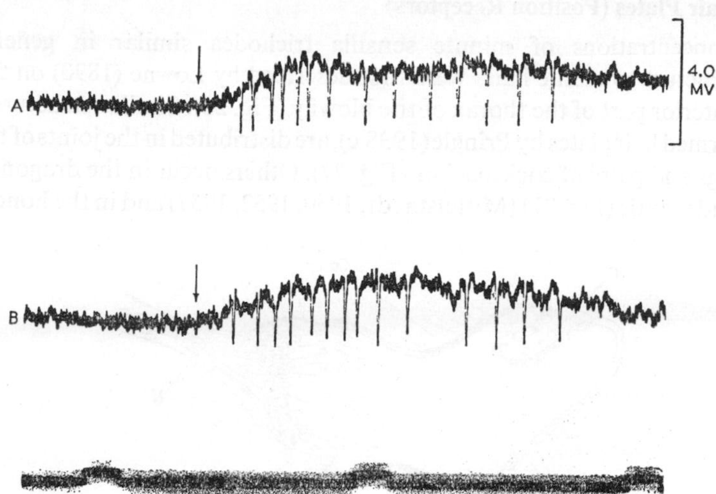

FIG. 25. Response of a mechanosensory hair on the second antennal joint of *Melanoplus* to increasing mechanical stimulation. Approximate onset of stimulation is indicated by arrow. The stimulus continues until the end of the record. A and B are responses to successive stimuli of approximately the same size. Positive at the recording electrode is down. Time marks recur at 0·2-second intervals. (Courtesy of M. L. Wolbarsht.)

most common on those areas where positioning is important. They are found, for example, in the genital regions and between joints. They are proprioceptors.

PROPRIOCEPTORS

Proprioceptors may be defined as sense organs capable of continuous response to deformations (changes in length) and stresses (tensions and compressions) in the body (Lissmann, 1950). They provide some of the information necessary for the animal to maintain certain relations of one part of the body with another and of the body as a whole with respect to gravity. In this capacity they are assisted by other receptors, as photo- and tactile receptors, for example, whose primary function may lie in another realm. In other words, the insect maintains position by assessing much information from a multitude of receptors.

Five kinds of sensory structures are known to take direct part in proprioception: hair plates, campaniform sensilla, stretch receptors, chordotonal organs, and statocyst-like organs.

Hair Plates (Position Receptors)

Concentrations of minute sensilla trichodea similar in general structure to tactile hairs were first described by Lowne (1890) on the anterior part of the thorax of the blowfly (Fig. 26). Similar structures, termed hair plates by Pringle (1938 c), are distributed in the joints of the legs and palpi of cockroaches (Fig. 27). Others occur in the dragonfly and mantis (Fig. 27) (Mittelstaedt, 1950, 1952, 1957) and in the honey-

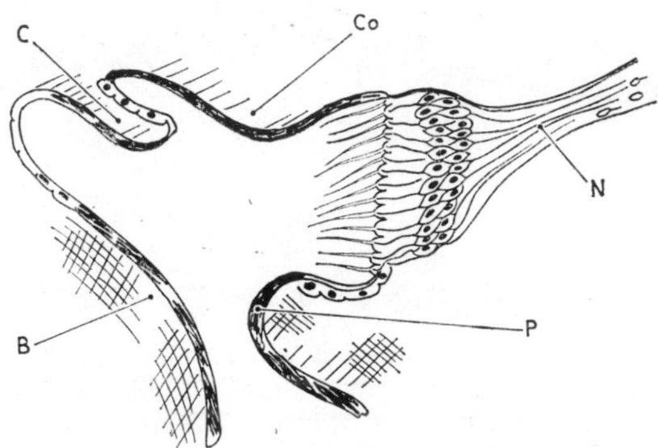

FIG. 26. The prosternal organ of *Calliphora*. B, basal part of head; C, neck sclerite; Co, connecting membrane; N, nerve; P, prothorax. (Redrawn from Lowne, 1890.)

bee (Lindauer and Nedel, 1959). Single hairs of varying size and shape were found in the body articulations of the cockroach by Diakonoff (1936). Hair plates are undoubtedly a common feature among insects. In all cases the sensilla are stimulated by folds of the intersegmental membrane or contact with adjoining surfaces as the joints are moved.

The hair plates of the cockroach have been studied in some detail (Markl, 1962; Peters, 1962). The discharge of these receptors is proportional to the degree of bending of the hairs as the joint is flexed. The initial frequency may be 800 or more per second (Fig. 29). The rate of adaptation is very slow. Thus, the hair plates act as 'position' organs and behave independently of muscular tension.

The proprioceptive function of hair plates is strikingly illustrated by Mittelstaedt's (1952, 1957) analysis of prey capture by mantids. Successful prey capture is a problem of absolute optic localization.

Mantids lying in ambush detect their prey visually. The eyes being immovable, the head is turned so that the prey is always faced. Although the mantis may then turn its body to line it up with the prey, it can capture a prey which sits at a considerable lateral deviation from the median plane of the thorax. If the prey is close enough it is seized by a rapid (10–30 milliseconds) stroke of the prothoracic legs. The accuracy of hitting in normal mantids is about 85 per cent. Since

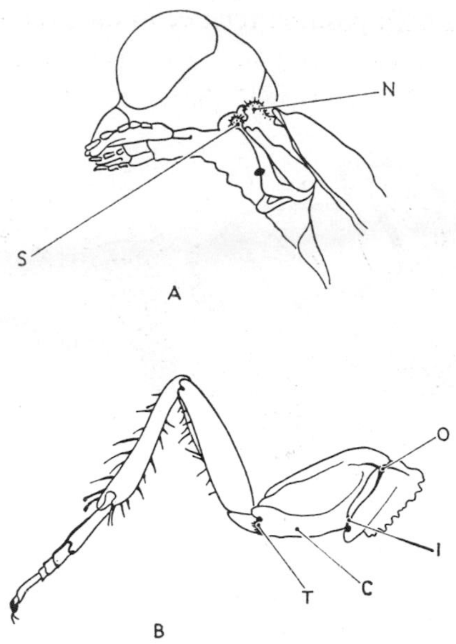

FIG. 27. A. Proprioceptors of the neck region of the mantis. S, sternocervical hair plate; N, tergocervical plate. (Redrawn from Mittelstaedt, 1957.) B. Proprioceptors of the second leg of *Periplaneta*. C, coxa; I, inner coxal hair plate; O, outer coxal hair plate; T, trochanteral hair plate. (Redrawn from Pringle, 1938 c.)

the speed of the stroke is so great, its direction is not controlled by watching the difference between its direction and that of the prey. Its direction is predetermined by information concerning the position of the prey relative to the plane of the prothorax. Thus, the message steering the stroke must contain information about the direction of the prey relative to the head and of the position of the head relative to the prothorax. The first information is provided by the compound eyes; the second, by hair plates in the neck region. Two pairs of plates are involved; the sternocervical plate (Pringle, 1938 c) and the tergocervical plate (Mittelstaedt, 1952) (Fig. 27). The role of these sensory systems was demonstrated by the following series of experiments. If the innervation from all hair plates is cut so that no information is forthcoming from these organs the accuracy of hitting drops to 20–30 per cent. With deafferentation of the left side only, missing increases, and there is a tendency to strike to the right. In other words, proprioceptive information coming only from the right misleads the animal into believing that its head is turned to the right whereas it is not. If the head is held in a fixed position relative to the prothorax by a balsa-

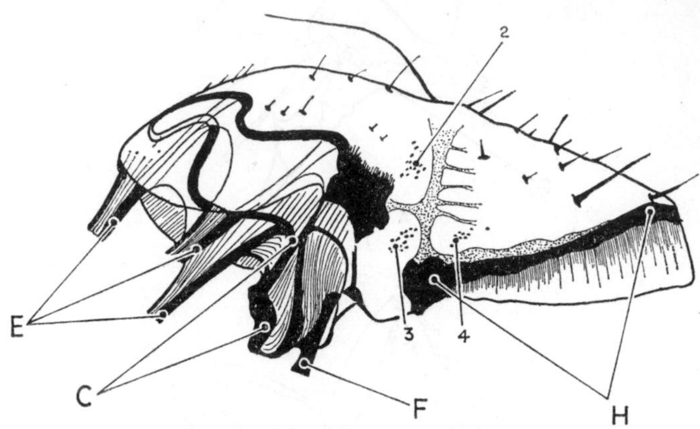

FIG. 28. Ventral view of the campaniform sensilla in the trochanteral region of the third right leg of *Periplaneta*. C, coxo-trochanteral condyle; E, extensor trochanteris and its accessory apodemes; F, flexor trochanteris; H, trochantero-femoral hinge joint; 2, 3, 4, groups of campaniform sensilla. (Redrawn from Pringle, 1938c.)

wood bridge so that the neck region is not touched accuracy of hitting decreases to 25 per cent if the head deviates from the body axis by 10–30 degrees. The prey is missed to the left if the head has been turned to the right, and vice versa.

If head fastening and unilateral extirpation of proprioceptors are combined the effects of both are superimposed, the loss of one-half of the neck receptors being equivalent to a deviation of the head of less than 20 degrees. If the free head is loaded with an extraneous force performance remains normal until the load surpasses twice the head weight at twice its diameter. In short, direction of stroke depends on feedback processes which control the position of the head. Fixation movements of the head are steered by the difference between the optic-centre message (a function of the angle between prey and

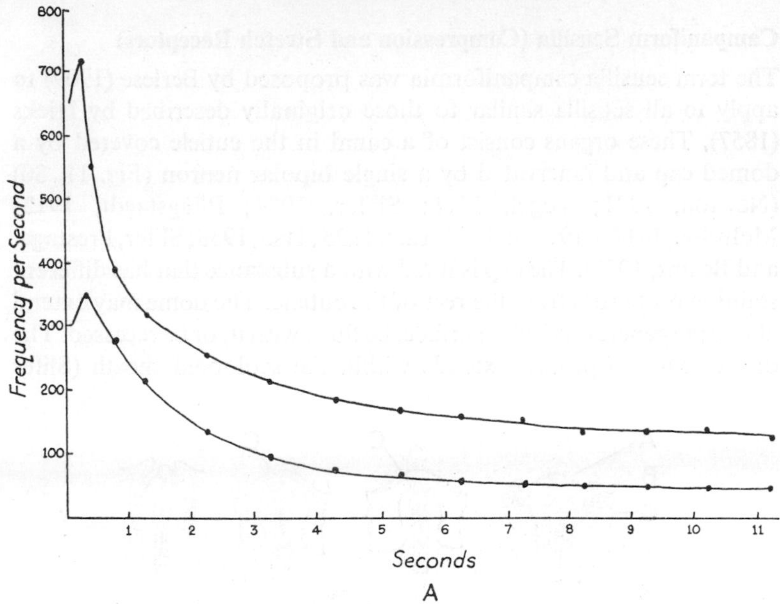

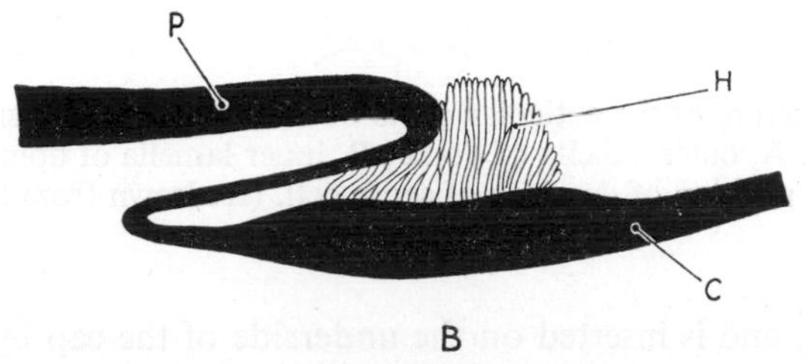

FIG. 29. A. Adaptation of a nerve-ending in the inner coxal hair plate of *Periplaneta* to a stimulus of a constant deflexion of the hairs. Two records from the same preparation. B. Diagram to illustrate the method of excitation of the inner coxal hair plate by a fold of the intersegmental membrane. C, coxa; H, hair plate; P, pleuron. (Redrawn from Pringle, 1938c.)

fixation-line) and the proprioceptive-centre message (a function of the angle of the head with respect to the body axis). If fixation movements have come to rest the direction of stroke is determined by the optic and, to a lesser extent, by the proprioceptive-centre messages, which then both contain the required information (Mittelstaedt, 1957).

D

Campaniform Sensilla (Compression and Stretch Receptors)

The term sensilla campaniformia was proposed by Berlese (1909) to apply to all sensilla similar to those originally described by Hicks (1857). These organs consist of a canal in the cuticle covered by a domed cap and innervated by a single bipolar neuron (Fig. 11, 30) (Newton, 1931; Vogel, 1911; Sihler, 1924; Pflugstaedt, 1912; McIndoo, 1914 a, 1914 b; Snodgrass, 1935; Hsü, 1938; Slifer, Prestage, and Beams, 1959). The cap is lined with a substance that has different staining properties from the rest of the cuticle. The dome may extend above the general cuticular surface, be flush with it, or be recessed. The distal neuronal process extends within the scolopoid sheath (Slifer

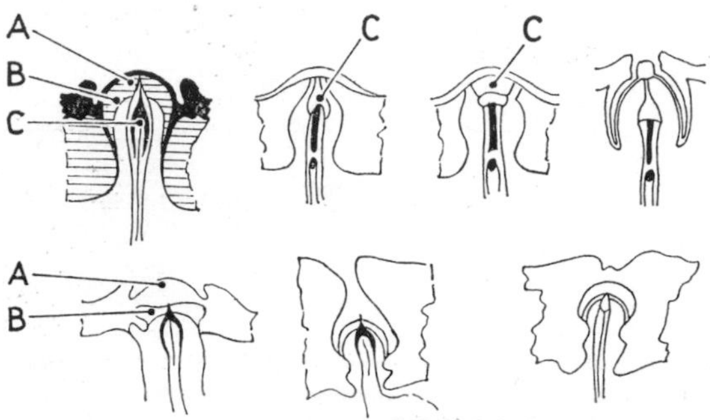

FIG. 30. Structure of the cuticular parts of various types of campaniform sensilla. A, outer lamella of dome; B, inner lamella of dome; C, cuticular connexion of dendrite of sense cell. (Redrawn from Snodgrass, 1935.)

et al., 1959) and is inserted on the underside of the cap by a highly refractile body.

These sensilla occur on practically all parts of the body. One of the earliest suggestions that they are proprioceptive organs came from Demoll (1917), many of whose speculations concerning the mechanism of action were given substance by the work of Pringle (1938 b). It is interesting that there is no known case of these sensilla occurring on a part of the cuticle free from strain. They are concentrated especially where stresses are set up by muscular contractions (e.g., leg, wing, haltere, ovipositor, and mandibular joints). A model has been constructed by Pringle (1938 b) to explain their probable action (Fig. 31).

A thin, flat surface such as the cuticle can be subjected to bending by forces at right angles to its plane or shearing in its plane, as illustrated by a sheet of rubber stretched over a rectangular frame (Fig. 31). When the surface is distorted by changing the rectangle to a parallelogram there is tension in the direction *AC* and compression in the direction *BD*.

Any force applied to a hollow cylinder sets up shearing forces (see Fig. 31). This is the situation as it occurs in a homogeneous surface to which forces are applied evenly. Insect limbs do not conform to this ideal, but, as Pringle pointed out, the important point is that on a hollow structure such as the insect exoskeleton all stresses can be ex-

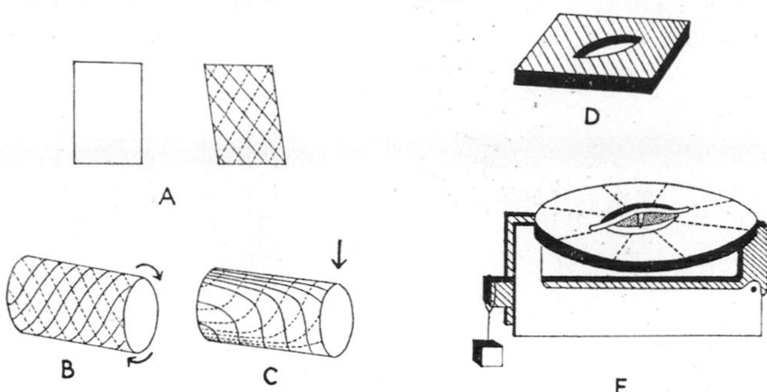

FIG. 31. Diagram to illustrate the resolution of shear forces into compression and extension components. A, a flat surface; B and C, a hollow cylinder subjected to twist and bend. Continuous lines, extension. Broken lines, compression. D, model representing actual sensillum; E, model constructed in a circular framework for measurement of the effect of compression in different directions. (Redrawn from Pringle, 1938b.)

pressed as shearing, which can be resolved into compression and extension components.

Based upon these ideas, the probable mode of action of a campaniform sensillum can be explained in terms of a second model (Fig. 31). In a sheet of rubber stretched over a frame a circular or oval hole corresponding to the cuticular canal of the sensillum is cut. A domed strip of paper is fastened across the long diameter of the oval aperture. This corresponds to the longitudinal thickening frequently seen in the dome of the sensillum where the nerve fibre is attached. The rest of the cap, assumed to be more elastic, is omitted from the model. The assumption of differential elasticity of the two parts is essential to the theory.

Distortion of the model from the rectangular shape causes the hole

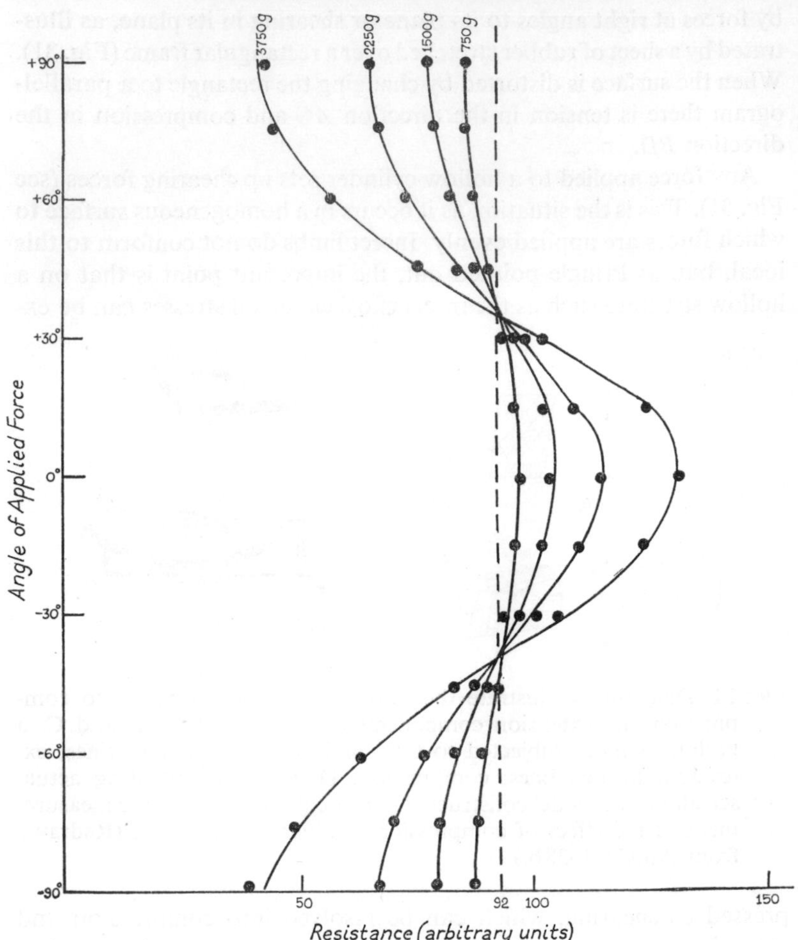

FIG. 32. Graph obtained from the model in Fig. 31E showing the relation between the angle of the applied compression force and the resistance of the electrolytic cell for various values of the compression force. (Redrawn from Pringle, 1938 b.)

to be lengthened in one direction and shortened in another. As a result of this action, the paper strip humps up in the middle. If the end of the neuron is imagined as being inserted on the underside of the middle of the strip it will be stretched by movement in one direction and compressed by that in the other. The magnification of movement is very large.

In order to provide some measurement of the force involved,

Pringle constructed another model in which there were two strips of paper, one on each surface (Fig. 31). The movement measured between the two and the relation between the angle of the applied compression force and the resistance of the detecting electrolytic cell is shown in Fig. 32.

If it be assumed excitation occurs only with increased doming, then the neuron will be excited when the compression component of the shear force makes an angle of less than a certain critical value with the

FIG. 33. Details of the orientation of the groups of campaniform sensilla on the third leg of *Periplaneta*. (Redrawn from Pringle, 1938 b.)

direction of thickening of the cap membrane. The sensitivity of the sensillum will depend, among other things, on the absolute length of the long diameter of the cap. Sensilla with parallel orientation will respond to the same type of shear force. Each group will act as a unit and, if innervated from the same fibre, will extend the range of these fibres quantitatively but not qualitatively (Fig. 33). This condition occurs in the sensilla of the palps (Pringle, 1957).

Although there is yet no direct evidence that the sensillum has undirectional sensitivity, considerable circumstantial evidence supports the idea. In many instances groups of sensilla are orientated in the same direction. The sensilla on the tarsus have their long diameters parallel to the length of the leg (similarly in the palps) and when the tarsus is pressed against the ground the compression lines in the cuticle of the upper surface, where these sensilla are located, will also be longitudinal. It must be the compression component which is effective.

Electrical recordings have shown clearly that these sensilla are most sensitive to pressure on the cuticle (Pringle, 1938 b). Adaptation is slow and incomplete.

Stretch Receptors

Certain of the Type II receptors for which no function had been known have recently been shown by Finlayson and Lowenstein (1955, 1958)

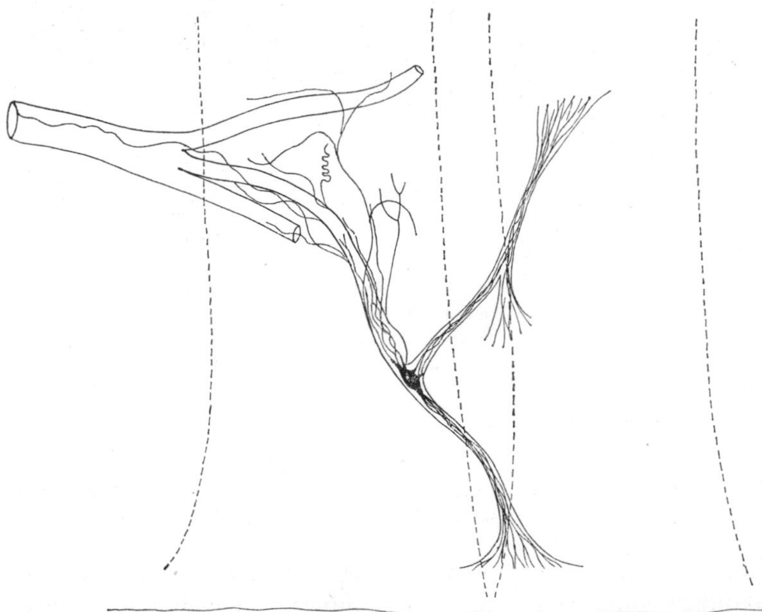

FIG. 34. Stretch receptor in the right side of the fourth abdominal segment of *Periplaneta*. The broken lines indicate the posterior ends of the fourth and fifth muscle bands, counting from the dorsal mid-line. (Redrawn from Finlayson and Lowenstein, 1958.)

to be stretch receptors analogous to the stretch receptors of Crustacea discovered by Alexandrowicz (1951, 1952 a, 1952 b, 1954, 1956) and to the muscle spindles of vertebrates. First described by Zawarzin (1912 a) and Rogosina (1928) in dragonfly larvae, they have now been found in

Orthoptera, Hymenoptera, and Lepidoptera by Slifer and Finlayson (1956) and Finlayson and Lowenstein (1955, 1958).

Three types of stretch receptors are known: those associated with connective tissue, those associated with muscle, and those consisting of a specialized muscle fibre. They are represented by receptors in dragonfly larvae, bees, and cockroaches, by those in Orthoptera, and by those in moths respectively.

Each connective tissue receptor is a multipolar neuron embedded in a strand of connective tissue which stretches either from an inter-

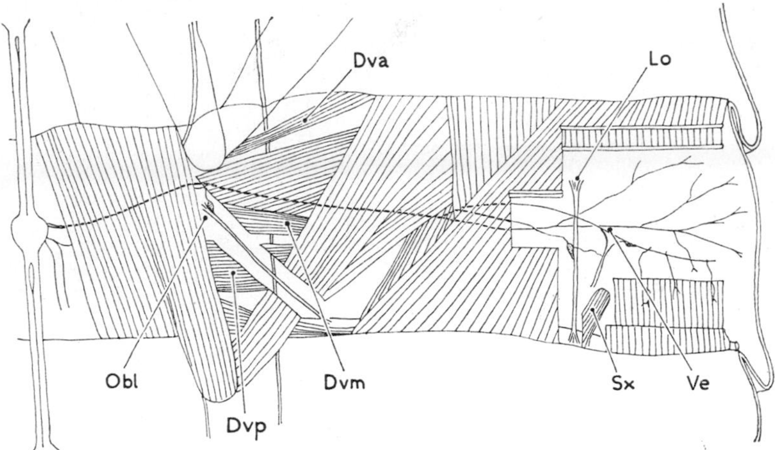

FIG. 35. Right half of the sixth abdominal segment of a full-grown larva of *Aeschna juncea* with various muscles cut to reveal the three stretch receptors. Dva, dorso-ventral anterior muscle; Dvm, dorso-ventral median muscle; Dvp, dorso-ventral posterior muscle; Sx, sextic longitudinal tergal muscle; Obl, oblique receptor; Lo, longitudinal receptor; Ve, vertical receptor. (Redrawn from Finlayson and Lowenstein, 1958.)

segmental fold or from a nerve to a point on the body wall (Fig. 34). In the cockroach *Periplaneta americana* a pair has been found in the dorsal region of abdominal segments two to seven. In dragonfly larvae (*Aeschna juncea*) three pairs of receptors have been found in each abdominal segment one to eight (Fig. 35). In the honeybee there is a pleural pair in each abdominal segment three to six. In all cases the neuron is encapsulated in connective tissue. The capsule is multinucleated. Detailed studies with light- and electron microscopy of the abdominal stretch receptor of the cockroach *Blaberus* (Osborne and Finlayson, 1962; Osborne, 1963) have shown that the terminal regions of the dendrites are naked, that is, not invested by Schwann cells, and embedded in the connective tissue matrix. There are no connexions with the collagen-like connective tissue fibrils. They resemble very closely the sensory terminations of the vertebrate muscle spindle and Pacinian corpuscle.

In Orthoptern (Acrididae) a pair of muscle receptor organs is present in each of abdominal segments one to ten in the region of the mid-dorsal line. The receptor organ is usually attached to the medial edge of one of the longitudinal muscle bands, although it may be nearer the

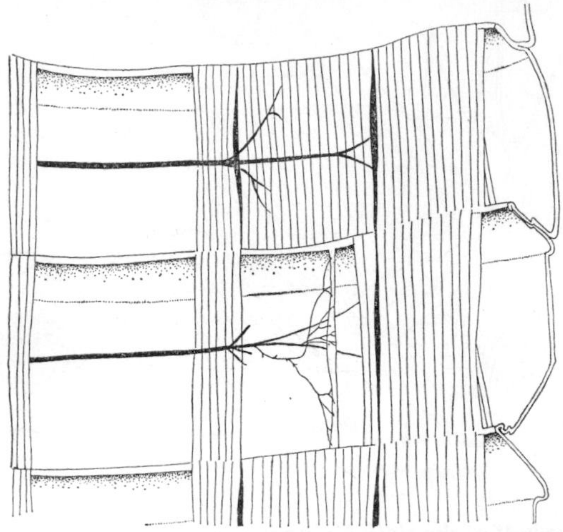

FIG. 36. Dorsal longitudinal muscles of the third and fourth abdominal segments of a pupa of *Antheraea pernyi*, with a part of the band in the fourth segment removed to show the receptor. Motor and sensory innervation of the receptor are shown. (Redrawn from Finlayson and Lowenstein, 1958.)

middle. Each consists of a large multipolar neuron surrounded by a thick nucleated capsule and a modified muscle fibre. There are also many neurilemma cells. The muscle fibre originates near the anterior end of the segment, and is inserted on the anterior end of the following segment. The fibre possesses striations. Attached to it are numerous thick connective tissue fibres which also extend to adjacent muscle fibres. The axon of the receptor joins the ventral branch of each segmental tergal nerve.

The most complex receptors are those in the larvae, pupae, and adults of Lepidoptera. In the larvae there is a pair in the meso- and meta-thorax and abdominal segments one to nine (Fig. 36). They are present in the abdominal segments of pupae and adults but have not been found in the thorax. The receptor consists of a multipolar receptor cell, a modified muscle fibre, and motor innervation to the fibre (Fig. 37a). The neuron is enclosed in the usual connective-tissue sheath.

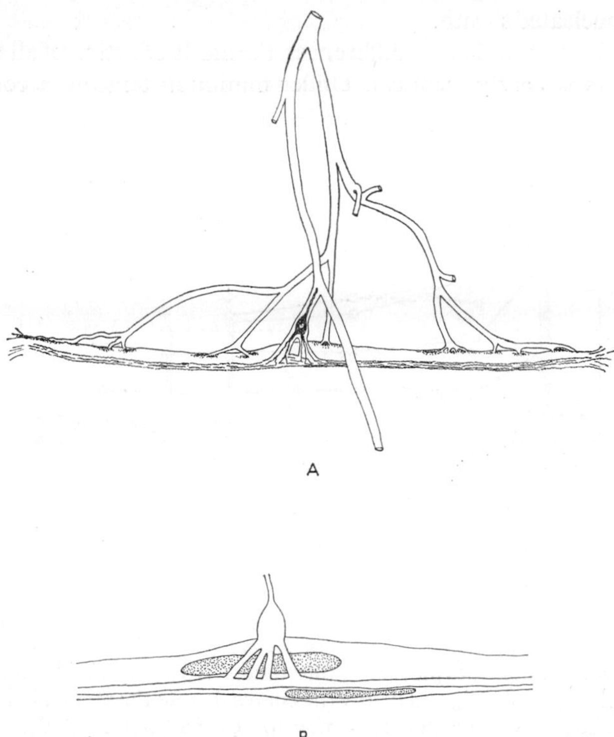

FIG. 37. A. Diagram of the structure and innervation of a lepidopteran stretch receptor, based on a preparation from the right side of the fifth abdominal segment of a pupa of *Antheraea pernyi*. The receptor is short because no tension is applied. B. Diagram showing the relative sizes and positions of the two giant nuclei, the neuron sheath, and the fibre tract of a lepidopteran stretch receptor. (Redrawn from Finlayson and Lowenstein, 1958.)

Its dendrites sometimes run on finger-like extensions of the sheath, which is continuous with a tubular sheath extending along the edge of the receptor (Fig. 37b). The muscle which constitutes the bulk of the receptor has fainter striations than normal muscles. At the centre there is a clear swelling with a giant nucleus (100–360 μ). Adjacent to this is another large nucleus. This muscle has its own separate motor innervation. The resemblance of this receptor to the vertebrate muscle spindle is striking. Both have rich motor innervation, an absence of striations in the central region, and much nuclear material (nucleus in the insect; nuclear bag in the vertebrate). In Crustacea and other insects there is no giant nucleus, but there is, as already described, a richly nucleated sheath.

Despite morphological differences, the mode of action of all of these receptors is nearly identical. Under minimum tension, a condition

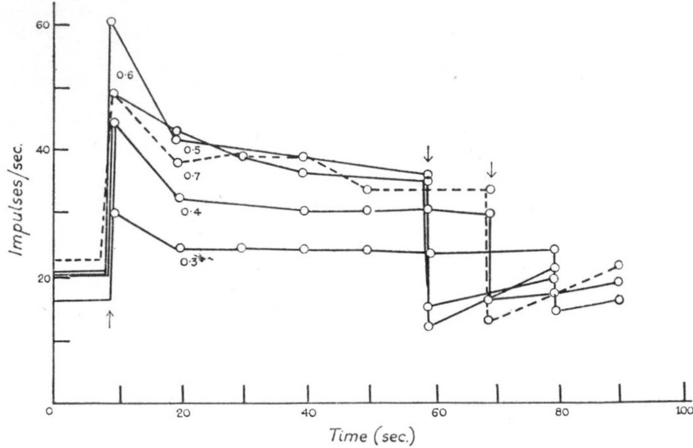

FIG. 38. A series of curves showing the discharge frequencies from the stretch receptor of the larva of *A. pernyi* in response to stretch of different intensities plotted against time. Arrows indicate beginning and end of stretch. Figures below the curves denote the stretch in mm. The broken line indicates response to 'over-stretch'. (Redrawn from Finlayson and Lowenstein, 1958.)

approaching the normal situation, the receptor discharges impulses at the rate of 5–10 a second. Under zero tension it is silent. The basal rate is maintained for hours. When the receptor is stretched there is a large increase in the frequency of discharge (Fig. 38). This drops very rapidly to a new level which is maintained for a long period. Upon release there is a post-stimulatory reduction in discharge. The relatively large drop in initial discharge is probably due both to neuronal adaptation and a mechanical accommodation to stretch. Over what may be judged a normal range of stretch there is a linear relation between the intensity of stretch and the frequency of impulses (Fig. 39). Beyond a certain point this relationship breaks down, probably because of 'over stretch', i.e., extension beyond the physiological range. The slowly adapting receptors clearly serve a static function.

The corresponding organs in Crustacea possess two neurons, a 'fast' and a 'slow' one; that is, a phasic and a static receptor. It turned out when the insect organs were examined with phasic stimulation that the single neurons were in fact dual-purpose receptors (Lowenstein and Finlayson, 1960). At rest the discharge activity is, within certain limits, a linear function of absolute length or total displace-

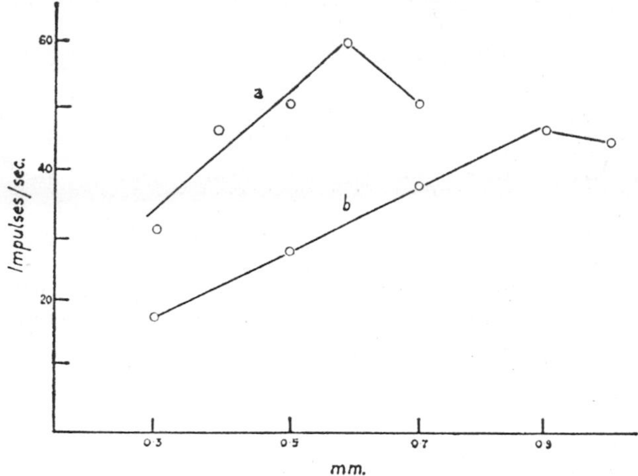

FIG. 39. Peak discharge frequencies plotted against intensity of stretch. A, larva of *A. pernyi*; b, longitudinal receptor of larva of *A. juncea*. (Redrawn from Finlayson and Lowenstein, 1958.)

ment. With plastic alternation of stretch and relaxation the impulse activity is a combined function of displacement and velocity. At low stimulus frequencies the phase relation of maximum response is approximately constant, and maximum activity coincides with maximum slope (= max velocity) (Fig. 40). Impulses begin to drop out as higher stimulus frequencies (1·5–5 c/s) occur (Fig. 41). Above 5 c/s the organ fails to signal phasic stimuli accurately, although the response is still in phase with the stimulus. Up to this point the stimulus-response relationship is linear (Fig. 42).

This receptor is thus seen to respond to displacement at low stretch velocities, but from 3 to 4 c/s onward there is no response activity at maximum displacement and during relaxation. Lowenstein and Finlayson (1960) were convinced that the decline of activity after the velocity peak of the stretch is passed is accentuated by post-excitatory

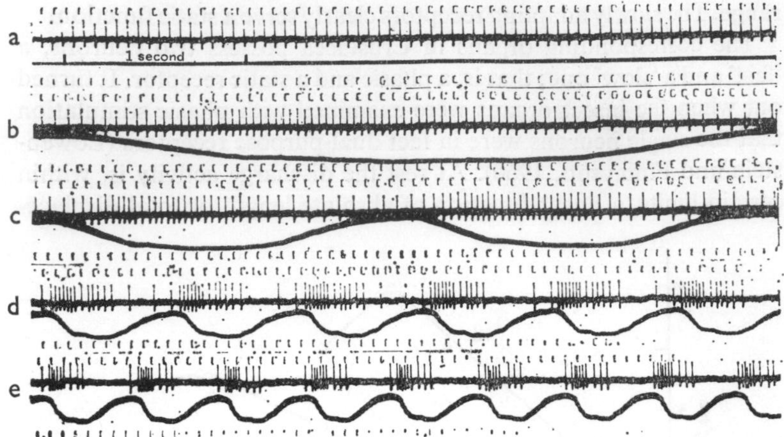

FIG. 40. Response to phasic stimulation during a continuous experiment with a range of frequencies of alternation between stretch and relaxation. a, resting discharge; b–e, frequency of stimulus and velocity of stretch respectively, 0·25 c/s, 4·3 mm./sec.; 0·5 c/s, 7·3 mm./sec.; 1·5 c/s, 22·2 mm./sec.; 2 c/s, 33·6 mm./sec. (Redrawn from Lowenstein and Finlayson, 1960.)

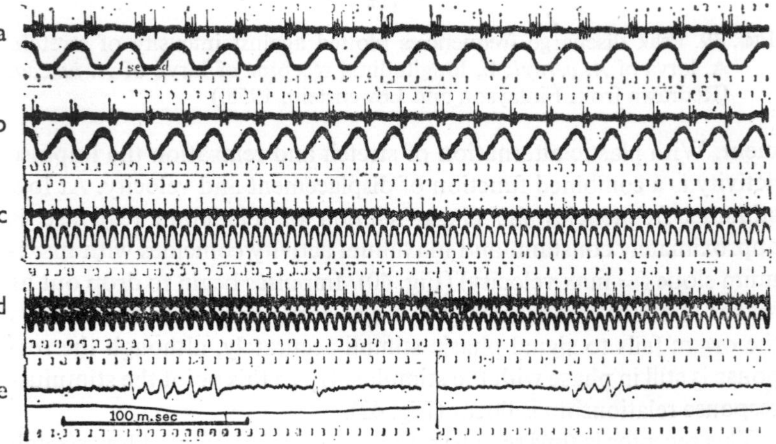

FIG. 41. Continuation of experiment in Fig. 40. a–e, 4 c/s, 67·2 mm./sec.; 5 c/s, 71 mm./sec.; 15·5 c/s, 89 mm./sec.; 18·5 c/s, 59 mm./sec.; recordings of responses in a and b respectively at ten times speed. (Redrawn from Lowenstein and Finlayson, 1960.)

inhibition. Thus, the gradual disappearance of response to displacement and the transition from a static to a dynamic response is related to the post-excitatory silencing.

The range of accurate frequency monitoring is more than adequate to keep pace with such rhythmic activity as respiratory movements. In their static capacities these stretch receptors are able to provide information as to the relations of one part of the body with respect to

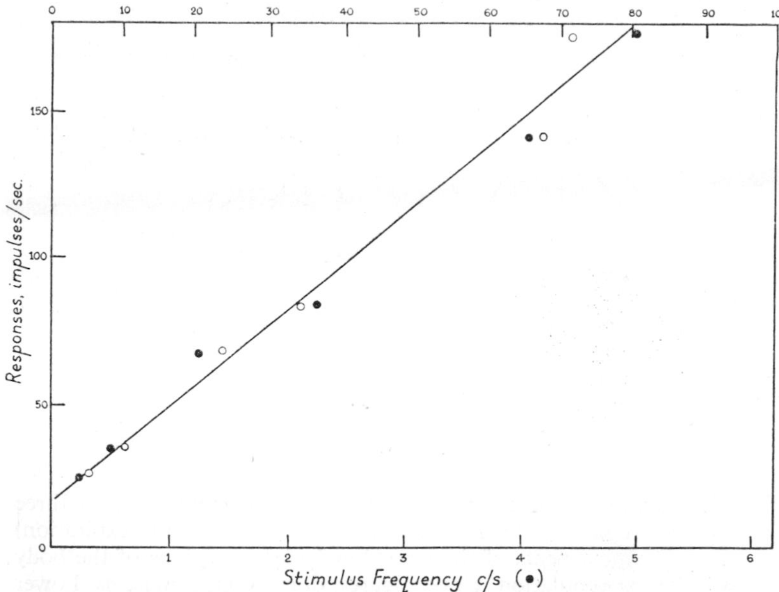

FIG. 42. Stimulus–response relationship. Frequency of phasic stimulus (solid circles) (abscissa). Velocity of stretch (open circles) (abscissa). Impulse frequency (ordinate). (Redrawn from Lowenstein and Finlayson, 1960.)

another. In the dragonfly larvae, for example, the three pairs of receptors are well adapted to supply information for analyses of body movements. As Fig. 43 illustrates for dragonfly larvae, the oblique receptor will be stretched during respiration (A) and relaxed during expiration (B). In longitudinal abdominal movement, as, for example, jet propulsion locomotion, the vertical and longitudinal receptors will act antagonistically.

Chordotonal Sensilla

Cord-like sensilla devoid of a specialized exocuticular component and stretching from one point of the body wall or its derivatives to another are peculiar to insects and have been found in every species in which they have been sought (Siebold, 1844; Leydig, 1851; Graber, 1882 a, 1882 b; Eggers, 1924, 1928; Snodgrass, 1926; Debaisieux,

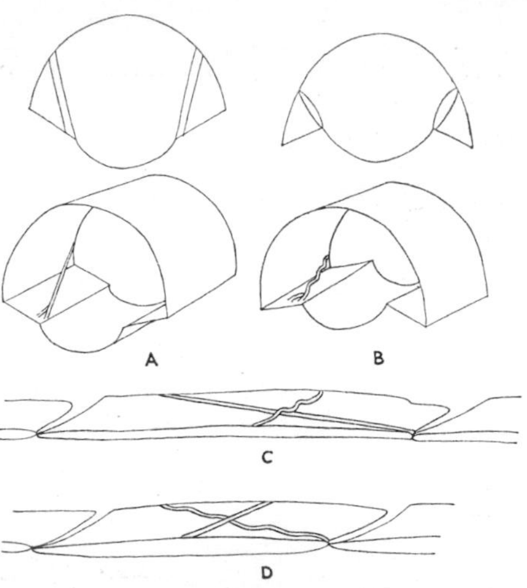

FIG. 43. Diagrams to illustrate probable alterations in tension of the three stretch receptors of *Aeschna* larvae. A (inspiration) and B (expiration) show the movements of the sternal and pleural regions of the body wall during ventilation. Upper figures, dorso-ventral muscles. Lower figure, oblique receptor of right side. The oblique receptor will be stretched during A and relaxed during B. C and D illustrate probable effects of longitudinal movement on longitudinal and vertical receptors. (Redrawn from Finlayson and Lowenstein, 1958.)

1935, 1938; Debauche, 1935; and others). They are widely distributed in the body. In all insects they occur in the appendages of the mouth and in the legs. They are universally present at the bases of the wings (Fig. 44) and halteres (Fig. 45) and in the antennae (Graber, 1882 a, 1882 b; Schon, 1911; Vogel, 1912; Lehr, 1914; Eggers, 1928). They occur segmentally in the abdomen. In many species simple chordotonal organs are associated with the tracheal system (Demoll, 1917; Larsen, 1955). They are especially numerous in larval insects, where they stretch from one point on the body wall to another and criss-

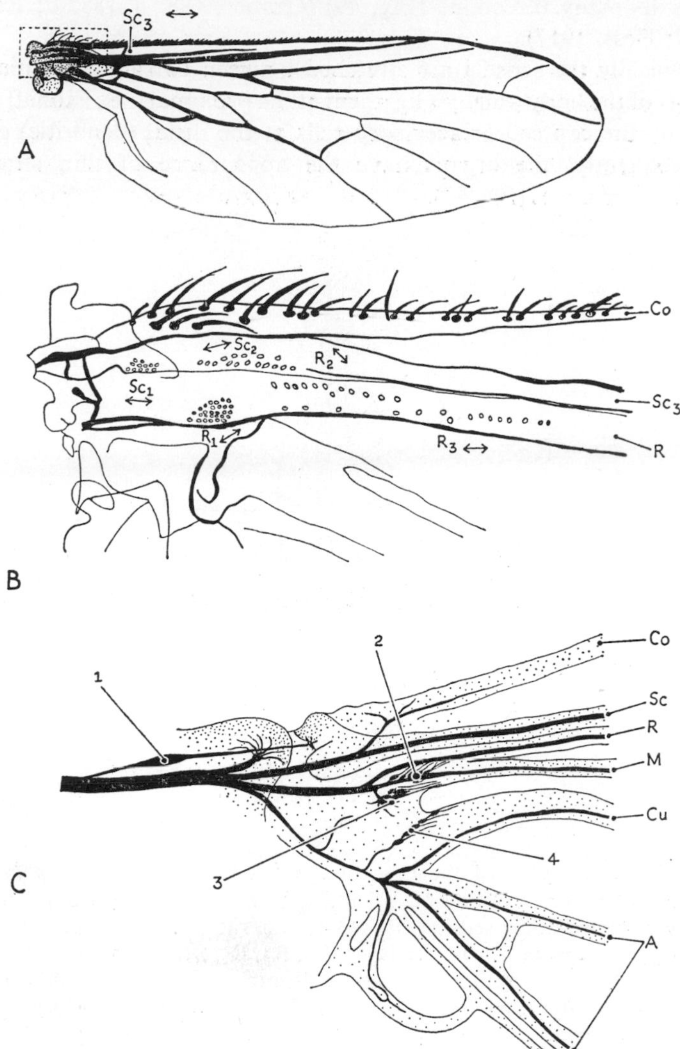

FIG. 44. A. Right wing of *Empis*. B. Enlarged view of insect showing location and orientation of campaniform sensilla. R_1, R_2, R_3, radial groups; Sc_1, Sc_2, Sc_3, subcostal groups with arrows indicating the orientation of the long axes of the sensilla. C. Right wing of *Panorpa communis* showing the location of chordotonal sensilla. 1, 2, 3, 4, ante-alar, radial, medial, and cubital sensilla respectively; Co, costa; Sc, sub-costa; R, radius; M, media; Cu, cubitus; A, anal. (Redrawn from Pringle, 1957 after Zácwilichowski.)

cross in many directions (Fig. 49) (Graber, 1882 a, 1882 b; Radl, 1905; Hess, 1917).

Typically the sensilla are stretched between two undifferentiated points of the body wall by a ligament at the proximal (i.e., axonal) end and by the cap cell or accessory cells at the distal (dendritic) end. Consequently, the organs have the appearance of thin strands (Fig. 46) or sheets (Fig. 47).

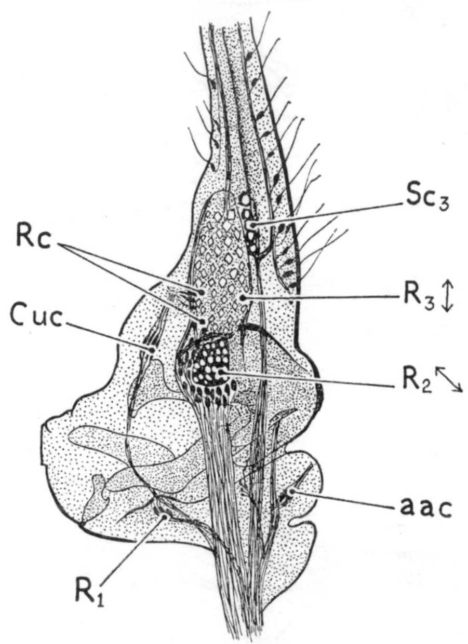

FIG. 45. Dorsal view of the base of the left haltere of *Tipula paludosa* showing the location and orientation of the group of campaniform and chordotonal sensilla. Rc, Cuc, aac, radial cubital, and ante-alar chordotonal organs respectively; R_1, R_2, R_3, Sc_3, radial and subcostal groups of campaniform sensilla with arrows indicating long axes of sensilla. (Redrawn from Pringle, 1957 after Zácwilichowski.)

The structure of chordotonal sensilla is very complex and has yet given no clue as to their exact mode of action. Each sensillum consists of one bipolar neuron and a minimum of two companion cells which are probably homologous with the trichogen and tormogen of other sensilla (Schwabe, 1906; Schon, 1911; Vogel, 1912; Snodgrass, 1926; Eggers, 1928). The three cells are arranged in overlapping linear fashion. One, the enveloping cell, surrounds the proximal portion of the dendrite; the other, the cap cell, surrounds the remaining length of the dendrite. As in the case of other sensilla, the dendrite of the neuron is enclosed terminally in a ribbed scolopoid sheath. This is invariably capped with a darkly staining, peg-shaped apical body (Fig. 48). In some instances there is a terminal strand extending from the apical body to the distal point of attachment of the sensillum.

Although they were originally thought to be exclusively audio-receptors, it is now known that they are not organs of constant function. A proprioceptive function has been demonstrated for many,

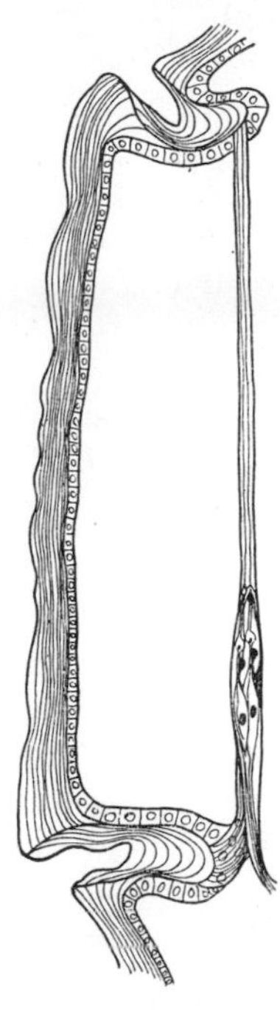

FIG. 46. Longitudinal vertical section of a pleural tubercle of *Monohammus confusor* showing a simple chordotonal organ. (Redrawn from Hess, 1917.)

and it is likely that all not associated with tympanic membranes or grouped to form sub-genual and Johnston's organs (which have a mixed proprioceptive and exteroceptive function and in Culicidae and Chironomidae are auditory) will eventually be proved to be proprioceptive. Their association with skeletal articulations, tracheae, pulsatile organs, and blood cavities has led to hypotheses that they are concerned with position, passive body movements, active muscle movements, blood pressure, tracheal air pressure, and vibrations (Radl, 1905; Demoll, 1917; Hertwick, 1931; Debaisieux, 1938). It can actually be seen by direct observation in many cases that the organs change in length as the insect moves (Radl, 1905; Larsen, 1955).

Proprioceptive chordotonal organs are usually much simpler than those concerned with sound reception, although there are some noteworthy exceptions (e.g., the tympanic organ of noctuid moths). Whereas the auditory organs may consist of tens to thousands of chordotonal sensilla, organs subserving a proprioceptive function consist of very few sensilla, sometimes only one.

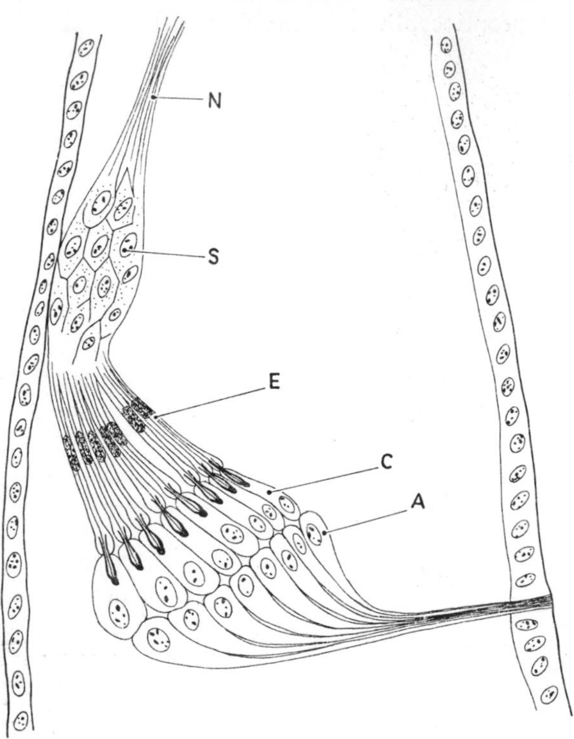

FIG. 47. Subgenual organ of *Formica sanguinea*. A, accessory cell; C, cap cell; E, enveloping cell; S, sense cell; N, nerve. (Redrawn from Schön, 1911.)

In the water bug *Aphelocheirus*, Larsen (1955) discovered a single chordotonal sensillum attached to each of the large tracheal sacs of adults and larvae. He suggested that the sensilla are concerned with respiratory behaviour. When air pressure within the animal falls, as it does according to Larsen, and when an animal in poorly oxygenated water has used up its air supply, there is a decrease in the volume of the air sacs. The decrease triggers the chordotonal sensilla, and the animal can attempt to move to a more favourable environment before acute respiratory distress ensues.

It has been suggested that other chordotonal sensilla in the abdomen of insects may act as rhythmometers in respiration (Eggers, 1928;

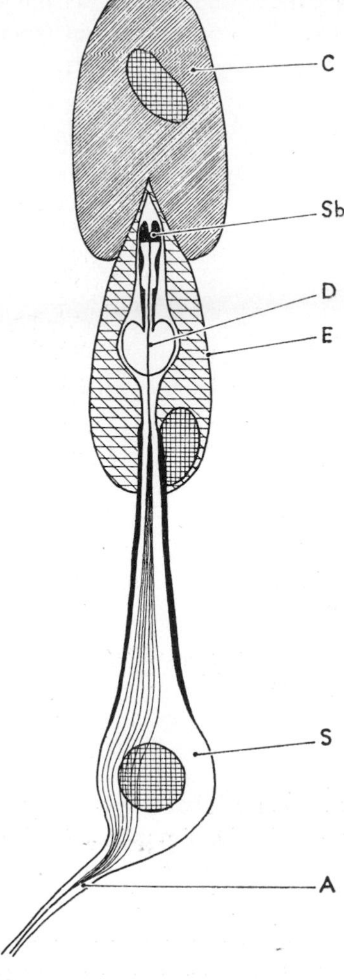

FIG. 48. Diagrammatic representation of a chordotonal sensillum. C, cap cell; E, enveloping cell; S, sense cell; Sb, scolopoid body; D, dendrite; A, axon. (Redrawn from Schwabe, 1906.)

Hughes, 1952). In *Dytiscus* and *Locusta* complicated sensory activity has been recorded in afferent segmental nerves of the abdomen (Hughes, 1952). Three patterns of impulses have been recorded, indicating that there are some end-organs that discharge during inspiration, others that discharge during expiration, and some whose discharge is inhibited during inspiration. Some end-organs with fibres in the segmental nerves respond to whistling, ground tapping, and respiration, others to sound only, others to respiratory movements only. Those responding to sound are sharply tuned to about 100 c/s, and the only parameter of the stimulus to which their frequency of discharge is related is intensity. Since the segmental nerves from which these signals were recorded are known to contain fibres from seg-

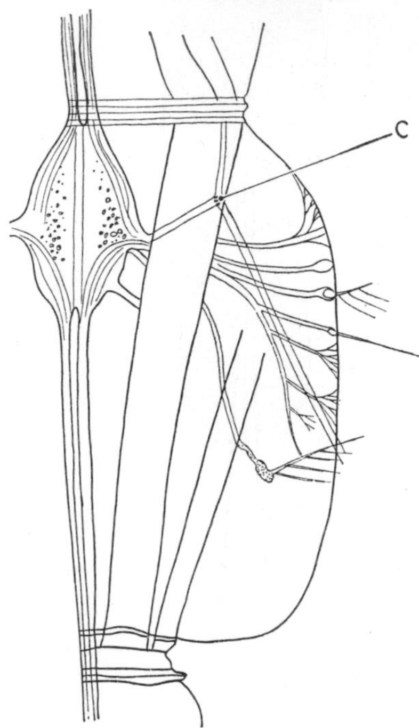

FIG. 49. A segment of the larva of *Corethra plumicornis* showing the location of one of the segmental chordotonal organs (C). (Redrawn from Graber, 1882.)

mental chordotonal organs, it was suggested that they are the sensilla involved in these activities (Hughes, 1952). Pumphrey (1940) also suggested that the activity recorded from the segmental nerves of locusts arises in chordotonal sensilla and not in hairs as formerly believed (Pumphrey and Rawdon-Smith, 1936 c). It should be remembered, however, that the Type II neurons of stretch receptors are also sensitive to respiratory movements and to periodic motion, so that further investigation of chordotonal responses is needed.

Johnston's Organ

In 1855 Johnston discovered in the antennae of culicine mosquitoes the compound chordotonal organ that now bears his name. Its structure was not investigated in any detail until nearly forty years later (Child, 1894). Since then it has been found to be almost a constant feature of insect antennae, and much intensive study has been given to its structure (e.g., Lehr, 1914; Eggers, 1923, 1924, 1928; Debauche, 1936; Richard, 1956, 1957; Urvoy, 1958). In its classical form it is basically a hollow cylinder or truncated sphere in the second antennal segment (pedicel), where it stretches from the base of the segment distally to the synovial membrane of segment three. The sensilla comprising the organ vary in number from tens to hundreds in the different species. Although the sensilla differ from those in other chordotonal organs in that they lack caps or apical bodies, both Eggers (1923, 1928) and Snodgrass (1926, 1935) agreed that they are chordotonal sensilla.

Each sensillum consists of a bipolar neuron, a scolopoid sheath, a cap cell, and an enveloping cell (Eggers, 1928). As seen with the light microscope, the scolopoid sheath, which is ribbed like most, becomes attenuated distally into a bundle of thin fibres. The fibres from a number of sensilla are grouped together for common insertion into a pore, cleft, or some other attachment on the synovial membrane. In the simpler Johnston's organs, where the total number of sensilla is small, each bundle with a common point of attachment is clearly separate from every other bundle. This arrangement suggests that the Johnston's organ is really a compound structure composed of many chordotonal organs. The closed cylinders of the complex Johnston's organs are a consequence of the extraordinarily large number of sensilla that must terminate in the limited space of the pedicle (Eggers, 1928).

The organ is enormously developed in Culicidae and Chironomidae. So many sensilla are crowded into the pedicel that the neurons lie in several layers, and the cap and enveloping cells are so forced out of position that they were originally described as supporting rods (Child, 1894). Furthermore, there is a corresponding modification of the synovial membrane to accommodate the large number of sensilla. The base of the third segment in male culicine mosquitos, for example, flares to form a reinforced circular plate from which rigid spines extend radially far into the pedicel. The sensilla are attached to these spinous processes. In these and other species where the organ is a hollow cylinder both its inner and outer surfaces are covered with epithelium that is a continuation of the hypodermis. In one case (Hymenoptera) every sensillum is individually ensheathed in epithelium. In addition to Johnston's organ there are smaller more typical chordotonal organs present in the scape, pedicel, and flagellum of many insects.

Everyone who has ever looked at Johnston's organs is impressed by the fact that they are ideally situated to respond to movements of the third antennal segment with respect to the second. This means, essentially, movement of the entire flagellum of the antennae with respect to the base, since all antennal muscles are located in the scape and insert on the pedicel.

The stimuli for motion of the antennae may be many. Johnston (1885) surmised that the organs of Culicidae were sensitive to airborne sounds, and Mayer (1874) demonstrated that the long hairs on the shaft of the flagellum could be set in motion when a tuning fork was struck near by. Child (1894) decided that in Culicidae and Chironomidae the organ has an auditory function, but otherwise is a tactile organ. The legend has grown up that Johnston's organs in general are auditory organs, but Demoll (1917) and Eggers (1928) went to great pains to point out that the only evidence for an auditory function to date, and that not conclusive, was the observation of Mayer (1874) for Culicidae. They therefore considered Johnston's organs to be organs concerned with movements of the antennae used actively as tactile appendages and with passive movements induced by air currents.

As might have been suspected from the fact that the Johnston's organ is a compound and complicated organ, the kinds of mechanical stimuli to which it can react are varied. A study of the action potentials produced in the antennae of the blowfly (*Calliphora erythrocephala*) revealed that the majority of sensilla house phasic receptors, but that some of these respond to torsional movements independent of direction, while others are sensitive only to movements in one of the two possible directions (Burkhardt, 1960). When wind blows on the antenna it causes the arista to act as a lever arm which rotates the funiculus outwards around its long axis (Burkhardt and Schneider, 1957). A typical electrical response from a single rotation consists of a large (+ 5 mV) action potential (on-wave) followed by a series of decreasingly small action potentials during the course of stimulation and ending with a large off-wave at the termination of stimulation. The small potentials are released by oscillations superimposed at the time of rotation. The amplitude of the on-wave increases with stimulus intensity. It seems that the on-wave represents the summation of many synchronously discharging neurons. The change in amplitude with change in stimulus intensity is a reflection of the differences in threshold of the contributing units.

The time-course of the off-wave differs slightly. If the direction of rotation of the funiculus is reversed the on-wave now resembles the off-wave at the end of the stimulus for the original direction of rotation, and vice versa. Burkhardt (1960), by way of explanation, suggested that some of the receptors respond to turning in one direction only, while others respond to turning in any direction. The geometrical arrangement of sensilla is such that mechanical stress in a particular direction serves as a stimulus; however, different sensilla are oriented differently with respect to the axis of rotation. Directional sensitivity of this sort had already been described for *Locusta* by Uchiyama and Katsuki (1956) on the basis of action potentials recorded by means of a microelectrode. There is no support for the suggestion of Kuwabara (1952 b) that the Johnston's organ is stimulated by changes in the pressure of body fluid in the pedicel caused by its moment of inertia during antennal movement.

The pattern of discharge following rhythmic stimuli of short duration changes as the frequency of stimulation changes. As the intervals between stimuli are shortened below 20–30 msec., the off-wave of one stimulus approaches more closely the on-wave of the succeeding stimulus. When intervals are double the duration of stimuli the on- and off-waves present a picture of regularity resembling the pattern elicited by air-borne sound (Burkhardt and Schneider, 1957). The response to sound frequencies up to 500 c/s reported by Burkhardt and Schneider (1957) probably arises from rigidly synchronized discharges at the beginning and end of each torsional vibration stimulus (Burkhardt, 1960). As the duration of stimulus is decreased the on- and off-waves approach one another, and eventually the off-wave disappears. It appears to be inhibited by the on-wave rather than to sum with it. Thus, minute changes in stimulus pattern elicit marked alterations in the spatio-temporal excitation pattern in Johnston's organ (Burkhardt, 1960).

Other patterns of excitation can also be detected in antennae, but the identity of the sensilla in which they originate is not known. There are a few unknown tonic receptors (Burkhardt and Schneider, 1957) (also in *Locusta*, Uchiyama and Katsuki, 1956), by means of which a constant deflexion of the antenna can be signalled. When subjected to steady air-flow, however, the antennae appear to tremble. Under these circumstances the phasic receptors would register on- and off-waves and thus could also register a mean deflexion (Burkhardt, 1960). In short, Johnston's organ can provide the central nervous system with rather accurate information about the strength and time course of antennal deflexion.

THE ROLE OF MECHANORECEPTION IN LOCOMOTION

Walking

Locomotion requires the co-ordination of moving parts. Although it is possible that movements associated with locomotion can arise from an innate central pattern, especially in the case of flying, as Wilson (1961) has shown for the desert locust (*Schistocerca gregaria* Forskål), a steady stream of information about the position of parts relative to one another and about the magnitude of forces acting upon them is undeniably necessary. In so far as flight is concerned, Weis-Fogh (1956) and Pringle (1957) favour a complete reflex explanation of movements. The consensus now is that walking, too, is reflexly controlled (Pringle, 1940; Hughes, 1957, 1958).

In addition to feedback loops from the moving parts, locomotion also requires information about the orientation of the insect as a whole in the gravitational field. The source of all of this information is predominantly the mechanoreceptors. All types of mechanoreceptors provide the service, and one of the marvels of the central nervous system is its ability to integrate all of the incoming signals so that the necessary adjustments in the performance of the effectors can be made quickly and accurately.

In walking, for example, the reflex action of the leg muscles is evoked by stimulation of mechanoreceptors. Most of the muscles of the insect leg are innervated by two nerve fibres only, a 'quick' and a 'slow' (Hoyle, 1957). Stimulation of the quick fibre is followed by a large electrical change and a rapid twitch, whereas stimulation of the slow fibre is followed by a smaller electrical change and a tonic contraction. In the cockroach *Periplaneta americana* L., as Pringle (1940) has shown, the depressor reflex is evoked by stimulation of campaniform sensilla on the trochanter; the levator response, by touch on the upper side of the leg or on the tibial spines. Most of the campaniform sensilla are located and oriented so as to be stimulated by forces produced in the leg when the insect is standing normally. The situation may actually be much more complicated than this because of the possibility of the muscles being compound ones (Becht, 1959) and because of the large number of mechanoreceptors (tactile hairs, hair plates, campaniform sensilla, chordotonal sensilla) and their complicated innervation (Nijenhuis and Dresden, 1952; Dresden and Nijenhuis, 1958). That the situation is indeed complicated is further suggested by the detailed cinematographic studies of Hughes (1952, 1957) on normal cockroaches and amputees. As various legs are amputated, the mechanical aspects of walking change. There is a corresponding change in proprioceptive feedback, with the result that gait and other aspects of walking are altered.

In the stick insect (*Carausius morosus*) the posture in walking is regulated by feedback control via hair plates which measure the angle between the coxa and trochanter-femur (Wendler quoted by Mittelstaedt, 1961). In the normal insect the body is held free from the ground as a result of this feedback. The distance above the ground remains the same even when the insect is carrying four times its weight. If the sense organs are eliminated the insect touches the ground under its own weight.

Flying

Flight, of all forms of locomotion, is the most demanding of information. Whether one believes that the basic co-ordination of flight is an inherent function of the central nervous system modulated by sensory feedback (Wilson, 1961) or that flight is more exclusively a matter of reflex control (Weis-Fogh, 1956; Pringle, 1957), it is certain that its initiation, maintenance, adjustment, and termination can be effected by means of elaborate sensory mechanisms. A brief survey of the problems involved will indicate the role of the mechanical senses. A complete treatment is given by Pringle (1957).

The most specific and universal reflex for initiating flight is the 'tarsal reflex' originally described by Fraenkel (1932). When the feet of most insects are removed from the substrate, flight commences. (There is a similar reflex in giant water bugs, *Lethocerus americanus* and *Benacus griseus*, whereby breaking of contact with the substrate initiates swimming movements [Dingle, 1961].) So essential to flying insects is this reflex that in some species (*Phormia*, *Calliphora*, *Vespa*) amputation of the legs interferes with the ability to cease flying. Conversely, contact with the substrate terminates flight. The electrophysiological studies of Pringle (1938 b, 1940), have shown that at least in *Periplaneta* the principal receptors involved are sensilla campaniformia on the trochanter and femur. On the other hand, amputation of the tarsi of flies abolishes the reflex (Fraenkel, 1932; Friedman, 1959).

In *Periplaneta* another flight-initiating reflex has been described by Diakonoff (1936). This is a change in the relative positions of the pro- and mesothorax, the so-called 'fall-reflex'. The sense organs concerned are small trichoid sensilla functioning in a manner similar to that of hair plates. A similar mechanism can cause flight to commence in giant water bugs (Dingle, 1961). Giant water bugs are also stimulated to fly by action of wind on sensilla trichodea located on the head between the eyes.

Although some insects (*Drosophila*) may continue to fly to exhaustion without further mechanical stimulation (Chadwick, 1939; Wigglesworth, 1949), others (e.g., *Muscina* and *Schistocerca*) require continuous stimulation. In the case of *Muscina stabulans* a flow of air against the antennae, causing the arista-bearing segment to move with respect to the second joint, results in the legs being flexed in the flying position. Air flow against the antennae also seems to be necessary for sustained flight (Hollick, 1940).

In *Schistocerca* ten groups of sensilla trichodea bilaterally arranged on the leading surfaces of the head are sensitive to wind. When they are stimulated the forelegs are flexed in flight attitude and continuous flight occurs (Weis-Fogh, 1949, 1956). They assist in stabilization in a horizontal plane (yaw), as is shown by the fact that the locust turns if a jet of air is directed on the hairs from the side rather than from the front (Weis-Fogh, 1949). Whether they are static or phasic receptors or both has not been satisfactorily ascertained. It has been observed that they do not vibrate in the wind; they are damped. The hair plates on the legs of *Periplaneta*, which these resemble, are sensitive both to continuous deformation and the vibrations of a loudspeaker (Pringle, 1938 c). According to Weis-Fogh (1956), 'wind on the wings' is also an adequate stimulus for the maintenance of flight in *Schistocerca.*

Maintenance and alterations of flight velocity depend in considerable measure upon information supplied by the Johnston's organ. The detailed experiments with *Calliphora* (Burkhardt and Schneider, 1957), *Aedes* (Bässler, 1957, 1958), and *Apis* (Heran, 1957, 1959) have revealed its hitherto unsuspected role. When insects are flying, air currents impinging on the antennae cause the Johnston's organ to be stimulated. As a result of the sensory information received, flight velocity is reduced and the antennae are actively brought forward. Forward alignment reduces the angle of attack of the air current, with consequent reduction in the intensity of stimulation. Heran suggested that proprioceptive information about the position of the antennae relative to the head supplements information from Johnston's organ for steering flight velocity.

When the funiculi of the fly's antennae are rotated in their sockets and fixed in the position which they would normally assume if wind were blowing on them the flies fly much more slowly than controls (Burkhardt and Schneider, 1957). In aphids flight is impaired when the flagella of the antennae are removed; however, when artificial flagella are supplied as replacements control is regained (Johnson, 1956).

Change in velocity of flight can be effected in a number of ways. The experiments of Hollick (1940) with *Mucina* showed that these flies shift the path travelled by the wing tip cranially if they are subjected to a current of air from in front and if they are in possession of their antennae. In the absence of antennae, there is no shift. Wing-beat amplitude is also altered as a result of information received through the Johnston's organ. Bees reduce the wing-beat amplitude in the face of air currents, but if they lack antennae the reduction is less marked (Heran, 1959). In the case of *Aedes* there is a greater wing-beat amplitude in air currents when antennae are lacking than in still air when antennae are intact (Bässler, 1957, 1958).

Burkhardt and Schneider (1957) had pointed out that the antennae of *Calliphora* also respond electrophysiologically to sound in the range 150–250 c/s, the same range as the wing-beat frequency. They proposed that this response might possibly be employed to register the acceleration due to each wing-beat, since the funiculi of the antennae vibrate at this frequency as a result of the discontinuous air stream arising with each wing thrust. Support for the hypothesis is derived from the observation that the resonance frequency of the bee's antennal flagellum also agrees well with the wing-beat frequency, and the Johnston's organ is most sensitive to vibrations of 200–350 c/s (Heran, 1959). No tonic component similar to that detected in *Calliphora* can be seen in electrical activity in the bee's antenna. Furthermore, if vibrations too fast for the flagellum to follow are forced upon the antenna it is bent outwards but no longer vibrates, and the bees do not respond to the change in position (Heran, 1959).

Information from the Johnston's organ is also used to correct yaw. In turning about the vertical axis the angle of attack of the antenna on the outside of the turn becomes larger. Since intensified current on an antenna reduces wing-beat on the same side, a passive rotation produces an active torque in the opposite direction by which the straight flight course is stabilized (Heran, 1959).

Other monitoring of the movements of the wings occurs as a result of stimulation of wing receptors. As many investigators (e.g., Vogel, 1911, 1912; Lehr, 1914; Erhardt, 1916; Eggers, 1928; Hertwick, 1931; Zácwilichowski, 1936) have shown, the wings of insects are elaborately equipped with sense organs (Fig. 44). These are sensilla trichodea, sensilla campaniformia, and chordotonal sensilla. They are strategically situated to respond to wind on the surfaces of wings or to forces acting on the veins. With the exception of one chordotonal organ, all sensilla are located distal to the hinge; consequently, they will be subjected to strains and distortions set up by aerodynamic and inertial torques, but not elastic torques (Pringle, 1937). Several investigators have shown by electrophysiological monitoring that considerable information is fed back to the central nervous system by these sense organs (Sotavalta, 1954; Wolbarsht and Dethier, 1958; Wilson, 1961).

The sensilla trichodea are clearly tactile. Although Pringle (1957) did not exclude the possibility that they react to air flow, he suggested that this is improbable, because the small fibre diameter precludes rapid enough impulse conduction to meet the demands of quick flight reflexes. On the other hand, it is known that these hairs in *Phormia* fire at great speed and adapt very rapidly (Wolbarsht and Dethier, 1958), hence might respond to turbulence. The loss of control during the few wing-beats necessary to allow time for nervous conduction might be inconsequential considering the high rate of wing-beat in most insects.

The sensilla campaniformia are distributed singly and in groups. The former are usually circular, hence not markedly directional in their sensitivity. Grouped sensilla are usually oval. The direction of the long axis is uniform within a group but differs from one group to another. As Pringle (1938 b) has demonstrated, each group constitutes a unitary organ selectively sensitive to strains whose compression axis is oriented parallel to the direction of the long axis of the sensillum dome.

The location of each group is such that the sensilla are maximally sensitive to a particular direction of torque in the vein wherein they lie. Pringle (1937) has discussed at length the probable mode of action of these sensilla in relation to the torques acting on the wing during flight. Probable modes of action of the chordotonal organs have been deduced with less certainty (Pringle, 1937).

Any flying machine must possess stability, that is, a tendency to return to a characteristic attitude when displaced if it is to be controllable in the air (Pringle, 1950). In this respect insects are able to control lift and to stabilize reflexly in all three planes of rotation, that is, to correct for pitch, yaw and roll. In insects with four wings much of the required information derives from mechanoreceptors on the wings. As a result, changes in pronation, supination, and angle of attack of the wings are made until stable flight is achieved. Details of the response characteristics of the various sensory structures of the wing, however, are poorly known.

More information is available about the halteres of Diptera. These structures, homologues of the hind wings, are radically specialized as balancing organs. They are lavishly equipped with all types of mechanoreceptors whose homologies can be traced to those of the wings of non-dipterous insects (Pflugstaedt, 1912; Zácwilichowski, 1936). Essentially, each is a heavy mass of tissue on the end of a thin stalk. The folding of the base is very complicated, consisting of a main hinge and a condyle of secondary articulation (Fig. 45) (Pringle, 1948). In these regions are concentrated, in *Calliphora*, for example, about 418 mechanoreceptors. They include the following sensilla as described by Pflugstaedt (1912):

Campaniform Sensilla

- Dorsal scapal plate
- Ventral scapal plate
- Basal plate
- Dorsal Hicks papillae
- Ventral Hicks papillae
- Undifferentiated papilla

Chordotonal Sensilla

- Large chordotonal organ
- Small chordotonal organ

All but thirty-five are located in the three plates and the large chordotonal organ. It is significant that the axons from these sensilla do not fuse as is the case with the campaniform sensilla in the palps of the cockroach (Pringle, 1938 b, 1948). The arrangement of sensilla is basically the same in all families of Diptera (Brauns, 1939). It has been suggested (Pringle, 1948) that strains produced by vertical oscillation of the haltere are detected by the dorsal and ventral scape plates, the dorsal and ventral Hicks papillae, and the small chordotonal organ. Strains produced by gyroscopic torques are presumed to be detected by sensilla of the basal plate and the large chordotonal organ.

The undifferentiated papilla may be sensitive to all strains in the cuticle of the base.

The beat of the two halteres is synchronized. They are oscillating masses which generate forces at the base of the stalk as the whole fly rotates (Pringle, 1948). They are thus gyroscopes, but it is questionable that they act as direct stabilizing gyroscopes (Schneider, 1953). It is more likely that their action is indirect, in that the activity of their sense organs signals the nervous system to set up the necessary corrections in the flight mechanism (Pringle, 1957). There is convincing experimental evidence that they are instrumental in the control of yaw (Pringle, 1948; Faust, 1952; Schneider, 1953), pitch (Faust, 1952), and roll (Faust, 1952).

Finally, in the control of flight there are visual stimuli (e.g., Schaller, 1960). Movement in the visual field is employed directly by *Calliphora* in incorrecting yaw (Schneider, 1956) and roll (Faust, 1952; Schneider, 1956). Vision is also employed indirectly (Autrum and Stöcker, 1952; Mittelstaedt, 1950) to correct roll, as the following example of dragonfly (*Anax*) behaviour illustrates.

The head is a broad, heavy object, and rotations of the body produce movement in the neck region. The position of the body relative to the head is signalled by two pairs of prothoracic hair plates. When the head of a flying or stationary dragonfly is twisted there is a compensatory twisting of the wings. In flight this corrects rolling; when the insect is perched it assists in the maintenance of balance. In nature the insect moves its head so that the light intensity is always greatest dorsally. By means of proprioceptive feedback from the hair plates, the body is then rotated until it is aligned with the head (Mittelstaedt, 1950).

Swimming

Insects that swim beneath the surface of water are faced with orientation problems more nearly resembling those encountered in the air than on land. They can move freely in three dimensions in a homogeneous medium and must possess stability, just as must flying insects. In *Notonecta*, *Naucoris*, and *Macrotorixa* the normal swimming position also represents the stable equilibrium position. This position is maintained in the imago of *Naucoris* and *Macrotorixa* by the distribution of air and the position of the legs; in *Notonecta* larvae, principally by the location of the centre of gravity of the body mass (Oevermann, 1936). When these insects are blinded, deprived of the air film on the surface of the body, and artificially weighted so that the position of stable equilibrium is altered they are still able to orient with respect to gravity (Oevermann, 1936). No special localized static organ has been found; however, in *Notonecta, Plea, Naucoris,* and *Corixa* the Johnston's organ is employed in conjunction with a bubble of air to mediate position sense (Rabe, 1953). *Notonecta* and *Plea* swim ventral side uppermost. When they are properly oriented an air bubble trapped between the antennae and the surface of the head causes by its buoyancy the antennae to be deflected away from the head. If the insect is turned upside down the antennae are then deflected towards the head. In each instance the deflexion activates the Johnston's organ. If the bubble is removed, *Notonecta* placed in darkness will swim dorsal side up (that is, reversed) because the antennae by their own weight lean away from the head. For *Corixa,* which swims dorsal side up, the mechanism is the same but acts in reverse (Rabe, 1953).

Lack of a specialized static organ is characteristic of many aquatic species, and it appears that much assistance is derived from exteroceptors. Blinded insects, while not losing their ability to retain their normal attitude and position with respect to gravity entirely, do tend to show locomotory aberrations (Oevermann, 1936; Tonner, 1938; Hughes, 1958; Dingle, 1961). Compensatory movements to rotation cease when eyes are blackened, and some species show a tendency to swim in spirals when unilaterally blinded. In larvae of *Acilius sulcatus* and *Dytiscus marginalis,* which possess twelve simple eyes (stemmata), Schöne (1950) has shown that the structure and arrangement of these eyes are especially suitable to mediate optical orientation in space by sensing the distribution of brightness in the visual space. In rotations around the longitudinal axis a displacement of the ratio of excitation between the right and left groups of eyes occurs; in rotations around the transverse axis a change in the quotient front : back forms the basis of regulation.

Exteroceptive information concerning water movement is received via the antennae. It is assumed that Johnston's organ is involved. A swimming *Dytiscus* holds its antennae at a slight angle to the median line. Any deviation from the axis of swimming causes the antennae to bend (Hughes, 1958). Some proprioceptive information is necessary in any case. Giant water bugs possess hair plates on the trochanters at the coxo-trochanteral joints which are important for the co-ordination of swimming (Dingle, 1961). When the legs are flexed, as when grasping a stem or when flying, the hair plates are stimulated by a covering fold of cuticle. When the legs float freely in the water in an extended position the hair plates are no longer stimulated by the fold, and swimming occurs. Destruction of the hair plates interferes with normal swimming.

By analogy with marine invertebrates, especially Crustacea, it might be expected that statocysts would be common in aquatic insects. Such organs are ideally constructed for responding to gravity in a medium where cues are few. Aside from a series of questionable cases studied by Wolff (1922) and Studnitz (1932), however, no true statocysts have been reported. In the larvae only of many Limnobidae (Diptera) there is located on the terminal segment a pair of small sacs, open to the outside, and equipped with muscles by which water can be pumped in

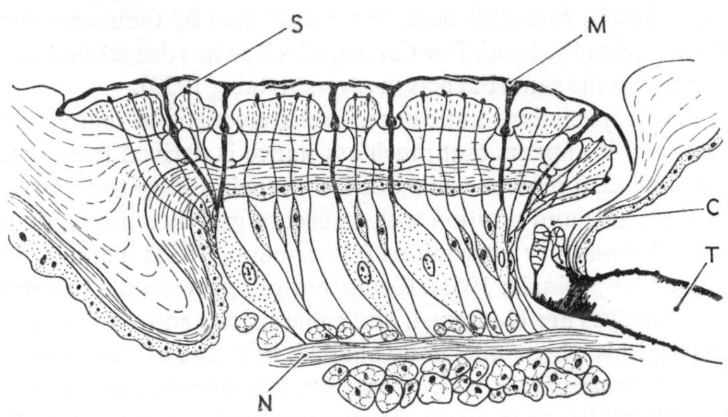

FIG. 50. The organ of pressure sense of *Nepa*. T, trachea; N, nerve; M, membrane of overlapping expanded margins of scale sensilla; C, closed spiracle; S, sensory papilla. (Redrawn from Thorpe and Crisp, 1947.)

and out (Fig. 51). Invariably each pouch contains a few minute particles either formed by the larva itself or picked up from the outside. As the muscles of the sac contract and relax, the particles are rattled about the interior.

In the interior of the sac are usually two sensory hairs, one at the blind end or deepest part of the sac, the other, in a lateral position. Wolff (1922) was convinced that these organs were not static in function. Studnitz (1932), on the other hand, after proving that unilateral or bilateral destruction of the organs abolished the positive geotaxis characteristic of the normal larvae, concluded that they were indeed statocysts.

In water bugs (*Nepa* and *Aphelocheirus*) there are elaborate mechanoreceptive organs which appear to be designed to respond to pressure changes and are presumed to have a static function. The organs in *Nepa*, situated adjacent to the spiracles of the third, fourth, and fifth abdominal segments, consist of groups of peg-shaped sensilla alternating with umbrella-shaped sensilla (Fig. 50). According to Hamilton (1931), the whole is covered by a thin membrane which does occlude the adjacent spiracle, but Thorpe and Crisp (1947) considered the membrane to consist of the overlapping umbrella-like portions of the sensilla which do indeed cover the spiracle. Baunacke (1912) considered these organs to be hydrostats. After he ascertained that a blinded *Nepa* placed on an underwater seesaw would reverse its direction of crawling as the inclination was reversed, he eliminated the

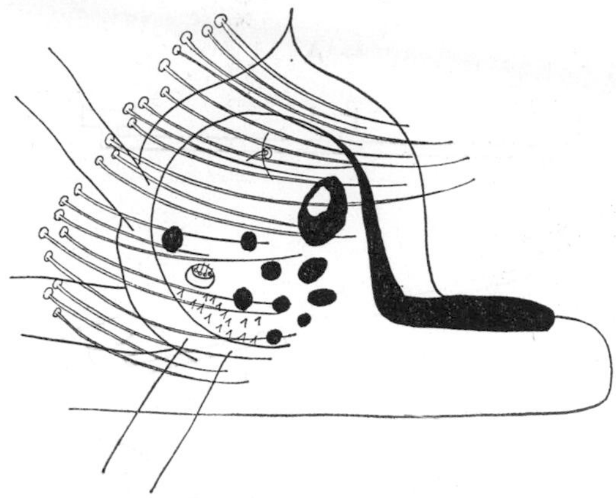

FIG. 51. Statocyst in the larva of an aquatic dipteran (Limnobiidae). The black objects are particles in the cavity. (Redrawn from Wolff, 1922.)

organs. Elimination abolished the bug's response to the change of inclination. Oevermann (1936) and Thorpe and Crisp (1947) confirmed these observations. Oevermann, however, demonstrated that there must be proprioceptive information from the legs, because a weighted insect can still make position corrections.

Baunacke (1912) believed that the three pairs of organs act as a system and respond to relative changes in pressure. In other words, the lowest pair (on the fifth sternum) are under greater pressure than the upper pair (third sternum) when the bug is in certain attitudes. For this system to work the gas-filled cavities of all of the sense organs must be in communication with one another via the tracheal system. According to Hamilton, who described the organs as covered with a membrane sealing them from the trachea, this is not so, but Thorpe and Crisp maintained that there is communication. They performed a series of extirpation experiments that are in agreement with Baunacke's hypothesis (Fig. 52). In the control (*A*) bugs on a seesaw gave sixty-eight correct performances out of ninety-two. *B* did not

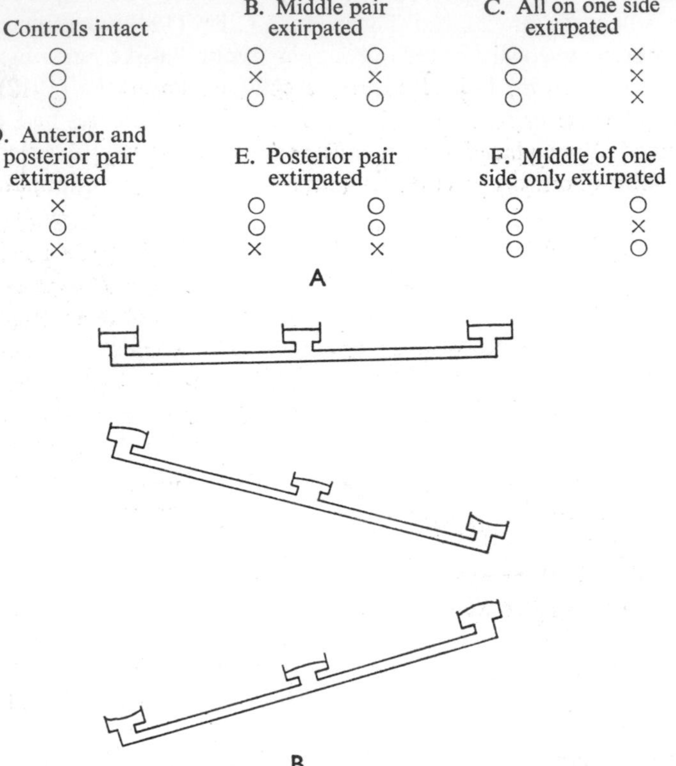

FIG. 52. A. Diagram illustrating the various operations performed on the three pairs of pressure organs in *Nepa*. (Redrawn from Thorpe and Crisp, 1947.) B. Diagram to illustrate the principle of action, when tilted in water, of a system of distensible membranes enclosing an air space and connected by an air-filled tube, of three pressure receptors of one side of *Nepa*. (Redrawn from Thorpe and Crisp, 1947.)

differ statistically from *A*, *C* and *D* were generally negative; *E* responded fairly well and *F* less well. It was concluded that the three pair of organs in *Nepa* were indeed co-ordinated as a differential manometer system.

A less-complicated organ occurs in adults of the predatory water bug *Aphelocheirus* (Fig. 53). There is a pair of oval sensory plates on the second abdominal sternum. Each consists of a shallow ovoid depression in which the usual plastron hairs are replaced by large hydrofuge hairs ($\pm$ 60,000 per sq. mm.), among which are delicate innervated sensilla trichodea (Fig. 53). It is assumed that increases of

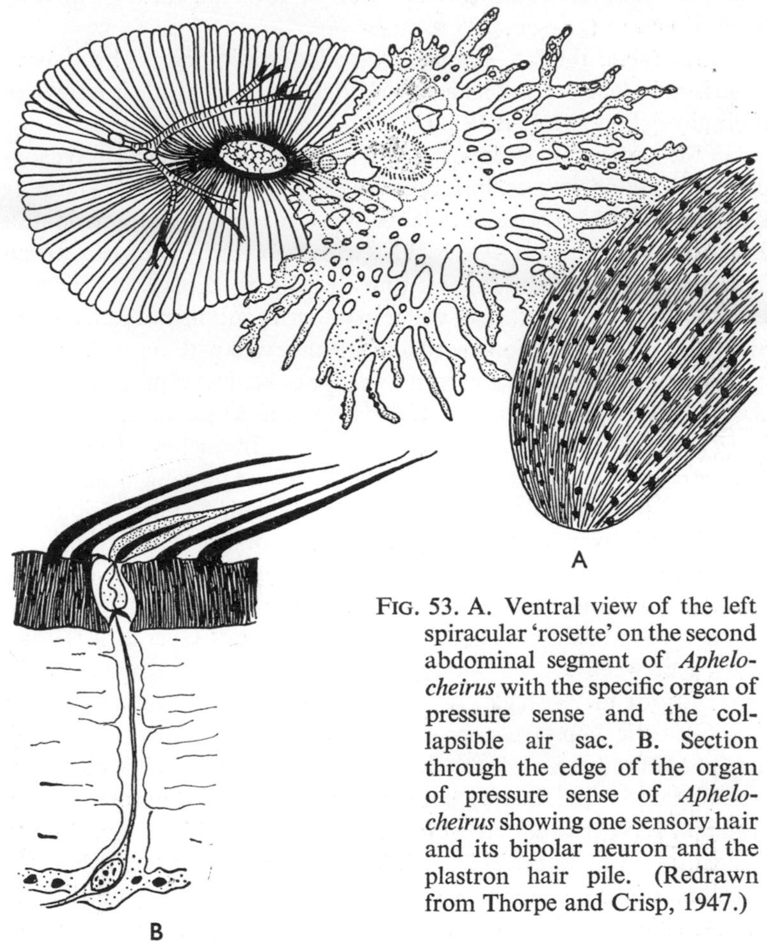

FIG. 53. A. Ventral view of the left spiracular 'rosette' on the second abdominal segment of *Aphelocheirus* with the specific organ of pressure sense and the collapsible air sac. B. Section through the edge of the organ of pressure sense of *Aphelocheirus* showing one sensory hair and its bipolar neuron and the plastron hair pile. (Redrawn from Thorpe and Crisp, 1947.)

pressure due to water currents and turbulence, depth, or the animal's position with respect to gravity are registered because the large slanting hairs press down upon the sensilla (Thorpe and Crisp, 1947). Unilateral damage causes the animal to swim in spirals, but this is only indirect proof of their static function (Larsen, 1955).

The air space around the pressure organs is continuous with tracheal air spaces; hence, if the organs are to give meaningful information regarding external pressure changes the internal air pressure must be kept constant. Thorpe and Crisp (1947) have suggested that large tracheal air sacs near these organs damp internal pressure changes. A different interpretation of the function of these air sacs has already been discussed (Larsen, 1955).

Comparable, though simpler, so-called static organs have been described in *Ranatra*, *Lethocerus*, and *Belostoma*, but little is known of their physiology (Möller, 1921).

On the surface of water insects do not encounter the same sensory problems as underwater, but, because of the great speed of swimming that is possible, obstacle avoidance is a problem. Some imaginative experiments by Eggers (1936 b, 1927) with the whirligig beetles *Gyrinus marinus* and *G. natator* suggest that the antennae play a prominent role. Beetles on the surface of water in a small container (diam. 35 cm.) are able to avoid collisions with one another and with the walls of the container. If the walls of the container are coated with paraffin so that the meniscus is convex instead of concave or if the surface of the water is carefully cleaned of all dust particles the frequency of collisions against the walls increases markedly. When swimming beneath the surface of the water the beetles also hit the wall. Neither vision, nor detection of waves bouncing from the walls, nor air pressure produced by the beetle moving towards the walls appear to be involved in obstacle avoidance. Eggers postulated that detection of the meniscus and detection of the resistance of the surface dust layer as it is compressed between the beetles and the wall informs the beetle of the proximity of the obstacle. It was presumed that the antennae, and possibly their Johnston's organs, are the sensing elements involved. Ordinarily the Johnston's organ is not highly developed in Coleoptera (as compared with Diptera), but in *Gyrinus* it is fairly complex, and the antennae have peculiar structural modifications which, according to Eggers, permit the pedicel to glide on the water surface while the flagellum sticks up into the air. The pedicel would be very sensitive to irregularities (menisci) in the water surface and to the resistance of floating particles such as dust; when moved, it would cause counter-movements of the flagella, with a consequent stimulation of Johnston's organ. Amputation of the antennae results in an increased number of collisions.

RESPONSES TO GRAVITY

As the foregoing discussions have implied, insects lack receptors designed specifically for the detection of gravitational force. Information required for maintenance of primary orientation is derived secondarily by the central nervous system from many receptors whose primary function may have little to do with responses to gravity. The precision with which some insects respond to gravity and the importance of a critical evaluation suggests that there may be some receptors whose information is critical. Bückmann (1954) has demonstrated, for example, that the staphylinid beetle *Blidius bicornis* Grm., which burrows in sea sand, responds to gravity with a precision of the order of one angular degree. This precision is not inferior to that exhibited by other animals which possess statocysts (Bückmann, 1955 a). Centrifugation experiments have indicated that neither light nor surface features are cues. Unfortunately the nature of the required sensory information is not known. In any event, the antennae are not required (Bückmann, 1955 b).

Another insect for which a precise response to gravity is critical is the honeybee. In order to be able to communicate the direction of food sources by transposing the angle of flight with respect to the sun to an angle of dancing with respect to gravity in a dark hive, the bee must be able to assess very accurately the direction of gravitational force. Vowles (1954), working with ants, had shown that the antennae were of importance in these species. Iron filings were cemented to various parts of the bodies of ants climbing a vertical surface. The ants were then suddenly subjected to a magnetic force. Only when the filings were on the funiculi of both antennae did the ants suddenly change orientation. This result plus the knowledge that different orientations with respect to gravity normally impart different rotational forces on the funiculus led to the hypothesis that the Johnston's organs are involved in geotaxis.

With the honeybee, however, the antennae are not so critical. Instead, hair plates in the neck region and at the articulation of the thorax and abdomen play a prominent role (Lindauer and Nedel, 1959). When the bee is standing on a horizontal surface the hairs of the pro-thorax are in even contact with the back of the head. When the bee crawls up a vertical surface the head will incline towards the sternum because of its low centre of gravity. In this position the more ventral hairs of the hair plate will experience maximal shearing forces. The less the substrate is inclined towards the vertical, the smaller the shearing forces on the whole organ. When the bee is crawling down a vertical surface the head will incline dorsally and the dorsal areas of the hair plate will be maximally stimulated. When a bee on a vertical surface turns to the right or left the hair plates on different sides of the thorax will be unequally stimulated. In this mechanism there is potentially a very fine capacity for analysing the position angle on the vertical plane. The degree of bending of individual hairs and the spatial distribution of bend in the hair plates as a whole could provide the necessary information (Lindauer, 1961). Severing the nerves to these organs, immobilizing the head, or changing the centre of gravity of the head by weighting it results in impairment of responses to gravity and ability to orient communication dances correctly with respect to gravity. The hair plates at the articulation of the thorax and abdomen function in a similar fashion. They appear to be subordinate to the cervical organs, however, because they alone are unable to regulate responses to gravity when the cervical organs are eliminated or when the head is fixed or weighted.

A comparative study of the occurrence and structure of hair plates at the joints of representatives of five families of ants, the honeybee, and *Vespa saxonica* has shown that these setal fields occur at the antennal, cervical, petiolus, and gaster joints and on the joints between the thorax and coxae and coxae and trochanters (Markl, 1962). By removing sense organs, disconnecting the various joints, or cementing the joints in abnormal positions, Markl was able to demonstrate that the cervical hair plates are the most important for gravity reception. The others in decreasing order of importance are the petiolus, the antennal, the coxal, and the gaster. In agreement with Vowles (1954) it was found that the antennal organs serve as gravity receptors but they represent only one, and by no means the most important, receptor system for gravity. In supplementing the results of Lindauer and Nedel (1959) it was shown that the receptors at the coxal joints but not those of the antennae serve for gravity reception in the honeybee. Since the hair plates are able to perceive active movements of the joints, it is argued that multiple development of hair plates is necessary if these organs are to serve as gravity receptors. Only a message in the same direction from one or more of the hair plates is related to gravity by the central nervous system, whereas aberrant responses from one or more areas are interpreted as joint movement independent of gravity (Markl, 1962).

CHAPTER IV

Sound Reception

The to-and-fro motion of a particle repeatedly displaced from equilibrium is termed vibration. In a continuous medium a vibrating particle causes periodic displacement of neighbouring particles by elastic forces. The resulting disturbance takes the form of periodic compressional waves. Sound reception is the process of detecting these waves whether they occur in gases, liquids, or solids. Whether one defines all vibration detection as 'hearing', restricts the term 'hearing' to the detection of air-borne sounds by specialized receptors and relegates other sound reception to a 'vibration sense' (von Buddenbrock, 1952), or limits 'hearing' to that condition where an animal behaves as if it has located a sound source (sound being defined as any mechanical disturbance whatever which is potentially referable to an external localized source) (Pumphrey, 1950) is not important to an understanding of how the receptors work. The crucial question, *physiologically* speaking, is to what extent insects can detect periodic motion or vibration in their environment and which parameters of the wave are detected. In this respect it is helpful to inquire first what kind of sounds or vibrations insects are exposed to normally.

Many sounds are produced by insects themselves. Many are incidental to ordinary movements, but nearly all orders of insects have members that produce specialized sounds. Frings and Frings (1958), in their review of the subject, have listed the following specialized methods of sound production: (1) tapping the substrate; (2) explosive expulsion of air or other material through a small orifice; (3) snapping a prosternal spine from a cavity in the mesosternum; (4) vibrating the body without flight to produce a buzzing, whining, or piping; (5) snapping the wings in flight; (6) snapping tymbals or tymbal-like organs; (7) stridulation (rubbing specialized surfaces of the elytra together or stroking the elytra with the hind femora); (8) expulsion of air over a specialized vibrating membrane. The sounds produced by insects are principally connected with sexual activity, territoriality, defence against predators, and maintenance of cohesion in flying swarms (Haskell, 1957). In addition to responding to sounds of these origins, insects respond aggressively to sounds produced by prey (e.g., the antlion to its prey) and defensively to sounds produced by predators (e.g., moths to the sounds of bats). Insects can also detect a certain amount of the white noise that fills the physical environment.

So far as is known, only two kinds of mechanoreceptive sensilla are sensitive to sound, sensilla trichodea and chordotonal sensilla, although there is nothing about the structure of campaniform sensilla or stretch receptors that precludes the possibility of their also responding to sound. Indeed, stretch receptors accurately signal phasic stimulation up to 5 c/s (Lowenstein and Finlayson, 1960). Hairs sensitive to sound do not differ fundamentally from those concerned with tactile and proprioceptive functions (hair plates on the legs of *Periplaneta* respond to loudspeaker sounds [Pringle, 1938c]) nor do the chordotonal sound receptors differ appreciably in structure from proprioceptive chordotonal sensilla. The more highly specialized chordotonal receptors, however, are grouped together and associated with elaborate accessory structures enhancing their sensitivity to sound. These organs include: tympanic organs, Johnston's organ in culicine mosquitoes, and subgenual organs.

TYMPANIC ORGANS

Morphology

Few external structural details escaped the eyes of nineteenth-century taxonomists, so it is not surprising that the occurrence of tympana was noticed in a number of insects. In some cases the structures were examined only with a view of their taxonomic usefulness; in others, guesses were made regarding their function. Those who guessed correctly believed the organ to be an instrument of sound production. Müller (1826), studying the paired tympana on the first abdominal segments of Acrididae, decided that they were organs of hearing. Tympanic organs were then discovered in the tibiae of the prothoracic legs of Tettigoniidae and Gryllidae (Siebold, 1844) and later in moths and butterflies. Among the Lepidoptera tympanic organs occur in the abdomen of adults in the super-families Geometroidea and Pyraloidea and in the metathorax of Noctuidea (Swinton, 1877; Jordan, 1905; Deegener, 1909; Eggers, 1911, 1919; von Kennel, 1912). Abdominal tympanic organs occur in the Cicadidae (Vogel, 1923 a) and in *Corixa* and a few other Hemiptera (Graber, 1882 a, 1822 b; Hagemann, 1910; Wefelscheid, 1912; Schaller, 1951), although in some of these forms the variation from an obvious tympanic organ makes those sensilla associated with tracheae look suspiciously like the proprioceptive chordotonal organs usually associated with tracheae in other species. Some chordotonal organs in the wings of Satyridae are associated with tympana (Vogel, 1912).

The detailed inner structure of tympanic organs was investigated thoroughly by Schwabe (1906), Eggers (1911, 1919, 1924, 1928), Vogel (1923 a), Hers (1938), Roeder and Treat (1957), and Treat (1959). These studies have been extended by the electron-microscope studies of Gray (1960).

All tympanic organs have certain features in common. These include: a thin cuticular membrane, a closely appressed internal tracheal sac, and a group of chordotonal sensilla. The sensilla may be

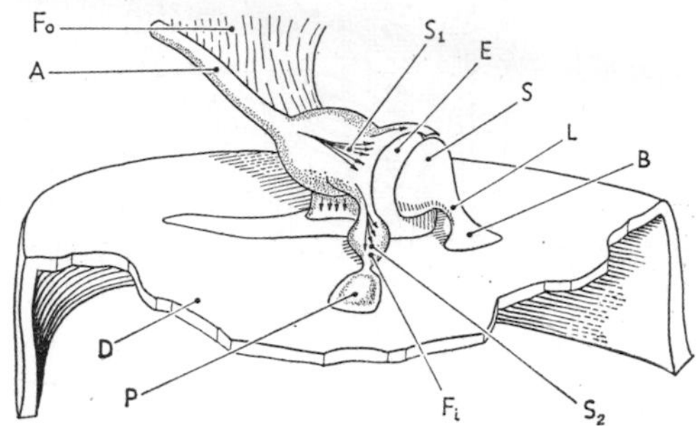

Fig. 54. Diagram to show the method of attachment of the neural elements to the inner surface of the tympanum of the locust. A, auditory nerve; Fo, fold; S_1 and S_2, location of sense cells; E, elevated process; S, styliform body; L, leg; B, base; D, drum; P, pyriform vesicle; Fi, fusiform body. (Redrawn from Gray, 1960.)

attached directly in the middle of the tympanum (Acrididae), to its far edge (Cicadidae), or to the trachea instead of the tympanum itself (Tettigoniidae and Gryllidae). They vary in number from two in certain moths to 1,500 or more in cicadas (Figs. 55, 57, 58, 59).

Of all these, the tympanic organs of Acrididae have undoubtedly been studied in greater detail than any others. The tympanum is a thin (2–3 μ), imperfectly ovoid area of exocuticle lying in a crater-like depression (sometimes likened to the auditory meatus of the human ear) formed by an incomplete rim of thickened cuticle (Fig. 54). The tympanum is further strengthened circumferentially as a consequence of a thickened cuticular invagination. It is thus a rigidly supported drumhead. It is lined internally, as is almost all cuticula, by a thin layer of hypodermal epithelium. Closely appressed to the internal side of the tympanum is a tracheal sac fed by a branch from the main trachea

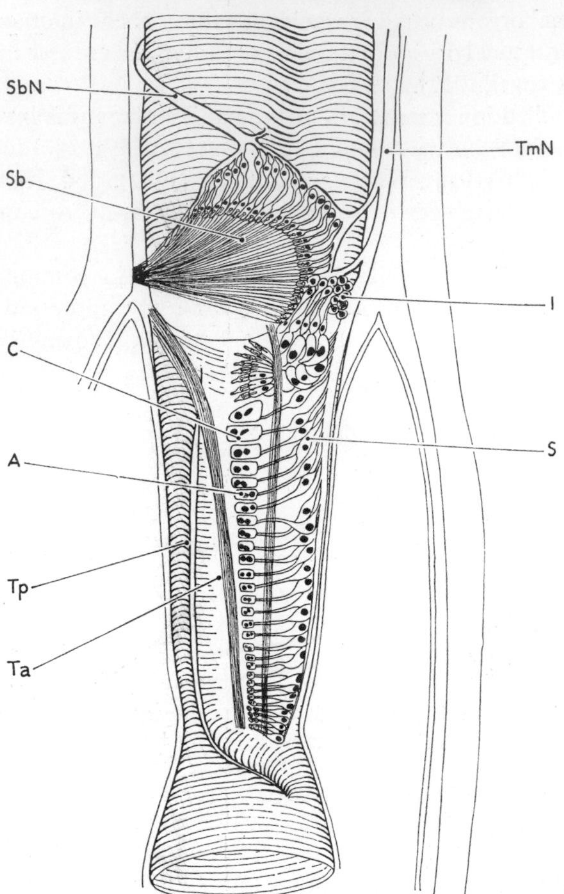

FIG. 55. Tympanic organ of the prothoracic leg of Orthoptera. Ta, anterior trachea; Tp, posterior trachea; Sb, subgenual organ; I, intermediate organ; A, acoustic organ; SbN, subgenual nerve; TmN, tympanic nerve; C, cap cells, S, scolopoid cells. (Redrawn from Schwabe, 1906.)

(analogous to the Eustachean tube), whose spiracle lies at the anterior border of the tympanum. The tympanum is in fact lined by two layers of epithelium, that of the hypodermis and that of the tracheal sac, and is bordered by air on both surfaces.

The tympanal nerve, a branch of the tergal nerve of the third thoracic ganglion, enters the region in a fold of the tracheal epithelium, branches, and attaches at several points of the drum (Fig. 54): the folded body (rinnenförmiges Körperchen), the styliform body (stielförmige Körperchen), the elevated process (zapfenförmige Körperchen), and the pyriform vesicle (birnförmiges Körperchen). These bodies are merely complex thickened areas of the drum. A small branch of the nerve goes to the folded body, where it innervates a few hairs and other sensilla. The main portion of the nerve, before branching to each of the four points of attachment, swells. This swelling has,

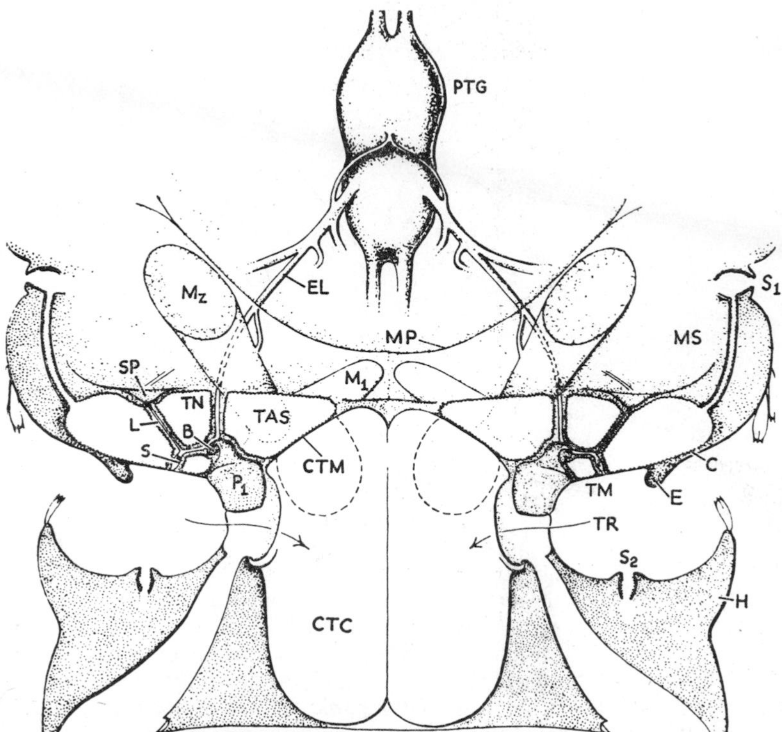

FIG. 56. Schematic dorsal stereogram of noctuid tympanic organ and related structures. B, Bügel; C, conjunctiva or accessory tympanic membrane; CTC, countertympanic cavity with external orifice indicated by arrow; CTM, countertympanic membrane; E, epaulette or nodular sclerite; EL, electrode site; H, hood; L, ligament; M_1, muscle originating on antero-median portion of metascutum and inserting on metapostnotum anterior to CTM; M_2, muscle originating dorsally on metascutum and inserting on epimeral band; MP, mesophragma; MS, metascutum; P_1, pocket I of tympanic frame; PTG, pterothoracic ganglion; S, sensillum; S_1, metathoracic spiracle; S_2, first abdominal spiracle; SP, scutal phragma; TAS, tympanic air sac lined with tracheal epithelium; TM, tympanic membrane; TN, tympanic nerve; TR, tympanic recess. (Courtesy of Roeder and Treat.)

unfortunately, been called a ganglion by Gray (1960). It is in fact the aggregation of most of the cell bodies (of which there are 60–80) of the neurons making up the sensilla. It is invested by two layers of cells, one of which is the epithelium of the tracheal air sac surrounding the nerve, the other being the accessory cells of the sensillum.

Prothoracic leg tympanic organs lie in the proximal region of the tibiae, one member on the anterior side, the other, posterior. They lie

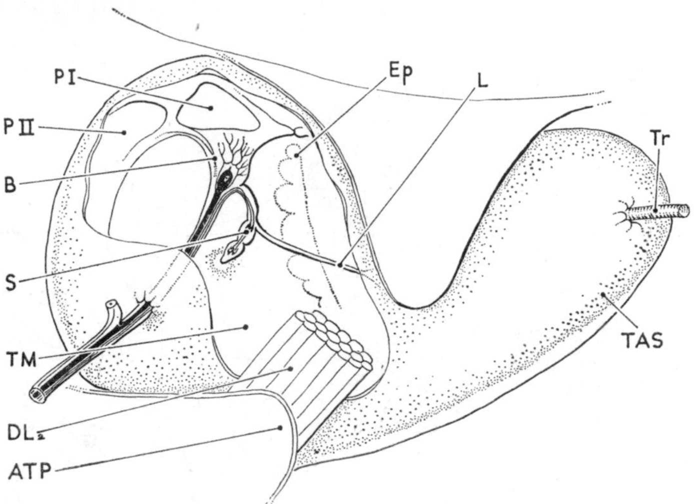

FIG. 57. Right tympanic air sac and associated structures of a noctuid as seen from within the metathorax. A portion of the air sac is represented as cut away to show the sensory elements. ATP, anterior tendon plate; B, Bügel; DL_2, second dorsolongitudinal muscle of metathorax; EP, epaulette; L, ligament connecting chordotonal organ with scutal phragma; PI, PII, pockets of tympanic frame; S, acoustic sensory cells; TAS, tympanic air sac; TM, tympanic membrane; Tr, tracheal twig from metathoracic spiracle. (Redrawn from Treat and Roeder 1959.)

thus back to back separated by two branches of a trachea, an anterior and a posterior (Fig. 55). Whereas in the Gryllidae the tympanic membranes lie on the exposed surface of the leg, they are sunken in the Tettigoniidae and are exposed to the outside only via a slit. The sensilla, of which there are about seventy in each leg, lie in a long row on the dorsal side of the anterior trachea. The dendrites and scolopoid bodies are oriented in such a way that they are not inserted on the tympanic membrane but instead on a membrane, presumably derived from the basement membrane of the hypodermis and trachea, bordering on the blood cavity of the leg. The cells thus stretch between the trachea and this membrane (Fig. 55). This organ is innervated by a purely sensory nerve, the tympanic nerve, originating from the first thoracic ganglion. This nerve also innervates part of the subgenual organ and the intermediate organ. The rest of thc subgenual organ is innervated by a branch of the leg nerve.

The metathoracic tympanic organ of Lepidoptera is the simplest organ of this type. It lies in the anterior wall of a deeply recessed cavity

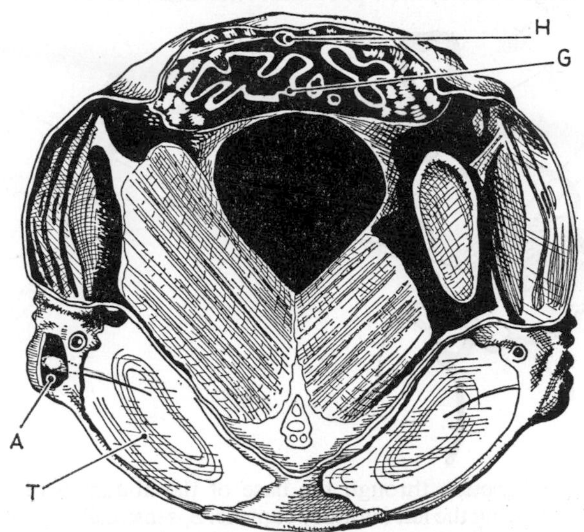

FIG. 58. The tympanic organ of the cicada *Tibicina haematodes* as seen when the abdomen is cut transversely. H, heart; G, gut; A, auditory cavity in which a window has been cut; T, tympanum. (Redrawn from Vogel, 1923.)

bounded posteriorly by parts of the first abdominal segment (Fig. 56). As in the Acrididae, the membrane is lined with hypodermal epithelium plus that of the associated tracheal sac. Two chordotonal sensilla are attached to the inner surface of the tympanic membrane. The axons, forming part of the tympanic nerve, extend anteriorly, receive support *en route* from a thin ligament, turn at an angle to receive further support from a cuticular projection, the Bügel, then continue on through the tracheal sac ultimately to join the pterothoracic ganglion (Fig. 57). Like the comparable structure in the locust, the nerve is ensheathed in tracheal epithelium.

The tympanic membrane faces only part of the tracheal air sac. The rest of it is faced by another membrane whose upper surface is exposed to the air by a narrow slit which is the orifice of a large counter-tympanic cavity. This cavity and membrane are regarded as accessory resonating structures.

The paired tympanic organs of cicadas are located ventrally in the region of the first and second abdominal segments. They differ from others described chiefly with reference to the point of attachment of the chordotonal sensilla. These, approximately 1,500 in number, occur in a single large bundle, their proximal ends attached to one corner of

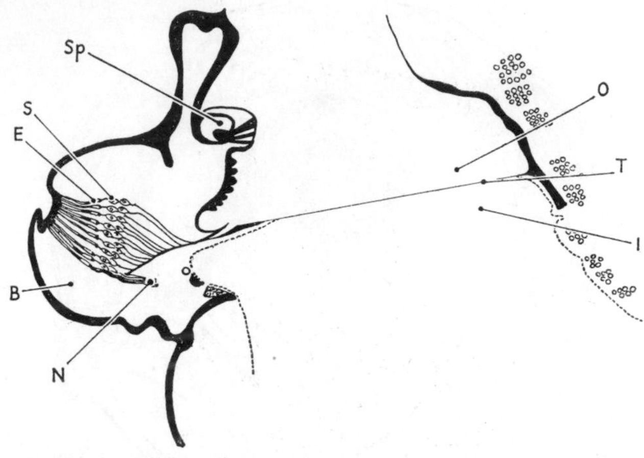

FIG. 59. Frontal section through the base of the abdomen of *Cicadetta coriaria* showing the left auditory capsule. S, sense cells; E, enveloping cells; N, nerve; B, blood; Sp, spiracle; O, outer air; I, inner air space; T, tympanic membrane. (Redrawn from Vogel, 1923.)

the tympanic membrane and their distal ends to the cuticle of the body wall (Figs. 58 and 59).

The tympanic organs of Orthoptera and Lepidoptera have two so-called tympanic muscles associated with them. The function of these muscles is unknown, although it has been suggested from time to time that they might be concerned with altering stresses on the tympanic organ. In moths it is certainly true that distortion of the skeletal elements of the tympanic organ reversibly changes the excitability of the sensilla (Roeder and Treat, 1957).

The Sensilla

The chordotonal sensilla, as viewed with the light microscope, are all basically the same. So far only those of the tympanic organ of the locust *Locusta migratoria migratorioides* have been examined with the electron-microscope. The relations between the various cells composing the unit are clearly revealed (Fig. 60). The axon and cell body of the neuron are enveloped in a Schwann cell. Each Schwann cell may envelope several neurons. Distal to the Schwann cell, at the base of the

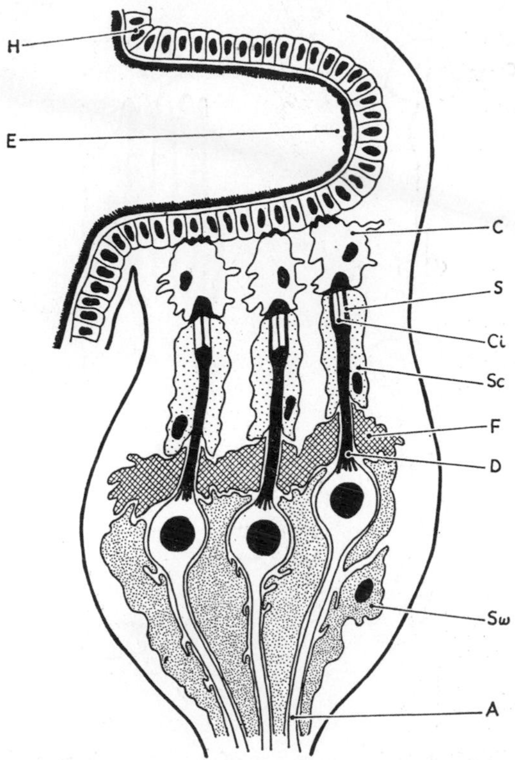

FIG. 60. A diagrammatic section through the sensory region of the locust tympanic organ to show the method of attachment of the sensory cells. H, hypodermis; E, elevated process; C, cap cell; Ci, cilium-like process; S, scolopoid body; Sc, scolopale cell; D, dendrite; Sw, Schwann cell; A, axon; F, fibrous sheath cell. (Redrawn from Gray, 1960.)

dendrite, lies another enveloping cell, the fibrous sheath cells (probably the Bindesubstanz of Schwabe). The remaining portion of the dendrite is enclosed in the enveloping cell (Hüllzelle of Schwabe, scolopale cells of Gray). Between this cell and the hypodermis lies the cap cell (Kappenzelle of Schwabe, Deckzelle of Eggers, attachment cell of Gray). These cells, as Schwabe (1906) observed, are in contact with each other by finger-like processes and interdigitate with the hypodermal cells by folds.

The scolopoid body exclusive of its cap is a hollow tube composed of several concentric rods. It lies within the cytoplasm of the enveloping cell. The apical body or scolopale cap is an extracellular body lying

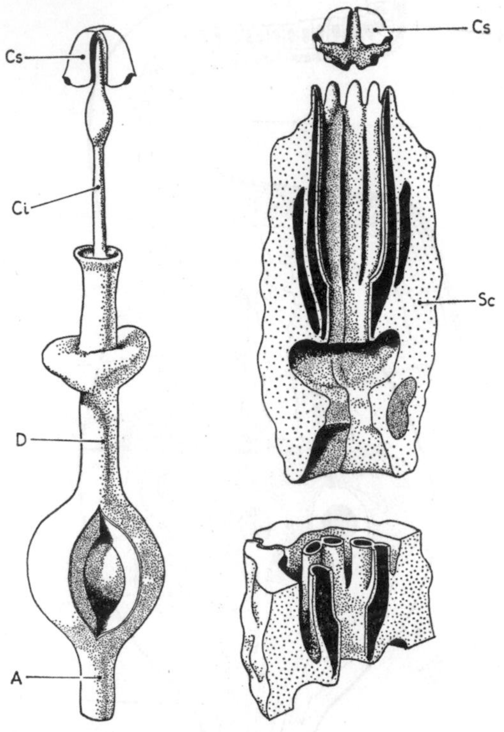

FIG. 61. Details of the scolopoid region of the tympanic organ of the locust. Cs, scolopoid-cap; Ci, cilium-like process; Sc, scolopale cell; D, dendrite; A, axon. (Redrawn from Gray, 1960.)

in a depression of the cap cell and fitted into a rim of the enveloping cell containing the fused ends of the scolopale.

As the dendrite proceeds from the cell body it presents a ring-shaped dilation just before entering the scolopoid body, a less-pronounced dilation followed by a marked reduction in diameter after it has entered the scolopale, and, finally, a subterminal swelling. Its tip is inserted into a channel in the cap (Fig. 61).

The axial fibre which can be seen by light microscopy is shown by electron-microscopy to be a very complicated cilium-like structure consisting of basal rootlets fusing into a root as they ascend within the dendrite (Fig. 62). Marked periodic cross striations are present. The distal portion of the cilium-like structure consists of nine fibrils

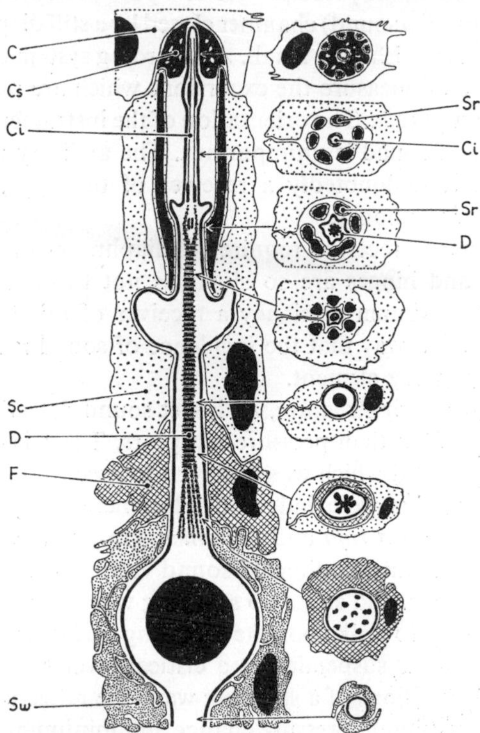

FIG. 62. Diagrammatic longitudinal section through the sensillum in the tympanic organ of the locust. Cs, scolopale cap; Ci, cilium-like process; Sc, scolopale cell; C, cap cell; F, fibrous sheath cell; Sw, Schwann cell; Sr, scolopale rod; D, dendrite. (Redrawn from Gray, 1960.)

surrounding a central core. Its resemblance to the typical motile cilium is so striking that Gray (1960) called it a cilium. Since there is no evidence that it is functionally a cilium, it seems inadvisable to identify it so completely with those structures. 'Cilium-like' is a more appropriate designation.

Mechanism of Action

It will be recalled that vibrational disturbance in a homogeneous medium produced both a local increase in pressure and a displacement of contiguous particles away from the source of disturbance. It follows that the waves resulting from this disturbance may be detected either by a device sensitive to pressure change or by one sensitive to displacement. As Pumphrey (1940) has stated in his discussion of the physics of sound detection, the prerequisites of a pure pressure receptor are a massive, opaque (to sound) chamber closed by a stiff diaphragm whose displacement is vanishingly small. A recording system coupled to the diaphragm would measure the excursions which are proportional to the pressure amplitude. The orientation of the instrument with respect to the source of sound is unimportant. The auditory mechanism of the mammal is undoubtedly a receiver of this type, as are most commercial microphones.

A displacement receiver requires a diaphragm or moving vane whose mass and hinges are so slight as not to offer resistance to motion. For maximum efficiency a receiver of this type should be oriented in such a way that the incidence of sound is normal to the plane of the moving element.

Judging from their structure, all insect sound-detecting organs are displacement rather than pressure receptors. There is one ingenious experiment reported which was designed to ascertain whether or not the sound receptors were indeed displacement receptors (Autrum, 1936). Ants (*Formica rufa* and *Myrmica* spp.) can respond to loud artificial sounds. Autrum directed sound vertically downwards upon a reflecting surface, and so set up standing waves. In one experiment ants were allowed to walk upon the reflecting surface; in another, they walked upon gauze suspended at a critical level above the surface. Under these conditions of a standing wave the reflecting surface was the region of maximum pressure change and minimum displacement, whereas at the gauze, this being an antinode, the reverse was true. Ants responded most vigorously when walking on the gauze; that is, they were most sensitive to displacement. Unfortunately, as Pumphrey (1940) pointed out, the sounds employed were extremely intense (10^{11} times human threshold at 1,000 c/s), and there is no indication as to whether the ants were responding to air-borne sound waves or to vibrations in the substrate. It is not known what organs were involved. As Pumphrey further pointed out, it is not necessarily true, as Autrum maintained, that velocity was the critical factor, since displacement, velocity, and acceleration are all maximal at an internode.

In any event, there is at this time absolutely no conception in terms of structure of the manner in which chordotonal sensilla operate.

As Gray (1960) pointed out for *Locusta*, displacement of the membrane is presumably transmitted to the cap cell. The cap appears to be rigidly seated on the scolopale, which in turn seems to be firmly locked to the dendrite. The cilium-like tip of the dendrite lies freely in the extra cellular cavity of the scolopale and cap. What moves in respect to what is obscure. Now that the electron-microscope is revealing more clearly the structural relationships of these sensilla, earlier speculations upon their mode of action based upon the partial knowledge provided by the light microscope have only historical value.

Function – Orthoptera

The earliest attempt to analyse thoroughly the function of tympanic organs was that of Regen (1908, 1912, 1913, 1914 a, 1914 b, 1924, 1926). As experimental animals he employed the cricket *Liogryllus campestris* and the long-horn grasshopper *Thamnotrizon apterus*. He demonstrated that females would orient to a telephone transmitting the sound of a male in another room and that two males could sing in concert. Between the Vorspiel (prelude) and the Nachspiel (coda) of the duet, that is, the beginning and end, where the two were in synchrony, there was almost always an intermediate period during which the chirps of the two alternated regularly. Furthermore, naïve (newly moulted adults) males could be induced to sing in concert with many kinds of artificial sounds ranging in frequency from ± 400 c/s to ± 28,000 c/s. All of these experiments proved that the insects were sensitive to air-borne sound. When both tympanic organs were amputated the responses were almost completely abolished (some residual sound perception remained), thus proving that the tibial tympanic organs were the principal sound receptors.

These conclusions were confirmed a few years later, when Wever and Bray (1933) recorded nerve activity in the forelegs of crickets (*Gryllus assimilis*) and tettigoniids (*Amblycorypha oblongifolia* and *Pterophylla camellifolia*) by means of electrodes inserted therein. The frequency range for crickets was 300–8,000 c/s; for the tettigoniids, 800–45,000 c/s. The electrical response was asynchronous at all frequencies. These experiments alone were not conclusive, because, by inserting their electrodes into the leg rather than directly upon the tympanic nerve, Wever and Bray might conceivably have been recording from tactile hairs and other chordotonal organs of the leg as well as from the tympanic organ (cf. also Wever, 1935). An attempt to circumvent these difficulties was made with *Decticus* by Autrum

(1941), who recorded from legs in which the subgenual organs presumably had been destroyed. Unfortunately, the precision of the operation was not confirmed histologically post mortem. In any event, the sensitivity to air-borne sound waves extended from 1,000 c/s to the upper limits of the stimulation apparatus (10,000 c/s). The higher the frequency, the lower the threshold. Responses at frequencies below 1,000 c/s were obtained only by employing intensities so high that it is doubtful that they truly fell within a physiological range.

The abdominal tympanic organs of two acridids (*Locusta migratoria migratorioides* and *Arphia sulphurea*) were sensitive over the range 300–10,000 c/s (Wever, 1935; Pumphrey and Rawdon-Smith, 1936 b)

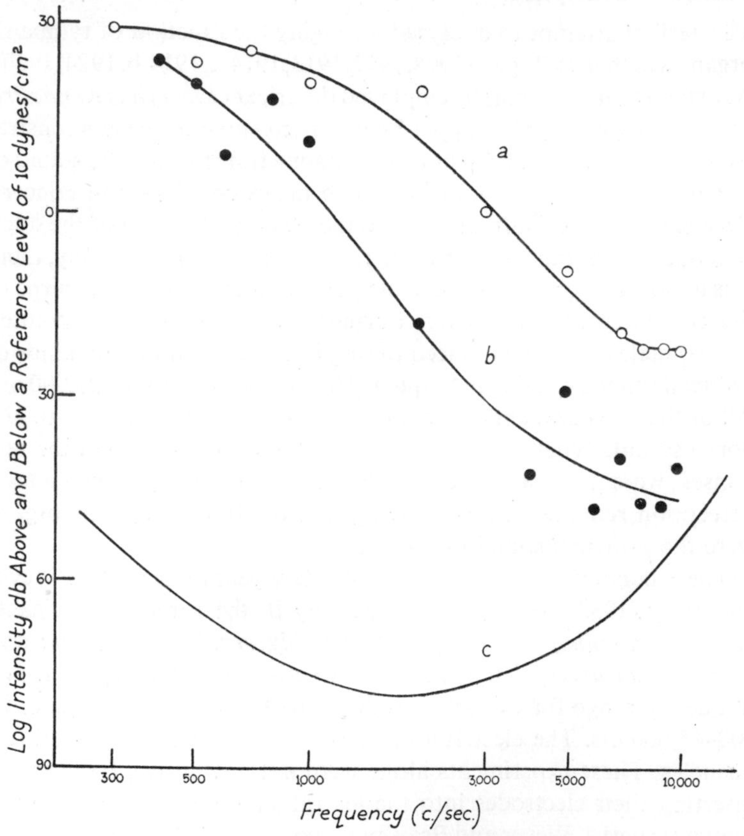

FIG. 63. a, Threshold curve for tympanic organs of *Arphia sulphurea* averaged from Wever's figures. b, Threshold curve for an isolated tympanic organ of *Locusta*. c, Human threshold subjectively determined (from Wegel, 1932). (Redrawn from Pumphrey, 1940.)

(Fig. 63). Again over the entire range the nerve response was asynchronous. Since 10,000 c/s was the limit of the apparatus used, it would appear that the tympanic organ is much more sensitive than the human ear at frequencies above 10,000 c/s. In the neighbourhood of 3,000 c/s, according to one report of Pumphrey and Rawdon-Smith (1936 c), the tympanic organ of *Locusta* exhibits maximum sensitivity. At this point the frequency is only 20 db above the ear of man at its maximal sensitivity. On the other hand, in an earlier paper (Pumphrey and Rawdon-Smith, 1936 b) it was indicated that the threshold continues to fall with increasing stimulus frequency (see also Pumphrey, 1940). A continuous fall was observed by Autrum (1941).

In any case, the tympanic organ is insensitive in the frequency range that is optimal for man and extends into the ultrasonic range. At its optimum the organ responds to a stimulus of about 7×10^{-10} ergs/sec., about the same as for man, and thus is operating at the physical limit. In contrast to the human ear, the tympanic organ of Orthoptera does not fatigue readily. No diminution in the response to a 2,000-c/s tone could be detected after continuous stimulation lasting one-half a minute (Pumphrey and Rawdon-Smith, 1936 c).

Although the tympanic organs are not the only receptors possessed by Orthoptera (there are in addition hair sensilla and chordotonal organs not associated with tympana), it is clear that they are the principal, if not sole, receptors involved in detecting noises produced by stridulation of the same and other species. Since Orthoptera can discriminate among the various kinds of calls and can distinguish between some artificial and genuine calls (Regen, 1926), it is obvious that the tympanic organ does have some specialized characteristics.

Songs of Acrididae are, on the whole, broad-band noises at 2–12,000 c/s with maxima at 4,000–8,000 c/s and intensities of 30–40 db, *re* 0·0002 dynes/sq. cm., at 10–30 cm. (Busnel, 1953; Haskell, 1955; Loher and Broughton, 1955). The Tettigoniidae also produce wide-band noises at frequencies up to 100,000 c/s (maxima 8,000–15,000 c/s) and intensities of 46–70 db (Borror, 1954; Busnel, 1953; Busnel and Chavasse, 1950; Pasquinelly and Busnel, 1955; Pielemeier, 1946 a, 1946 b; Pierce, 1948). Gryllidae produce relatively pure tones at 2,000–6,000 c/s and intensities of 40–60 db (Alexander, 1957; Busnel, 1955 a, 1955 b; Haskell, 1955; Pasquinelly and Busnel, 1955; Pierce, 1948).

The songs can be described physically by five parameters: frequency, intensity, wave form, phase, and the temporal distribution of sound units (Frings and Frings, 1958). Successive units may be combined to form more complex arrangements, and this in turn further multiplied.

The tympanic organ is sensitive to the entire frequency range of sounds produced by stridulation, but regardless of the frequency, the pattern of discharge in the tympanic nerve is asynchronous. From this it has been concluded that the organ is incapable of frequency discrimination, and this may indeed be so. On the other hand, there have been no recordings from single fibres in Orthoptera, and this should be done to clinch the argument, even though Pumphrey (1940) has argued on structural grounds that harmonic analysis, that is, different fibres responding to different stimulus frequencies, is impossible. The fact that no frequency discrimination has been observed in the moth tympanic organ, where the presence of only two fibres permits a precise analysis (Roeder and Treat, 1957), adds weight to the argument. It also supports the idea that there is no frequency pattern in the nerve mirroring the frequency pattern of the stimulus. On the other hand, it is possible that the insect itself may be able to analyse frequency to some degree by means of central interpretation of input from a number of organs each having a different frequency range (Katsuki and Suga, 1960; Suga and Katsuki, 1961).

Pumphrey and Rawdon-Smith (1939) proposed that the tympanic organ, being sensitive to intensity, detected changes in intensity, that is, amplitude of the sound wave, and that the different sounds of insects differed most importantly by the periodic changes (modulation) in intensity of the sound. In other words, any sound wave of a frequency within the detectable frequency range was merely a carrier wave upon which was imposed a pattern of amplitude modulation. By contrast, the human ear is very sensitive to frequency changes in the carrier wave but relatively insensitive to changes of the modulation frequency. This hypothesis was supported by records showing that an organ stimulated by an amplitude-modulated sound discharged volleys of impulses at the modulation frequency of the stimulating sound. These results were confirmed in a number of species by Haskell (1956 b), and as he pointed out, it would be reasonable to assume that the different pulse rates found in the different songs of various species would be the parameter signalled by the receptors, and hence the key to the recognition of songs. Busnel (1955) and his co-workers (Busnel, Loher, and Pasquinelly, 1954), on the other hand, have suggested as a result of experiments in which natural and artificial songs were played to species of *Chorthippus* that the essential element in songs that aids discrimination is 'transients' (sudden changes in intensity). To test the latter hypothesis Haskell (1956 b) played the identical stimulus again and again to a tympanic organ and recorded the pattern of discharge from the tympanic nerve. He found that the resultant volleys of spikes, although synchronous with the pulse frequency of the stimulus, were variable in themselves and that this variability bore no simple relationship to any quality of the stimulus. On the basis of this evidence he

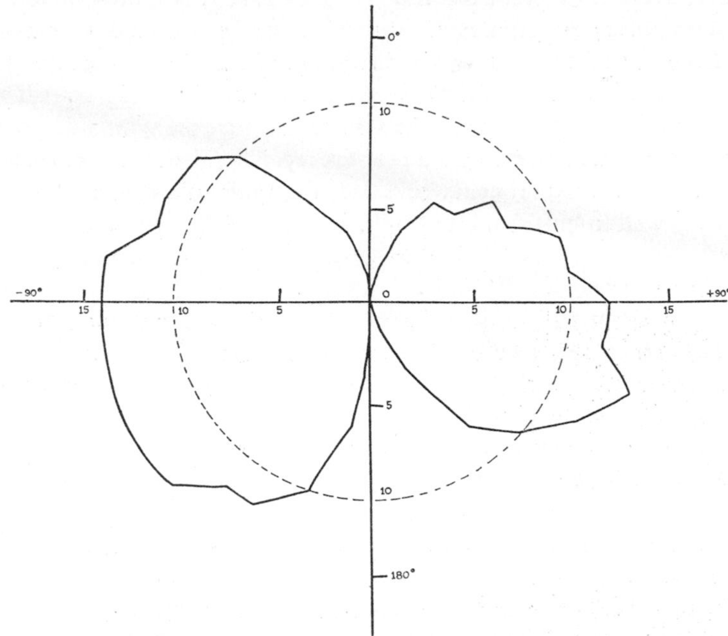

FIG. 64. Sensitivity of an isolated tympanic organ of *Locusta* plotted on polar co-ordinates as a function of direction of incidence of the test stimulus. Sensitivity (log reciprocal of threshold amplitude) is plotted radially and the minimum sensitivity is arbitrarily taken to be zero. The line 0–180 degrees lies in the sagittal plane of the animal, and for angles of positive or negative sign the test stimulus is incident on the external or internal aspect of the tympanic organ respectively. (Redrawn from Pumphrey, 1940.)

concluded that the characteristic of stridulation that permits inter-specific recognition is the pulse repetition of the songs. Many questions about sound recognition remain to be answered, however, and Haskell's (1956 b) discussion should be consulted.

One feature of the early field experiments that turned up repeatedly was the ability of the insects to localize sound. Regen (1924), for example, showed that unmated females could orient from a distance of approximately 10 metres to a chirping male. A female's path of approach was nearly a straight line. Even with one tympanic organ destroyed, orientation was possible, although the line of approach now became more devious. These observations suggesting that the tympanic organ has directional characteristics are supported by experiments in which sensitivity was tested to a stimulus given successively at different directions of incidence (Pumphrey, 1940). A plot on polar co-ordinates of the sensitivity of an isolated tympanum of *Locusta* as a function of the direction of incidence of the stimulus illustrates the pattern of the directional characteristics (Fig. 64). This finding is in agreement with the assumption that the tympanic organ is a displacement rather than a pressure receiver (also Autrum, 1955 c) Also, as these experiments revealed, the tympanic organ responds equally well to 'push' and to 'pull'.

Function – Lepidoptera

Moths and butterflies also are known to be sensitive to sound (Stobbe, 1911; Turner, 1914; Turner and Schwarz, 1914; Eggers, 1925, 1926 a, 1928; Frings and Frings, 1956, 1957). Many of the sounds employed for testing in early experiments were non-specific (e.g., squeaks of a glass stopper twisted in a bottle), and the responses, too, were not always specific (e.g., partial erection of the antennae, folding of the wings, flexing of the antennae, running, or flying). It was difficult to know what kind of sounds to employ as test stimuli for the simple reason that no one knew what sounds moths responded to in nature. One of the earliest speculations regarding the normal role of sound perception in behaviour was the suggestion of White (1877) to the effect that auditory receptors, in moths specifically, might assist in detecting the approach of insectivorous bats. This idea gained plausibility from a number of field and laboratory observations (Schaller and Timm, 1950; Webb, 1953; Treat, 1955), and was finally established on a firm experimental basis by Roeder and Treat (1957, 1961 a, 1961 b).

The principal sound receiver is the tympanic organ. The sensitivity of this organ in noctuids to air-borne sounds was demonstrated by Eggers (1925, 1926 a, 1928), first confirmed by the behavioural studies of Schaller and Timm (1950) and of Treat (1955), and ultimately by electrophysiological techniques. Other sound receptors must exist because, as is true with Orthoptera, there is still a residual response to intense sound after destruction of both tympanic organs (Stobbe, 1911; Eggers, 1925; Treat, 1955; Frings and Frings, 1957). Furthermore, species in which tympanic organs are not known to occur on the body are somewhat sensitive to sound. For example, the satyrid butterfly *Cercyonis pegala* responds to air-borne sounds of high intensity (100–110 db). It should be remembered, however, that there exist on the ventral surface of the basis of the wings of this insect chordotonal sensilla associated with minute tympanic membranes (Vogel, 1912), and some people have tendered the suggestion that sound reception by these organs is possible (Vogel, 1912; Pringle, 1957).

The tympanic organ is sensitive to very high sound frequencies. Responses in the frequency range 3,000–20,000 c/s have been recorded from the tympanic nerves of the moths *Phalera bucephala* (Notodontidae) and *Arctia caja* (Arctiidae) (Haskell and Belton, 1956). The very thorough investigations of Roeder and Treat (1957, 1959, 1961a, 1961b) with a number of noctuids have shown that the sensitivity extends up to stimulus frequencies of 100,000 c/s. These investigations have also revealed many of the characteristics of these organs. A resting discharge occurs at the ordinary noise level of the laboratory. It

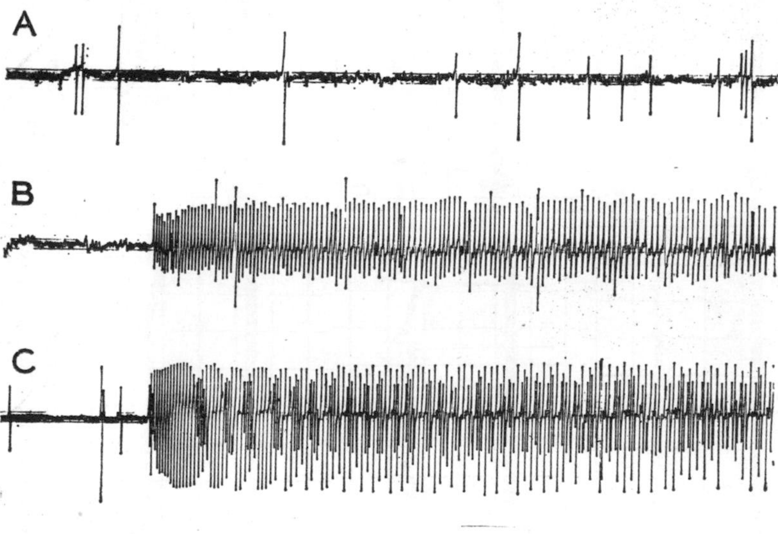

FIG. 65. Tympanic nerve activity in the noctuid *Prodenia eridania*. A, activity in the tympanic nerve at laboratory noise level. The large spike belongs to the non-acoustic unit. B, response in one acoustic unit to continuous sound of 70 kc/s. C, response in both acoustic units to 30 kc/s. Time marks, 100 c/s. (Courtesy of Roeder and Treat.)

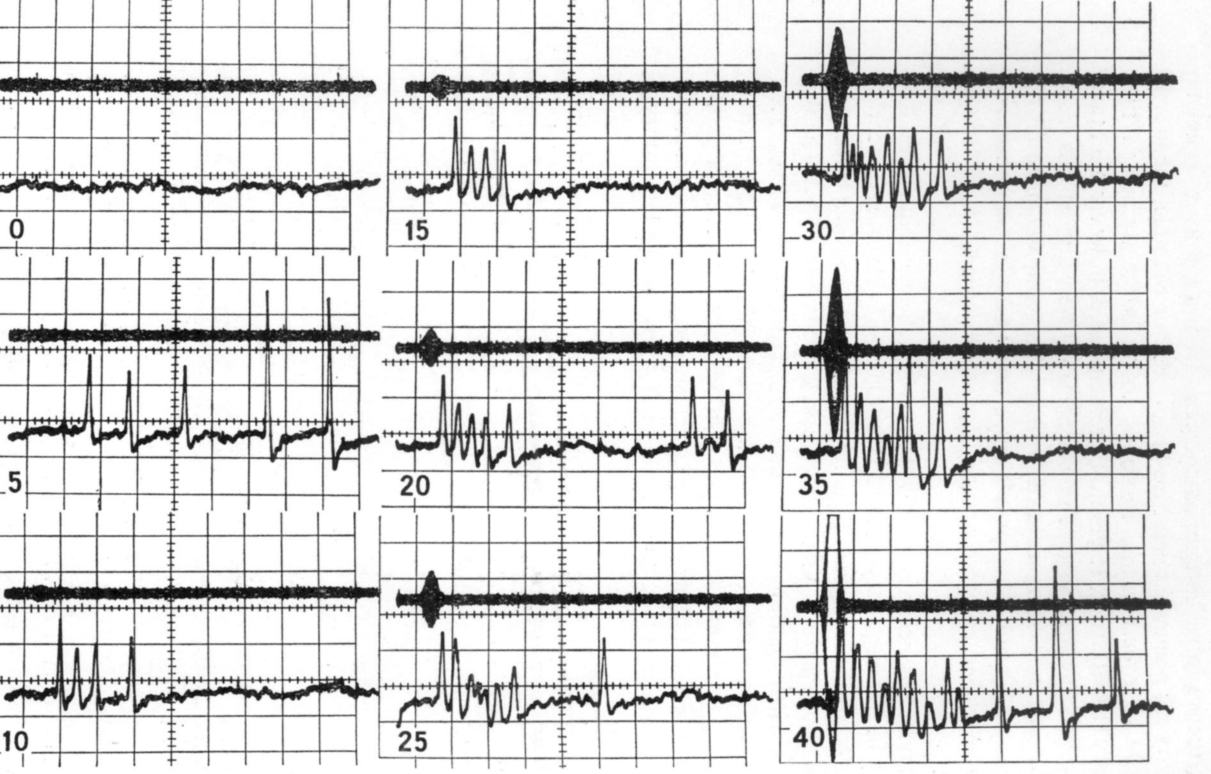

FIG. 66. Tympanic nerve responses (lower traces) of *Noctua c-nigrum* to a 70-kc sound pulse recorded simultaneously by a Granith microphone (upper traces). The numbers indicate the intensity of the sound pulse in decibels above a reference level (O). The threshold of the sensitive A cell lies between 0 and 5 db. The large spikes appearing in some of the records are from the B cell. The less-sensitive A cell responds in the 25-db recording.

takes the form of a series of discharges of a large spike at a steady frequency of 5–20 per second. Haskell and Belton (1956) believed these to be motor discharges, but in Roeder's and Treat's preparation they were clearly afferent. In addition, two species of small spikes discharge randomly, in all probability, as a result of low-level random noise in the laboratory. These two spikes represent the acoustic units of the tympanic organ; the large spike is a non-acoustic unit whose function is not clearly understood (Fig. 65).

Both acoustic units respond to sound by a high-frequency discharge which shows no change with stimulus frequency. The two differ only in their threshold. For both, the greatest sensitivity lies between 15,000 and 60,000 c/s. In response to a click, with many transients, or a short pulse (0·02–1 msec.) of pure sound at threshold, the more sensitive fibre responds after a latency of 3·5 msec. with one spike (Fig. 66). When the stimulus intensity is increased, the latency decreases and there is an after-discharge of two–three spikes at a frequency of 700 per second. A further increase in stimulus intensity brings in the second acoustic unit. The variety of overlap observed indicates that there is no regular alternation of activity or coupling of the units. Although one cannot state categorically that only two units are firing, this appears to be the case. It fits well with the histological facts.

Contrary to the situation found in orthopteran tympana, these organs adapt rapidly. From an initial frequency of about 1,000 spikes per second the discharge drops to 50 per cent of this value in the first 0·1 second and to 25 per cent by the end of the second.

Various operations on the tympanic organ prove that the effects observed electrophysiologically are truly indicative of activity in the two chordotonal sensilla. Touching the sensilla or disengaging them from the tympanic membrane terminates their activity. On the other hand, tearing the membrane or opening the air sac behind it fails to alter the response significantly. Occluding the external tympanic recess narrows the band of frequency reception to its middle range and raises the threshold.

These experiments are in agreement with the idea that this organ is a displacement-sensitive receiver. They show that the tympanum must be free to vibrate but that uniformly distributed elastic tension is not necessary. The direction of the displacement, in so far as the sensillum is concerned, is apparently not critical, since in many noctuids the axis of the sensillum is not normal to the plane of the tympanic membrane; instead, it forms an acute angle with it.

The function of the non-acoustic unit may be proprioceptive. If the acoustic sensilla are rendered inoperative resting activity may be recorded from the non-acoustic unit alone, but only so long as the attachment to that structure known as the Bügel is intact (Fig. 57). In this region is located a single Type II neuron (Treat and Roeder, 1959). The rate of discharge of this unit changes as various portions of the tympanic frame are distorted, as they would be during flight or as a result of activity of the two tympanic muscles (Fig. 56).

The fact that the moth tympanic organ exhibits after-discharge, a form of physiological amplification for stimuli of short duration, and rapid adaptation fits it very well for the reception of short, rapid bursts of sound of the sort given off by hunting bats. Furthermore, its maxi-

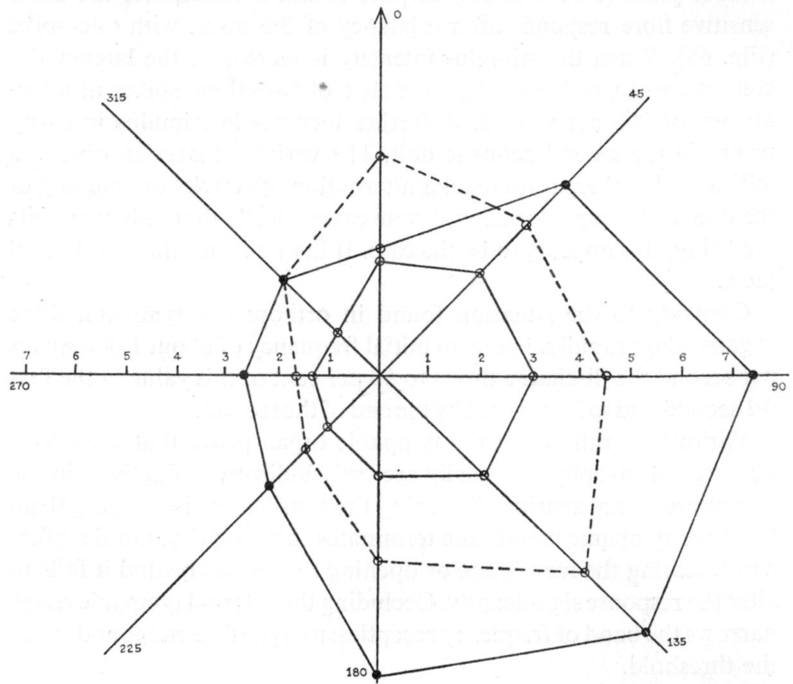

FIG. 67. Polar plot of the distances at which a 1-msec. click of fixed intensity elicits the same response from the right tympanic organ when placed at various angles relative to the median axis of the moth (0–180 degrees). The moth was headed towards 0 degree and inclined upward at about 30 degrees to the plane of measurements. Distances in metres from the moth are indicated on the 90–270-degree line. Open circles and solid line, *Acronycta*; broken line, *Graphiphora*; solid circles and solid line, *Lucania*. (Redrawn from Roeder and Treat, 1961.)

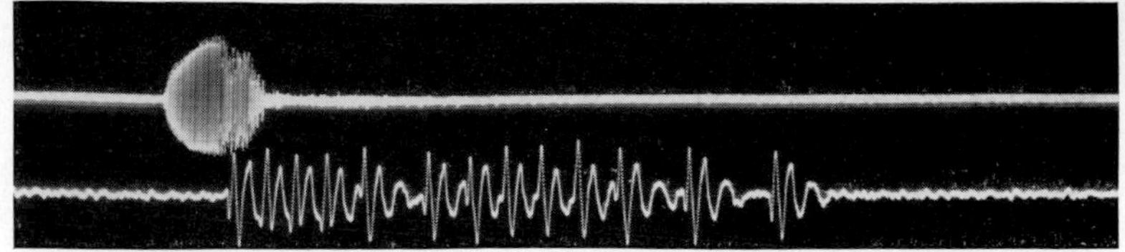

PLATE I. The cry of a flying bat (*Myotis*) recorded by a Granith microphone (upper trace) and the acoustic cells of the noctuid moth *Agroperina dubitans* (lower trace). Time mark, 10 msec. Made in collaboration with Dr Fred Webster. (Courtesy of Roeder and Treat.)

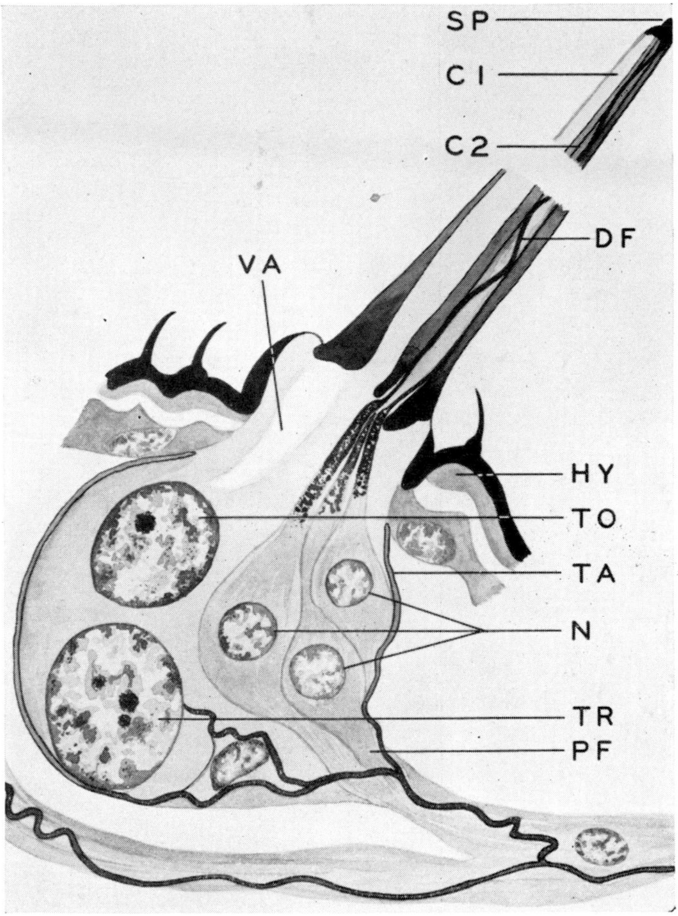

PLATE II. Triply innervated chemosensory hair of *Phormia* (pigment layer omitted). HY, hypodermis; DF, distal fibres (dendrites); PF, proximal fibres (axons); N, neuron cell bodies; TR, trichogen; TO, tormogen; C_1, thin-walled cavity; C_2, thick-walled cavity; VA, vacuole; TA, tracheole; SP, sensory papilla. (From Dethier, 1955.)

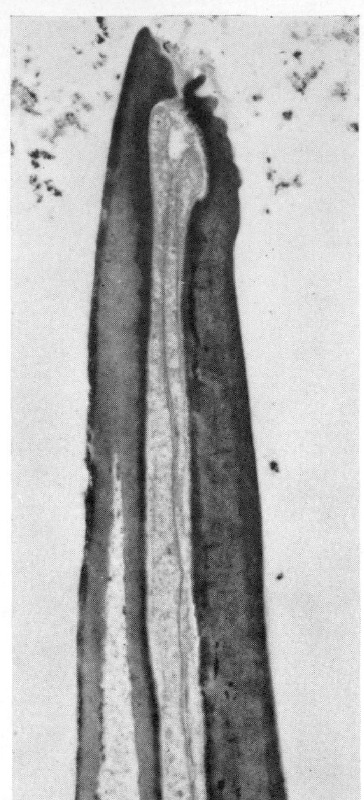

PLATE III. Electron-micrograph of the tip of a tarsal contact chemoreceptor of *Stomoxys calcitrans* (×20,000). (Courtesy of J. R. Adams.)

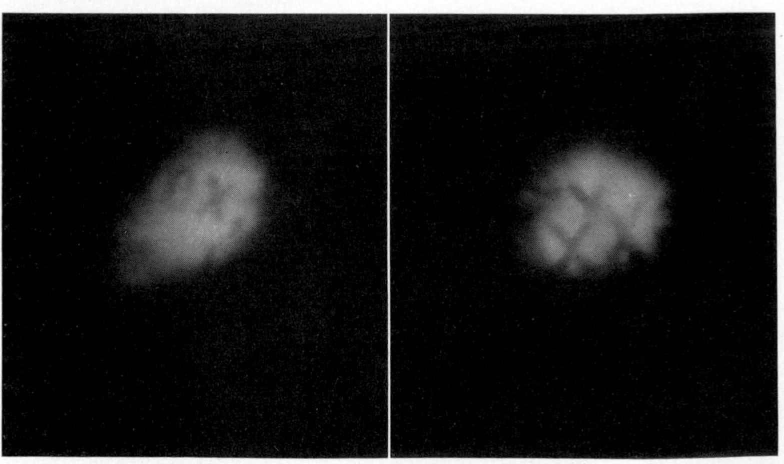

PLATE IV. Photomicrographs of images of newsprint formed by the corneal lens of ocelli of the caterpillar *Isia isabella*. ex is seen through a unitary type cornea; x, through a tripartite type. (From Dethier, 1942.)

mum sensitivity is in the range (15,000–60,000 c/s) corresponding to the predominant frequencies in the cries of flying bats of the family Vespertilionidae (Griffin, 1950, 1953). Actual tests in which electrical recordings were made from tympanic organs in the presence of bat cries prove beyond all doubt that the organs could be used for detecting these predators (Roeder and Treat, 1957) (Pl. 1). Behavioural studies (Roeder and Treat, 1961 a, 1961 b) have shown that free-flying moths take evasive action when they are stimulated by bat cries. This is random action, at least when the bat is near, in that it bears no particular relation to the flight path of the bat.

Like the tympanic organ of Orthoptera, the organs of moths are directional receivers (Roeder and Treat, 1961 a). Localization is theoretically possible with one, but is obviously more efficient with two. At low sound intensities, that is, when the bat is not too near, there is a differential response from the two organs, but as the intensity increases, when the bat would be close, the differential nature of the binaural response disappears (Roeder and Treat, 1961b) (Fig. 67).

Another role of the tympanic organ may be concerned with navigation during flight. It has been suggested (Hinton, 1955) that some moths may orient themselves by echo-location. Although no experimental proof exists, there is direct evidence that moths can detect the sounds of a flying moth and presumably those of their own flying (Roeder and Treat, 1957). This evidence suggests that moths might be able to detect the reflection of their own flight sounds from nearby objects, and hence to echo-locate. For this to succeed, however, numerous obstacles would have to be overcome, not the least of which would be the ability to distinguish between direct and reflected flight sounds.

Function – Hemiptera

Little is known about the tympanic organs of this Order. Males of the waterboatman, *Corixa*, stridulate. Females respond to the chirping, and other males chirp in chorus as long as the tympanic organs are intact (Schaller, 1951). These are the only insects for which a sensitivity to water-borne sound has been demonstrated.

HAIRS AS SOUND RECEPTORS

Many insects that lack tympanic organs are sensitive to sound waves in air. As early as 1779, Bonnet recorded that caterpillars respond to sound by thrashing about of the anterior portion of the body. Since that time many naturalists have recorded this phenomenon, a response brought about by convulsive contractions of the longitudinal muscles in the anterior trunk. Some species respond by a complete cessation of movement, a 'freezing'; some respond by 'freezing' followed by thrashing. The response probably serves as a protective device. It remained to Minnich (1925, 1936, 1937) to attempt a physiological investigation of the response. He studied seven species of butterfly larvae and eight species of moth larvae, bringing to a total of twenty-eight the number of lepidopterous larvae known up to that time to be sensitive to sound. It is likely that all caterpillars detect sound. The range of frequency sensitivity extends from 32 to 1,000 c/s. By cutting larvae into fragments and noting that the fragments responded, Minnich showed that the receptors for sound were diffusely distributed throughout the body.

Early experiments were confined to relatively hairy species, and in these the responses to sound were abolished when the hairs were loaded with flour dust or droplets of water. Upon removal of the dust or water, responsiveness returned. A steady stream of air directed against the hairs inhibited response. These experiments support strongly the idea that the hairs are the sound receptors. On the other hand, similar behavioural responses to sound were obtained with 'hairless' species. Although even these species possess minute setae, Minnich (1936) entertained doubts that sound reception here was indeed mediated by hairs. The question is still open.

In the belief that the sensory hairs of the hirsute caterpillars were resonant structures, that is, that different lengths and sizes would resonate to different frequencies of stimulus, Minnich (1936) attempted to fatigue the response to one frequency and test for a response to another. He found, in fact, that fatiguing at low frequency inhibited responses to all higher frequencies, but that the reverse was not true. As Pumphrey (1940) pointed out, these results are inconsistent with a hypothesis of reaction by resonance. He pointed out further that the results obtained in the experiments on fatiguing are explicable on the grounds that low-frequency stimuli will be much louder to the animal than those of equal intensity but higher frequency and would therefore probably have a greater fatiguing effect. This interpretation is based on a study of action potentials recorded from cercal hairs of cricket and cockroaches (Pumphrey and Rawdon-Smith, 1936 a, 1936 b, 1936 c).

The cerci of cockroaches and *Gryllus* and many other Orthoptera are clothed with extremely delicate, long, lightly hinged hairs (Sihler, 1924). They are typical sensilla trichodea. In *Periplaneta americana* there are several hundred on each cercus. Each hair is about 0·5 mm. long and ± 0·005 mm. in diameter. They move visibly to light puffs of air and to sounds of adequate intensity over a wide frequency range; that is, the response is not resonance. As Pumphrey and Rawdon-Smith (1936a, 1936b, 1936c) showed, these hairs are pure displacement receptors sensitive up to about 3,000 c/s. Threshold measurements over

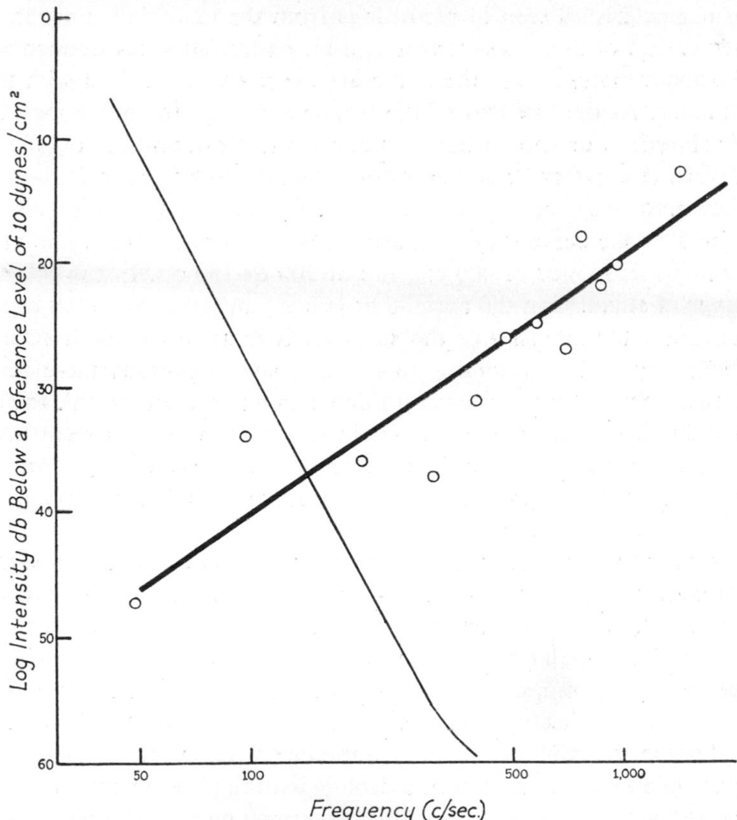

FIG. 68. Experimentally determined thresholds of the cercus of *Gryllus* for pure tones at various frequencies (solid circles). The heavy line represents a constant displacement amplitude of 560 Å. The light line represents the human threshold of hearing from Wegel's data. (Redrawn from Pumphrey, 1940.)

the frequency range 50 c/s to +1,000 c/s (Fig. 69) reveal that the response is to a constant displacement amplitude of 560 Å. (Pumphrey, 1940). If the hair acts as a rigid lever this finding suggests that the threshold displacement of the dendrite at the base of the hair cannot greatly exceed 0·5 Å. Pumphrey (1940) suggested that the 'spontaneous' activity recorded from nerves in silent surroundings may represent random movement of the dendrites by Brownian agitation of the molecules in their vicinity. Conditions are similar for the cricket and the cockroach.

In contrast to the tympanic organ, the cercal hairs exhibit a number of characteristics seen in recordings from the mammalian cochlear nerve. One of these is synchronization. At low stimulus frequencies the action potentials in the nerve are exactly synchronized with the stimulus. At the low end of the frequency range the nerve may be synchronized or show what Pumphrey and Rawdon-Smith (1936 a, 1936 b, 1936 c) term 'frequency doubling'. At high frequencies it may show frequency halving or quartering. Thus, at a stimulus frequency of 400 c/s the nerve may discharge at 400 c/s or at 800 c/s, and at a stimulus frequency of 400 c/s, fire at 300 or 150 c/s. In the 400 c/s range of stimulation the nerve that is firing in synchrony may begin halving if the intensity of the stimulus is reduced by about 10 db. Pumphrey and Rawdon-Smith (1936 c) suggested that these phenomena may exemplify the condition known as 'alternation'. In the mammalian VIIIth nerve the synchrony in the whole nerve at high stimulus frequencies is believed to result from each fibre firing to alternate sound waves and the different fibre groups being 180 degrees out of phase. In the cercal nerve the alteration is different in that all fibres fire to every other sound wave but all are in phase, that is, the whole nerve alternates, hence, the response frequency is halved or quartered. It was suggested, however, that true alternation of the mammalian type also occurs, at least during the first fraction of a second of response, when the nerve momentarily fires at 600–800 c/s. At higher stimulus frequencies the nerve responds asynchronously.

Another resemblance to the mammalian VIIIth nerve is the occurrence of equilibration, that is, a decline with time in the amplitude of massed spikes in the nerve. This phenomenon is interpreted as a reduction in the number of impulses at each sound wave with time as the result of the lengthening of the relative refractory period of each fibre.

Electrophysiological studies of the cercal sensilla of a number of Acrididae are in general agreement with the results just described; however, no clear evidence of equilibration or frequency halving or doubling was obtained (Haskell, 1956 a, 1956 b).

Hairs on other parts of the body, especially of Orthoptera, are believed also to be receptors sensitive to air-borne sound waves, but the evidence is not always convincing, because it is derived primarily from electrophysiological records of activity in segmental nerves known to carry fibres from other types of sensilla, particularly chordotonal sensilla. Pumphrey and Rawdon-Smith (1936 c), studying the locust, believed that the responses originated in trichoid sensilla. Later Pumphrey (1940) suggested that the segmental chordotonal organs were perhaps involved (see also Hughes, 1952). Working with a number of acridid species, Haskell (1956 a) inclined to the view that responses did indeed emanate from hairs because smearing the abdomen with vaseline abolished the response. In any event, the receptors involved fired asynchronously at all stimulus frequencies and required high stimulus intensities (+ 7 dynes/sq. cm.). Even after smearing with vaseline, however, a residual sensitivity to sound occurred, and Haskell (1956 a) suggested that in this instance the chordotonal organs might be involved. Other sensilla on the abdomen of grasshoppers, presumed to be sensitive to vibrations of the substrate, will be discussed later.

Little is known about the functions of hair sensilla sensitive to sound. It is unlikely that those in Orthoptera are concerned with reception of noises produced by stridulation (Haskell, 1952 a). In the cockroach stimulation of cercal hairs with a puff of air evokes the 'evasion response'. This kind of response is not well developed in locusts. In Orthoptera in general mechanical stimulation of the cerci seems to be of great importance during copulation, and perhaps this is the principal role of cercal hairs.

Hairs most highly developed for the reception of air-borne sounds differ in performance from tympanic organs in several respects: they respond over much lower frequency ranges; they respond synchronously with stimulus frequency over certain ranges and thus do exhibit a limited frequency discrimination; they fatigue fairly rapidly; they tend to equilibrate. Like tympanic organs, however, they are displacement receivers.

THE JOHNSTON'S ORGAN OF CULICIDAE

In the males of Culicidae and Chironomidae the Johnston's organ attains an extraordinary complexity manifested by such an enormous multiplication of sensilla that the pedicel is bulbous and a special internal cuticular framework has developed to serve as points of attachment for the many sensilla. This exceptional organ is demonstrably able to be stimulated by air-borne sound waves as Johnston (1855) and Child (1894) originally surmised.

When Mayer (1874) demonstrated that the hair (or fibrillae)

comprising the whorls on the antennae of male *Culex* vibrated in the presence of a vibrating tuning fork he did not indeed prove, as many authors have pointed out (e.g., Fulton, 1928), that the antennae are auditory organs. Nor did his experiments implicate the Johnston's organ. Furthermore, since the different forks employed gave different intensities, and hence stimulus energy could not be controlled, the fact that the hairs vibrated most extensively at 512 c/s is not especially significant. In an experiment with *Culex pipiens pallens* in which intensity was controlled, Yagi and Taguti (1941) found that the hairs which vibrated in the stimulus frequency range of 193–870 c/s vibrated most widely at 217 c/s. As Mayer had shown, maximum vibration occurs when the sound wave advances at right angles to the longitudinal axis of the hairs.

The literature is replete with accounts of mosquitoes reacting to sound. In a most extensive study Roth (1948) found that males of *Aedes aegypti* respond to the sound of a flying female and to artificial sounds of comparable frequencies by orienting to the source of sound and displaying the mating response, which consists of seizing and clasping. To sounds of other frequencies they: rub the antennae with the forelegs, rub the hind legs together, rub the abdomen or wings with the hind legs, jerk the body, suddenly fly, or suddenly become immobile.

The frequencies which induce the mating response are different for males of different ages. The effective range extends from about 100 to about 800 c/s, and the spectrum is narrower for non-virgin males. For virgin and non-virgin alike the effective band widens with age. This shift to higher frequencies has been correlated with the extension of the antennal fibrillae. When males first emerge, the hairs or fibrillae lie recumbent along the shaft of the flagellum. By 48 hours they are fully extended. This correlation suggests either that the apical fibrillae vibrate at higher stimulus frequencies than the lower or that a larger total of fibrillae must be set in motion at higher stimulus frequencies in order to mediate a response.

Males can be adapted to one frequency (as judged behaviourally) and still retain responsiveness to other frequencies (Roth, 1948). Since intensities were not controlled in these experiments, the significance is in doubt. With minor deviations the same story holds for *Anopheles quadrimaculatus*, *Culex pipiens*, and *Psorophora confinnis*.

The correlation between the degree of extension of antennal fibrillae and the extension of responses to higher stimulus frequency suggests that the fibrillae are concerned with sound reception; however, they are not innervated in mosquitoes. Early workers postulated that the vibrating fibrillae acted as mechanical amplifiers which set the flagellar shaft in vibration. The movement of the shaft with respect to the pedicel was presumed to be detected by Johnston's organ. In an extensive series of experiments with *Aedes aegypti* Roth (1948) obtained results that confirmed this hypothesis. The mating response of males to sound is abolished by completely removing the flagellum, joining the flagellum rigidly to the pedicel with shellac, or weighting the tips of the antennae with large beads of shellac. In all cases responsiveness returns when the shellac is removed. When the fibrillae are removed from the antennae greater intensities of sound are required in order to elicit responses.

Although no electrophysiological studies of the Johnston's organ of mosquitoes have yet been reported, these experiments of Roth, taken in conjunction with Burkhardt's electrophysiological analysis of the Johnston's organ of *Calliphora*, establish beyond reasonable doubt that this organ in *Culicidae* is indeed adapted to respond to air-borne sound waves.

PERCEPTION OF VIBRATIONS IN SOLIDS

It had been suspected for many decades that insects were sensitive to vibrations in solids because they gave clear behavioural responses when the substrate upon which they were standing or walking was subjected to this form of motion. No very meaningful experiments were performed, however, prior to the introduction of electrophysiological methods of analysis. By recording from leg and segmental nerves it has now been possible to demonstrate that there are rather specific responses by some insects to vibration. A few clues as to the identity of the sensilla involved have been obtained.

The two types of sensilla suited to the task are trichoid sensilla and chordotonal sensilla. It is to be expected that those parts of the body immediately in contact with the substrate, that is, the legs and abdomen, would be especially equipped with the requisite organs; however, aside from a few experiments showing that in *Locusta* there are hairs on the sternites which mediate responses to vibrations of the substrate (Haskell, 1956 a), there is no extensive work on areas of the body other than the legs.

The legs certainly possess elaborate sensory equipment. In addition to trichoid sensilla they invariably possess numbers of chordotonal sensilla (Eggers, 1928; Debaisieux, 1935, 1938). Generally the legs contain chordotonal organs at four locations; the femur, the proximal tibia (the subgenual organs), the distal tibia, the tarsus-pretarsus. The degree to which the organs are developed varies from Order to Order and species to species. The number of sensilla in a group varies from one to two hundred or three hundred. Each group, with the exception of the subgenual organ, is associated with an articulation of the leg. In the subgenual region there may be one or two concentrations of sensilla or none at all. The true subgenual organ lies immediately distal to the femur–tibia articulation. When a second group of sensilla occurs, it lies distal to the true subgenual organ. True subgenual organs have not been found in the thysanuran *Machilis*, the beetle *Rhagonycha*, or in Diptera, Heteroptera, Homoptera, and Neuropterpodea. Even the more distal organ is absent in *Machilis*, *Rhagonycha*, and Diptera (Debaisieux, 1938).

Subgenual organs are unusually diverse in structure, shape, and numbers of component sensilla. They are most highly developed in Orthoptera, Hymenoptera, and Lepidoptera and take the form of cones, or sails, or fans. They are unique in that they more or less completely occlude the dorsal blood sinus of the leg (Figs. 47, 56). At the same time they lie in close proximity to the main tracheal trunk. They are innervated by a branch of the leg nerve or, in the case of insects possessing a tibial tympanic organ, by a branch of the tympanic nerve and a branch of the leg nerve combined. They are supported proximally by their nerves and distally by accessory cells which form a ligament attached most often to the cuticula of the leg. Standard chordotonal sensilla comprise the sensory elements. In number they range from ten to forty. Extensive descriptions of these organs have been given by Schwabe (1906), Schön (1911), Eggers (1928), and Debaisieux (1935, 1938).

It has not been easy to ascertain just which of the many sense organs in the legs mediate responses to vibrations of the substrate. The most extensive experiments have been those of Autrum (1942, 1943), Autrum and Schneider (1948), and Schneider (1950). Data are based upon electrophysiological recordings of total activity in leg nerves while the preparation was 'standing' on a metal plate which was set into sinusoidal oscillations of measurable amplitude (Autrum, 1941). Tests were conducted with Orthoptera, Lepidoptera, Hymenoptera, and Coleoptera. In many, the prothoracic legs are the least sensitive; the mesothoracic, the most.

All of the insects tested fall roughly into two groups as regards sensitivity. In the less-sensitive group are the beetles, *Carabus*, *Silpha*, *Pterostrichus*, and the Hymenoptera, *Vespa* and *Bombus*. The more

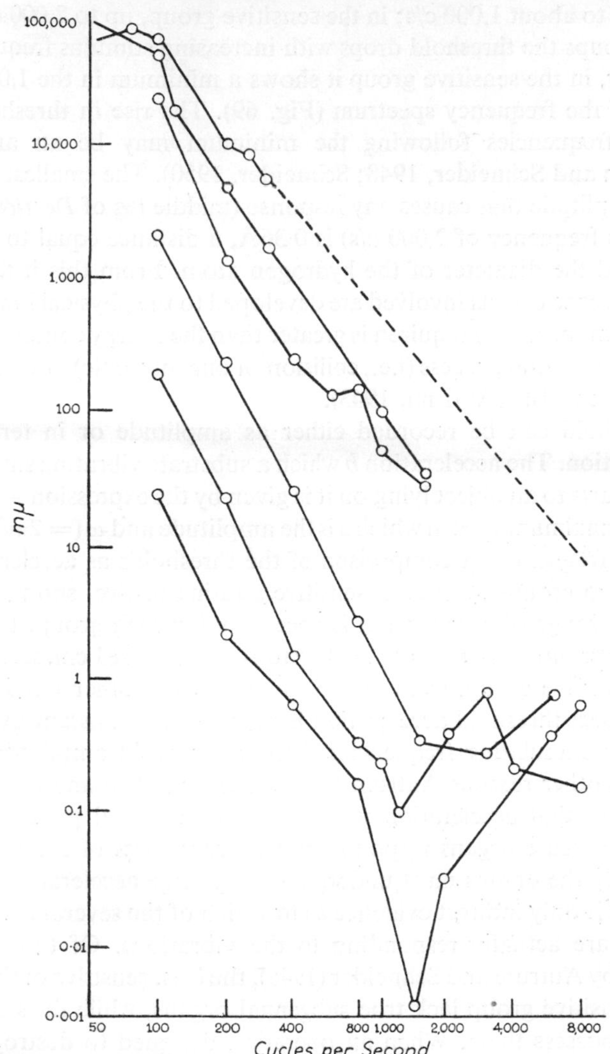

FIG. 69. Vibration thresholds in mμ (ordinate) in relation to frequency (abscissa) for insects representing three levels of sensitivity. (Redrawn from Autrum and Schneider, 1948.)

sensitive forms include the beetles *Geotrupes* and *Melolontha*, the butterfly *Pyrameis*, the cockroach *Periplaneta*, and the cricket *Liogryllus* (Autrum and Schneider, 1948; Schneider, 1950). In the insensitive group there are responses to stimulus frequencies ranging from 50 to about 1,000 c/s; in the sensitive group, up to 8,000 c/s. In both groups the threshold drops with increasing stimulus frequency; however, in the sensitive group it shows a minimum in the 1,000 c/s band of the frequency spectrum (Fig. 69). The rise in threshold at higher frequencies following the minimum may be an artefact (Autrum and Schneider, 1948; Schneider, 1950). The smallest measured amplitude that causes any response (middle leg of *Decticus* at a stimulus frequency of 2,000 c/s) is 0·36Å, a distance equal to about one-third the diameter of the hydrogen atom. From this it follows that the sense organs involved are developed to the physical limit, but the minimum energy required is greater than the energy content of the unitary elemental process (i.e., collision of one molecule) of which the stimulus consists (Autrum, 1943).

Threshold can be recorded either as amplitude or in terms of acceleration. The acceleration b which a substrate vibrating sinusoidally imparts to an object lying on it is given by the expression $-a \cdot \omega^2 \sin \omega t$ (maximum $a\omega^2$) in which a is the amplitude and $\omega (= 2\pi\nu)$ is the angular frequency. A comparison of the thresholds as accelerations of the two groups of insects, sensitive and insensitive, shows that a different range of acceleration is necessary for each group. For the sensitive group it ranges from $2 \cdot 10^{-14}$ to $10^{-1}g$ ($g = 981$ cm. sec.^{2}); for the insensitive group, from $3 \cdot 10^{-2}$ to g). On the other hand, for a given insect threshold acceleration is more nearly constant over the range of stimulating frequencies than is threshold amplitude. For this and other reasons Autrum and Schneider (1948) and Schneider (1950) felt that acceleration was the crucial physical parameter to which the sense organs respond and that regardless of the stimulus frequency the organs must undergo equally large accelerations.

There is only indirect evidence as to which of the several organs in the leg are actually responding to the vibrations. Of the species studied by Autrum and Schneider (1948), the least sensitive of those in the insensitive group lack true subgenual organs, while the sensitive species possess them. When an operation designed to destroy subgenual organs was performed on those species possessing them the threshold of response to vibration rose and the effective frequency band became narrow so that these sensitive insects now resembled insensitive ones (Autrum, 1941).

From these experiments it was concluded that the sensitive insects possessed an organ especially adapted to detect vibrations in the substrate and that this organ was the subgenual collection of chordotonal sensilla. The insensitive insects, on the other hand, were presumed to be reacting primarily to stimuli outside the normal biological range and doing so through the agency of organs not finely adapted for this function. Coating the legs with paraffin did not abolish the response so it is unlikely that hairs or spines mediate the response. As already pointed out, other chordotonal organs in the leg are associated with articulations. The articulations are also equipped with hair plates. Either of these groups could be concerned. Whichever types they are, it is probably the tarsal ones that are important in perception, since response to vibration is lost following amputation of the tarsi (Autrum and Schneider, 1948).

In flies (*Calliphora* and *Eristalis*), which are among the least sensitive insects, there is no subgenual organ of any sort. Responses are probably mediated through a tibial chordotonal organ which consists of three sensilla (Schneider, 1950). The upper frequency limit of this organ is about 100/cs. At frequencies up to this, the discharge in the nerve is synchronized with the stimulus. At higher frequencies it is asynchronous.

Autrum and Schneider (1948) decided that sensitivity is connected with the anatomical structure of the subgenual organs. Where these are fan-shaped, thresholds are low (e.g., Orthoptera); where they are conical and compactly constructed (e.g., Hymenoptera), thresholds are higher. On the other hand, the beetles *Geotrupes* and *Melolontha*, which lack true subgenual organs, are very sensitive to frequencies between 600 and 1,000 c/s and 600 and 1,500 c/s respectively and still are responsive to 4,000 and 8,000 c/s respectively (Schneider, 1950). Recordings obtained following successive amputations of lengths of leg suggest that the receptors are the ten chordotonal sensilla in the distal end of the tibia. In any case, sensitivity does not depend upon the number of sensilla. *Camponotus* sp? with a subgenual organ containing about twenty sensilla is as sensitive as *Apis* with about forty.

The curious anatomical position of the subgenual organ with respect to the blood sinus of the leg invites speculation about the functional association of this organ with the blood. Work with a model has shown that vibrations would establish vortices in the blood such that a rather constant pressure would be applied to the outer surface of the subgenual organ (Autrum, 1942). It has been postulated that the effect is a rectifying one and that it serves to permit the nerve to transmit frequencies higher than the 200–500 c/s that represent the top limit permitted by the refractory period of nerves (Autrum, 1942; Autrum and Schneider, 1948). While it is possible that vibrations act indirectly by means of disturbances in the blood, the argument that it is necessary in order to permit the organ to respond to higher stimulus frequencies is not valid. For example, alternation of firing in the various fibres, as in the cercal hairs, would accomplish the same purpose.

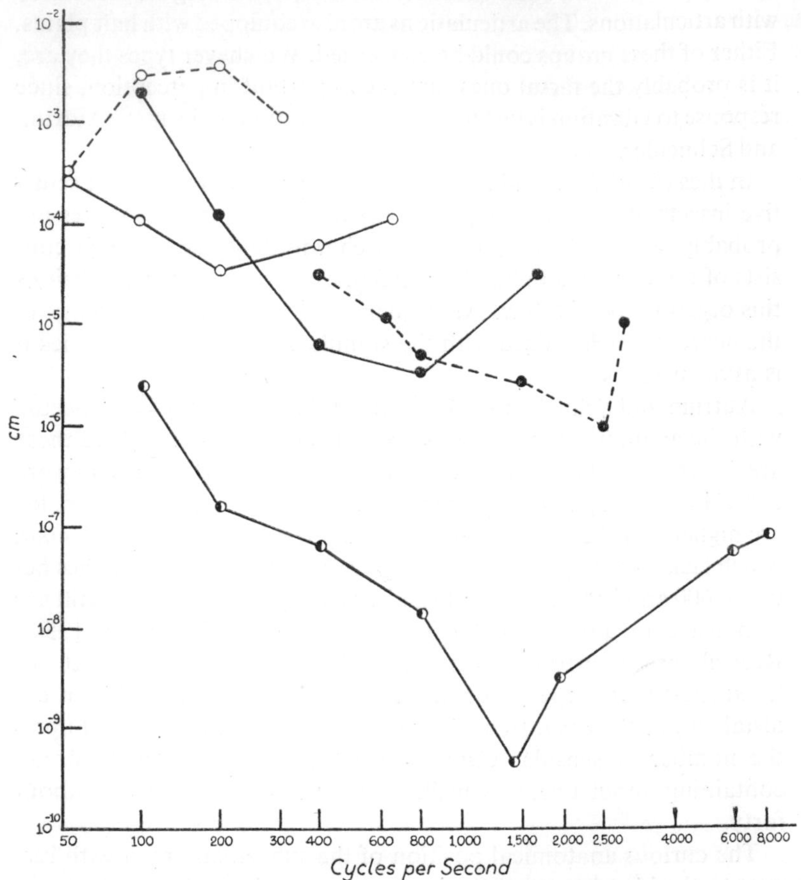

FIG. 70. Comparisons of the vibration thresholds of flies (○ - - - - ○), men (○———○), bullfinches (●———●), bees (● - - - - ●), and cockroaches (◐———◐). (Redrawn from Schneider, 1950.)

Those who would consider sensitivity to vibrations in solids a separate sense, compare the abilities of man, birds, and insects (the only animals for which threshold values are known) in this respect and find insects to be the most as well as the least sensitive. The cockroach at its optimum range is more sensitive by a factor of 10,000 than the bird which in turn is more sensitive than man (Schneider, 1950). Flies are among the least-sensitive animals (Fig. 70).

Pure vibrations at these high frequencies do not generally occur in nature, but such high frequencies undoubtedly exist as transients in the single pulse-like vibrations of the substrate to which insects are ordinarily exposed. Suddenness is the important factor, so perception of these transients, even without frequency discrimination, may be the contribution which the subgenual organs make to behaviour (Autrum, 1959).

CHAPTER V

Chemoreception

The accomplishment of many sexual, reproductive, social, and feeding activities of insects depends to a great extent upon the detection and assessment of specific chemical aspects of the environment. With the exception of feeding, where most of the chemical energy of the stimulating materials is utilized for purposes remote from the activity of the sense organ, the energy of compounds eliciting the other behaviour patterns serves merely to trigger excitation in receptors.

These receptors are not chemosensitive simply because of fortuitous anatomical location, or exposure to the environment, or the possession of permeable coverings (Dethier, 1962). On the contrary, they are inherently highly specialized and specific. Because of their specificity it would probably be more meaningful to speak of salt, sugar, or sex-attractant receptors than of olfactory and contact chemoreceptors; however, since our knowledge of their physiology is still fragmentary, the two broad but ambiguous categories are still convenient (cf. Dethier and Chadwick, 1948 a).

It was postulated long before being demonstrated that chemoreceptors generated impulses as did other receptors. There is nothing unique about this part of the train of events initiated by stimulation. At the opposite end of the train, a beginning is being made towards an understanding of the behavioural correlates (cf., e.g., Dethier, 1957). The great unknown now is the basis of specificity and the nature of the transducing mechanism (Dethier, 1956, 1962).

THE RECEPTORS

The identification of chemoreceptors (whose nature is never so obvious as that of photoreceptors and sound receptors) has probably been retarded more than that of any other sense modality by the tendency to assign the function of chemoreception to all sensilla whose structure conforms to some postulated norm. There is, therefore, a voluminous literature on the structure of chemoreceptors real and supposed (for detailed reviews consult Kraepelin, 1833; Röhler, 1906; Forel, 1908; McIndoo, 1914 a, 1914 b; von Frisch, 1921; Minnich, 1929 a; Marshall, 1935; Dethier and Chadwick, 1948 a; Dethier, 1953).

By observing the responses of insects (from which various appendages or parts thereof have been extirpated) to food, naturally occurring attractants, and odours to which they have been conditioned, it has been established that the principal sites of chemoreceptors are: antennae, maxillary and labial palpi or their homologues, legs, and ovipositors. Since all of these areas contain a large and heterogeneous population of sensilla, the assignment of a chemoreceptive function to specific ones has been an arduous and uncertain task (cf. Dostal, 1958; Schneider, 1961). Thus, despite extensive histological studies from those of Hauser (1880), Schenk (1903), and Vogel (1923 b) to the present time, the identity of chemoreceptors is known in fewer than a score of cases.

Olfactory Receptors

An olfactory function has been assigned to the following receptor types with a fair degree of certainty: in the honeybee, sensilla placodea (von Frisch, 1921; Dostal, 1958), sensilla basiconica, and possibly sensilla coeloconica (Dostal, 1958); in the dung beetles, *Geotrupes sylvaticus*, *G. vernalis*, *Necrophorus tomentosus*, *N. vespilloides*, *Silpha noveboracensis*, and *S. americana*, sensilla basiconica (Warnke, 1931, 1934; Dethier, 1947 a); in lepidopterous larvae, sensilla basiconica (Dethier, 1941; Morita and Yamashita, 1961); in the human louse, sensilla basiconica (Wigglesworth, 1941); in housefly larvae, sensilla basiconica (Bolwig, 1946); in *Drosophila*, sensilla basiconica (Begg and Hogben, 1946); in *Phormia regina*, sensilla basiconica (Dethier, unpublished); in saturniid moths, probably sensilla trichodea, sensilla basiconica, sensilla coeloconica (Schneider, 1961); in the grasshoppers *Melanoplus differentialis* and *Romalea microptera*, sensilla basiconica and sensilla coeloconica (Slifer, 1961).

The salient features of sensilla placodea as seen with the light microscope are illustrated in Fig. 11. Details of structure have been clarified by the electron-microscopic studies of Richards (1951) and Slifer (1961). The sensillum is essentially a thin circular or oval plate connected to the surrounding cuticle by a delicate circumferential membrane and equipped with twelve to eighteen bipolar neurons (Vogel, 1921, 1923 b). Each dendrite possesses one or two minute refringent bodies of unknown function, the Riechstabschen (Vogel, 1923 b). Furthermore, each dendrite ends in a cilium-like structure (Slifer, 1961) similar to that described in tympanic organs. From each cilium-like structure there extends a fibrous strand. The strands terminate on the extreme edge of the plate (Slifer, 1961). The antenna of a honeybee possesses from 3,000 to 30,000 sensilla placodea (Schenk, 1903; McIndoo, 1914 b; Vogel, 1923 b; Melin, 1941; Kuwabara and Takeda, 1956; Dostal, 1958). Although the behavioural experiments of von Frisch (1921) and Dostal (1958) support the idea that these sensilla are olfactory, it is still difficult to comprehend in what way their structure is particularly suited to chemoreception (see also Snodgrass, 1935; Slifer, 1961).

Sensilla basiconica are so variable in size, shape, and number of neurons that a general description is meaningless. Extensive electron-

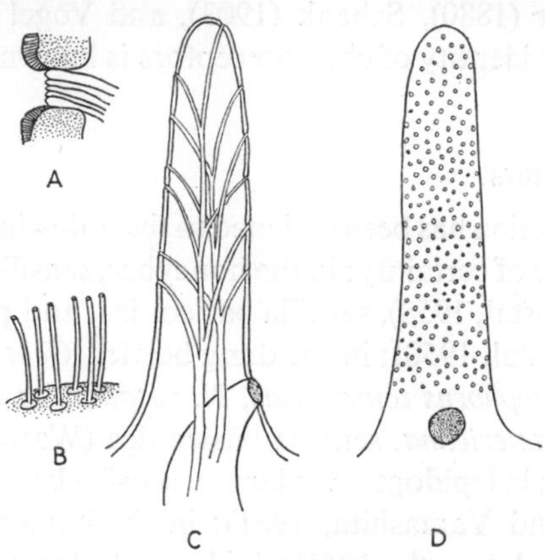

FIG. 71. Diagram of a thin-walled sensillum basiconicum from a grasshopper antenna. A, section through a perforation showing finger-like processes of dendrite; B, small portion of scolopoid sheath showing the dendritic processes passing through; C, longitudinal section of peg showing dendrite passing through scolopoid sheath at base; D, external surface showing permeable basal spot and numerous fine perforations of peg. (Redrawn from Slifer *et al.*, 1959.)

microscope studies have been made only of grasshoppers on the antennae of which two types occur (Slifer, 1961). The length of a typical thick-walled peg (sensillum basiconicum) is 20–50 μ (Fig. 14) (Slifer, Prestage, and Beams, 1957). The tip possesses an opening about 2 μ in diameter. A tubular cuticular sheath extends from this opening down the lumen of the peg, constricts in the region of its base, then again widens. It is the scolopoid sheath. The dendrites of the neurons, usually five, are conducted within this sheath to the tip of the peg, where, according to Slifer, Prestage, and Beams (1957), they are exposed to the air and bathed in a fluid derived from the vacuole of the tormogen and trichogen cells. At moulting the cuticular sheath is drawn out through the orifice at the tip of the peg.

The typical thin-walled sensillum basiconicum of the grasshopper antenna is 16 μ long and 3 μ in diameter at its base (Fig. 13). The scolopoid sheath, instead of extending to the tip as in the thick-walled pegs, makes a right-angle turn at the base of the peg and comes to the surface. At moulting the old sheath is pulled out through this area. The dendrites of the forty to sixty neurons enter the scolopoid sheath in the usual manner, but when the latter turns, they perforate its side and continue into the lumen of the peg (Fig. 71). Within this fluid-filled cavity each one branches once or twice and each branch terminates at one of about 150 openings on the peg's surface (Slifer, Prestage, and Beams, 1959). At its termination each branch is composed of about twenty-four parallel finger-like processes (Fig. 71). The long, hotly debated question as to whether the neurons of chemoreceptors are exposed to air, a question for which the conventional answer had been negative (cf. Dethier, 1954 b) would now seem to have been answered in the affirmative.

Contact Chemoreceptors

Receptors sensitive to stimulation by chemical solutions applied directly have been identified positively in Diptera, Lepidoptera, Hymenoptera, and Coleoptera. They are trichoid sensilla located on the legs and mouth-parts. Small sensilla basiconica on the labella of flies have also been identified as gustatory receptors. There is no doubt that there are also other types of gustatory receptors, but their identity still requires confirmation. For details regarding the location of contact chemoreceptors in various insects the review of Frings and Frings (1949) should be consulted.

The contact chemoreceptive hairs, as exemplified by those on the tarsi and labella of Diptera, are actually compound sensilla; that is, they are organs containing several kinds of receptors. In the black blowfly, *Phormia regina*, the receptors occur as groups of three, four, or five bipolar neurons associated with long (30–300 μ) hairs which characteristically possess two lumina (Pl. II). The cell bodies of the neurons lie in a subhypodermal position beneath the hair in association with the tormogen and trichogen cells and one or more neurilemma and tracheal cells. The entire group of cells is wrapped in a thin membrane which is continuous with the basement membrane of the surrounding hypodermis and with the sheath enveloping the nerve. The nerve consists of the axons of the receptor cells, which are believed to extend, without synapsing, to the central nervous system. The dendrites of the neurons extend into a scolopoid sheath and then up the thicker walled of the two lumina to the tip of the hair. In triply innervated hairs as originally described in *Phormia* by Grabowski and Dethier (1954) and Dethier (1955 a) the fibres from two neurons extend to the tip of the hair while the third terminates on the base. The existence in *Phormia* of hairs equipped with four neurons was only recently suggested by behavioural evidence (Dethier and Evans, 1961) and confirmed electrophysiologically (Mellon and Evans, 1961) and by electron-microscopy (Larsen, 1962). Hairs with three, four, and five neurons have been found in *Calliphora* (Sturkow, 1960; Peters, 1961).

The only part of the hair that is sensitive to chemical stimulation is the extreme tip, which in some hairs is prolonged into a terminal papilla into which the dendrites extend (Dethier, 1955 a; Dethier and Wolbarsht, 1956). In the stable fly *Stomoxys calcitrans* Adams (1961) has found that the terminal processes of the dendrites extend through a pore in the cuticle (Pl. III).

OLFACTION

Acuity

Although the behaviour of insects in their natural environment suggests that their olfactory sense may be extraordinarily sensitive by human standards, attempts to measure acuity accurately have not been outstandingly successful. With the exception of Schneider's work with *Bombyx mori* and associated species, electrophysiological measurements have not been made. All measurements of the performance of olfactory receptors have been based upon behavioural thresholds.

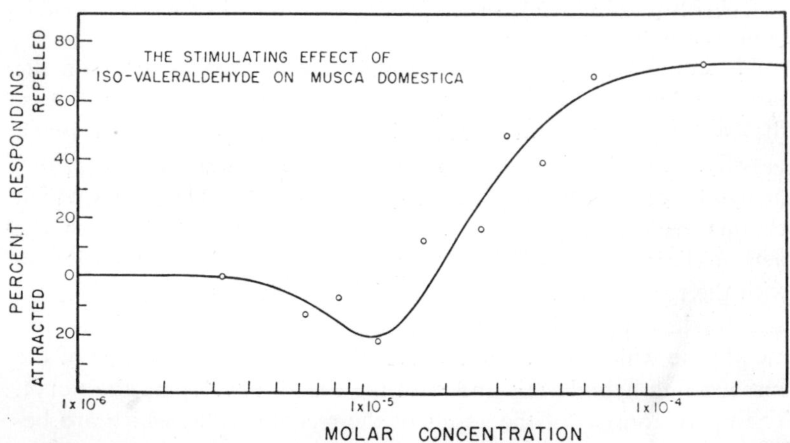

FIG. 72. Change in behaviour with change in concentration of the odour of iso-valeraldehyde. (From Dethier, 1954.)

As the concentration of a stimulating odour exceeds that necessary to stimulate the most sensitive receptor element, a behavioural response occurs in the form of antennal movements, movements of the mouth-parts, occasionally salivation or grooming movements whereby legs or antennae are drawn through the mouth-parts or rubbed against one another. A further increase in concentration results in an oriented movement which may carry the insect towards or away from the source of odour. If the initial response is towards the odour, an additional increase in concentration may cause a reversal in orientation (Fig. 72). An odour which is initially repellent usually remains so at all higher concentrations. An attractive odour may become repellent at higher concentrations (Dethier, 1947 b; Dethier, Hackley, and Wagner-Jauregg, 1952).

Measurements of acuity thus depend in large measure upon which behavioural threshold is chosen for testing. Numerous attempts to measure threshold have been made (Barrows, 1907; von Frisch, 1919; Wirth, 1928; Folsom, 1931; Warnke, 1931; Reed, 1938; Wieting and

TABLE 1

(From Schwarz, 1955)

Differences between the olfactory thresholds of man and honeybees

Odour	THRESHOLD CONCENTRATION: MOLECULES/CC AIR			
	Man	*Author*	*Bee*	*Difference*
Propionic acid	$4{\cdot}2 . 10^{11}$	v. Skramlik	$4{\cdot}3 . 10^{11}$	$1{\cdot}0 . 10^{10}$
Butyric acid	$7{\cdot}0 . 10^{9}$	v. Skramlik	$1{\cdot}1 . 10^{11}$	$10{\cdot}3 . 10^{10}$
Valeric acid	$6{\cdot}0 . 10^{10}$	v. Skramlik		
iso-Valeric acid	$4{\cdot}5 . 10^{10}$	Schwarz	$1{\cdot}6 . 10^{11}$	$11{\cdot}5 . 10^{10}$
Caproic acid	$2{\cdot}0 . 10^{11}$	v. Skramlik	$2{\cdot}2 . 10^{11}$	$2{\cdot}0 . 10^{10}$
Ethyl caproate	$1{\cdot}3 . 10^{11}$	Schwarz	$3{\cdot}8 . 10^{11}$	$2{\cdot}5 . 10^{11}$
Ethyl caprylate	$3{\cdot}7 . 10^{10}$	Schwarz	$5{\cdot}4 . 10^{10}$	$1{\cdot}7 . 10^{10}$
Ethyl pelargonate	$3{\cdot}1 . 10^{10}$	Schwarz	$3{\cdot}7 . 10^{10}$	$6{\cdot}0 . 10^{9}$
Ethyl caprate	$4{\cdot}2 . 10^{9}$	Schwarz	$5{\cdot}6 . 10^{9}$	$1{\cdot}4 . 10^{9}$
Ethyl undecylate	$1{\cdot}4 . 10^{10}$	Schwarz	$1{\cdot}8 . 10^{10}$	$4{\cdot}0 . 10^{9}$
Methyl anthranilate	$2{\cdot}6 . 10^{10}$	v. Skramlik	$1{\cdot}9 . 10^{9}$	$24{\cdot}1 . 10^{9}$
Phenyl propyl alcohol	$6{\cdot}5 . 10^{9}$	Schwarz	$2{\cdot}2 . 10^{9}$	$4{\cdot}3 . 10^{9}$
Nerol	$5{\cdot}7 . 10^{9}$	Schwarz	$3{\cdot}2 . 10^{9}$	$2{\cdot}5 . 10^{9}$
Ionon-α	$3{\cdot}1 . 10^{8}$	Zwaardemaker	$1{\cdot}5 . 10^{10}$	$146{\cdot}9 . 10^{8}$
Eugenol	$8{\cdot}5 . 10^{11}$	Ohma	$2{\cdot}0 . 10^{10}$	$8{\cdot}3 . 10^{11}$
Citral	$4{\cdot}0 . 10^{11}$	v. Skramlik	$6{\cdot}0 . 10^{10}$	$3{\cdot}4 . 10^{11}$

TABLE 2

(From Schwarz, 1955)

Olfactory thresholds for man and various insects

Odour	Species	Threshold concentration: Original value	Threshold concentration: Mol./c.c	Author
Skatol	Man	3·2 . 10^{10} M/50 ml.	1·84 . 10^{9}	v. Skramlik
	Necrophorus	0·00009 g./100 ml.W.	4·17 . 10^{14}	Abbott, 1937
	Geotrupes	0·003 – 0·009 mg./1.	1·83 . 10^{13} – –4·61 . 10^{14}	Warnke, 1931
	Hydrous	0·0000625 %		Ritter, 1936
Benz-aldehyde	Man	0·44 . 10^{-6} g./l.	2·49 . 10^{12}	Ohma
	Pieris rapae	580 . 10^{-7} g./1.	3·28 . 10^{14}	Dethier, 1941
	Malacosoma	435 . 10^{-7} g./l.	2·46 . 10^{14}	Dethier, 1941
Benzol	Man	2·0 . 10^{15} M/50 ml.	4·0 . 10^{13}	v. Skramlik
	Habrobracon	0·5 – 3·0 mg./l.	3·87 . 10^{15} – –2·3 . 10^{16}	Wirth, 1928
Ethyl alcohol	Man	1·6 . 10^{17} M/50 ml.	3·2 . 10^{15}	v. Skramlik
	Musca domestica	0·23 g./l.	3·01 . 10^{18}	Wieting & Hoskins, 1939
	Habrobracon	5 – 20 mg./l.	4·7 . 10^{16} – –1·8 . 10^{17}	Wirth, 1928
	Phormia regina	2·4 . 10^{-4} mol.	1·44 . 10^{20}	Dethier & Yost, 1952

Hoskins, 1939; Dethier, 1941; Crombie, 1944; Dethier and Yost, 1952; Hodgson, 1953; Schwarz, 1955; Fischer, 1957; Dostal, 1958; and others [see Dethier, 1947 b]). A few data are given for comparison in Tables 1 and 2.

Attempts have been made to correlate the acuity of olfaction in the various species with the numbers of sensilla, but the correlation is highly conjectural in as much as the identity of the receptors is uncertain in many species, and quantitative tests of acuity have not been undertaken. It is certainly true that some correlation exists between the number of receptors and behavioural response to odours. The number of olfactory sensilla in an insect varies from species to species. There may be as few as 9–10, as in the human louse, or there may be as many as 30,000 in the drone honeybee (Schenk, 1903; Vogel, 1923 b; McIndoo, 1914 a, 1914 b). Lice and lepidopterous larvae, which live on their hosts and have little apparent need for an extremely acute olfactory sense, possess few sensilla. In the life of the honeybee, on the other hand, many odours are encountered and are highly significant.

Among the Diptera Liebermann (1926) has shown that the so-called olfactory pits (Fig. 73) average 820 in dung-feeding species which depend largely upon odour for locating their food, while in the flower-visiting species, which depend more on vision, the average number is 494. Moreover, the pits are more numerous in males than in females. This difference is presumed to be related to the fact that males employ the olfactory sense in the search for females.

In an individual there is clearly a relation between threshold and the number of sensilla stimulated. The phenomenon was first investigated

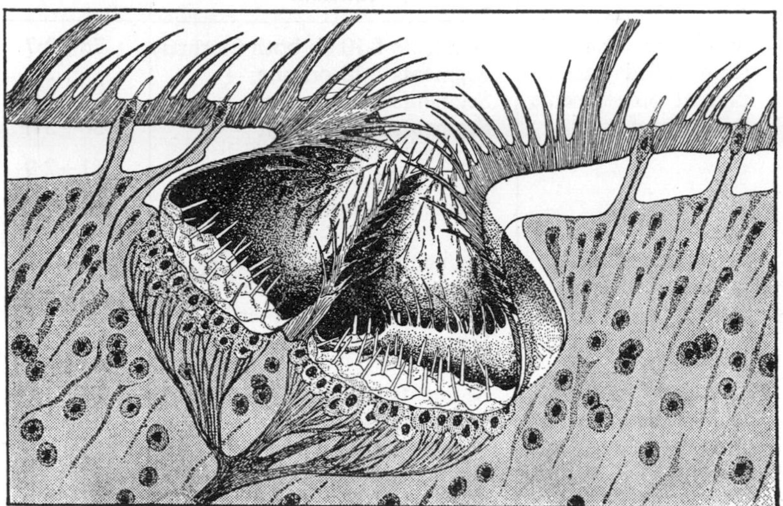

FIG. 73. Olfactory pit on the antenna of a dipterous insect. (From Liebermann, 1926.)

with hygroreception. Pielou (1940) suggested that a threshold number of receptors is required by *Tenebrio molitor* for a response. Detailed confirmation was provided by the experiments of Roth and Willis (1951 a), which showed that the percentage of response of a population of *Tribolium* was closely correlated with the number of sensilla basiconica remaining on each individual after surgical operation. The change in threshold with unilateral antennectomy is illustrated by the figures in Table 3 based on data of Roth and Willis (1951 b). For olfaction the first quantitative data were those of Dethier (1952 b), which showed that in *Phormia regina* there is a definite relation between the threshold and the number of receptors functioning. The data suggest that for a response to occur a given number of molecules must hit a given number of receptors and that the probability of a response can be increased by increasing either the concentration or the number of receptors.

TABLE 3

(From Dethier, 1952 b)

Effects of unilateral and bilateral operations in the responses of beetles given a choice between 0% and 100% R.H. at 27°C.

(Data from Roth and Willis, 1951b)

Species	*Receptor areas remaining on Antenna*	*% Response*
Rhyzopertha dominica (thin-walled sensilla present on segments 8–10)	Segments 1-10 on both (normal)	76±2·7
	{Segments 1-10 on one Segments 1-9 on other}	69±3·0
	Segments 1-9 on both	56±3·4
	{Segments 1-10 on one Segments 1-7 on other}	61±2·9
	Segments 1-7 on both	−0·1±7·0
Latheticus oryzae (thin-walled sensilla present on segments 7–11)	Segments 1-11 on both (normal)	87±3·1
	{Segments 1-11 on one Segments 1-10 on other}	73±3·2
	Segments 1-10 on both	46±2·7
Tribolium castaneum (thin-walled sensilla present on segments 9–11)	Segments 1-11 on both (normal)	80±1·0
	Segments 1-9 on both	75±2·9
	{Segments 1-9 on one Segments 1-8 on other}	78±3·6
	Segments 1-8 on both	31±5·4
Tribolium confusum (thin-walled sensilla present on segments 7–11)	Segments 1-11 on both (normal)	86±1·7
	{Segments 1-11 on one 0 segments on other}	76±3·0
	0 antennae	−0·2±2·2
	Segments 1-7 on both	23±1·6
	{Segments 1-7 on one Segments 1-6 on other}	12±3·9
	Segments 1-6 on both	5±4·1
	{Segments 1-11 on one Segments 1-6 on other}	75±2·1
	Segments 1-6 on both	5±4·1

A more detailed investigation of this phenomenon has been made by Dostal (1958), who studied the response of honeybees to the substance Nerol R ($C_{10}H_{18}O$), a synthetic constituent of rose oil. She showed that with successive amputation of one to six antennal segments the acuity of olfaction decreases only slightly. After extirpation of seven segments a pronounced decrease occurs, and amputation of eight segments abolishes all response. A comparison of the frequency distribution of sensilla on the antennae and the threshold of response reveals a logarithmic relationship which Dostal relates to the Weber–Fechner law. An examination of the data which Schanz (1953) obtained by measuring thresholds in the potato beetle after differential amputation of antennal segments reveals similar relationships.

Not all olfactory receptor fields of an individual are equally sensitive. As a rule response thresholds are lowest when the antennae are intact. Many insects lose their ability to respond to attenuated odours when the antennae are rendered inoperative, but can respond to higher concentrations as long as the palpi are still operative (Warnke, 1931; Frings, 1941; Dethier, 1941, 1947 a, 1952 b).

The Stimulus

As with man the number of gaseous materials, natural and synthetic, to which insects respond is very great. Many attempts have been made to relate stimulating effectiveness to some molecular property, and many data have been collected by workers interested in insect attractants and repellents. When these data can be translated into terms of threshold some interpretation is possible. One of the earliest of such studies was that of Cook (1926). It was designed to ascertain the relation between the optimum attractiveness to flies and the physical properties of aliphatic alcohols from C_1 to C_5 and esters from acetates to valerates. Within a homologous series acceptance threshold decreases with increased boiling point. The relationship is logarithmic.

Instead of ascertaining the relative stimulating effect of members of a homologous series by testing each member separately over a concentration range as Cook had done, one may derive the same information by testing a number of compounds simultaneously and employing the number of insects attracted as an index for efficiency. Employing this method, Speyer (1920) found that homologous alcohols and esters become more attractive as the chain length is increased. Increasing the chain length on the acid side of the ester molecule results in a more pronounced and uniform increase in effectiveness than do similar increases on the alcohol side. Comparable experiments with codling moths yielded similar results (Eyer and Medler, 1940). Olfactometric experiments with the blowfly *Phormia regina* have shown that the rejection threshold to homologous alcohols decreases logarithmically as the chain length is increased until a cut-off point is reached at or near C_{11} (Dethier and Yost, 1952). With aldehydes both rejection and acceptance thresholds reveal similar relationships (Dethier, 1954 a).

Mechanism of Olfaction

The nature of the process whereby the odour molecule initiates depolarization in the olfactory receptor remains a mystery despite numerous theories, of which those of Ehrensvärd (1942), Davies (1953 a, 1953 b), Mullins (1955 a, 1955 b), and Davies and Taylor (1959) are the more comprehensive. Analyses of relationships between threshold of response and molecular characteristics have contributed much of the groundwork for theorizing. On the basis of measurements made with *Phormia* (Dethier and Yost, 1952; Dethier, 1954 a) and with man (Mullins, 1955 a), it is clear that olfactory thresholds, stated as thermodynamic activities, for members of homologous series of aliphatic alcohols, aldehydes, and saturated hydrocarbons are nearly constant

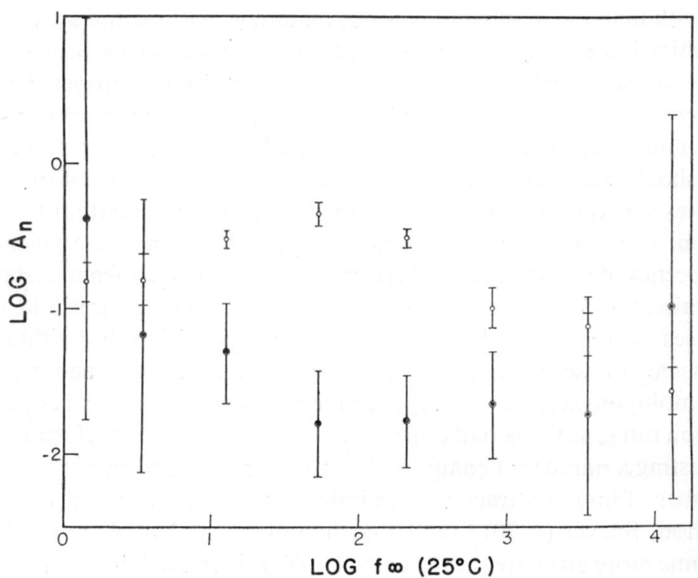

FIG. 74. Comparison in terms of thermodynamic activity of the stimulating effectiveness of the first eight normal alcohols acting in aqueous solution (open circles) on tarsal chemoreceptors and as gases (solid circles) on olfactory receptors of blowflies. In each case the value represents a threshold of rejection. The vertical lines represent 2·575 standard errors for aqueous thresholds and 2 for vapours. (From Dethier and Yost, 1952.)

over the middle range of chain length (Fig. 74). Olfactory thresholds for fatty acids measured in the dog (Neuhaus, 1953a, 1953b) and the honeybee (Schwarz, 1955) do not show such a precise relationship. For these two animals the thresholds, expressed as molecules per c.c. of air, are lowest in the region C_2 to C_4. Dethier (1954b) pointed out that the relationship observed with alcohols suggests that olfaction in these cases may involve the establishment of an equilibrium, and as such represents a physical rather than a chemical process which involves specific receptor substances (Dethier, 1956). Mullins (1954) further analysed the date of Dethier and Yost (1952) by plotting the product of the thermodynamic activity at threshold and the molal volume of the compounds against chain length and assigning a calculated membrane solubility parameter of 11·5. The analysis suggested that the vapour of the first three alcohols might not have been in equilibrium with the organism. Additional data and analyses indicated that olfaction does not involve an equilibrium process and that excitation is probably a result of the ability of the odour molecules to produce local disorder in the oriented molecular structure of the cell membrane (Mullins, 1955a, 1955b).

The theories of Ehrensvärd (1942) and Davies (1953a, 1953b) postulate that odour molecules must first adsorb into the plasma membrane of the olfactory neuron. Ehrensvärd suggested that the potential changes due to the adsorption actually initiated impulses in the receptor. The Davies theory envisions the adsorbed molecules as dislocating the membrane, thus permitting an exchange of sodium and potassium ions across it, with the consequent initiation of impulses. The effectiveness of compounds depends not only upon the concentration of adsorbed molecules but also upon their size and shape (Davies and Taylor, 1959). Olfactory threshold data for *Phormia*, as well as for dogs and man, confirm that both shape and adsorption are important factors (Fig. 75).

Electrophysiological studies thus far have not clarified our understanding of the receptor mechanism. Summed spontaneous activity in antennal nerves has been recorded by Boistel and Coraboeuf (1953), Boistel, Lecompte, and Coraboeuf (1956), Roys (1954), Smyth and Roys (1954), Schneider (1955, 1957a, 1957b), Schneider and Hecker (1956), and Morita and Yamashita (1961). Firing from individual neurons has occasionally been detected in the antennae of *Bombyx mori* and related species (Schneider, 1957b), but it has not been possible to ascertain from which type of sensillum the activity originated (Schneider, 1961). When the olfactory stimulus is extract of female sex attractant (*Bombyx mori*) hexadeca-diene-(10, 12)-ol-(1) (Butenandt, Bechmann, Stamm, and Hecker, 1959), electrical activity increases in the male antenna but not in that of the female. When cyclohexanon or sorbinol are employed as stimuli activity increases in both sexes. The spikes are superimposed on a complex slow potential which Schneider (1957 a) has termed the electroantennogram (EAG). The amplitude

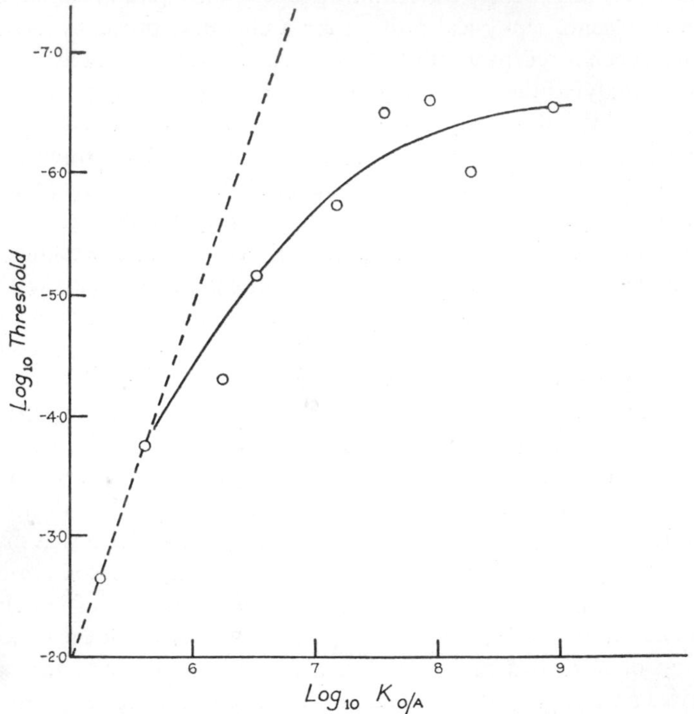

FIG. 75. Plot of the logarithm of the olfactory rejection concentration for blowflies against the adsorption constant at an oil/air interface ($\log_{10} Ko/a$). The broken line represents the slope expected if $1/p$ were to increase regularly with chain length. Threshold data from Dethier and Yost (1952). (Redrawn from Davies and Taylor, 1959.)

depends upon the concentration of the odour, and the wave form, on the kind of molecule. Many compounds in high concentration elicit an EAG (ether, ethanol, propanol, butanol, xylene, etc.), but at extreme dilution only the natural sex attractant elicits an EAG. Its wave form is characteristically different (Schneider, 1961). There are no significant differences in the normal EAGs of a male antenna when the stimuli employed are the glands of related saturniid species, although the conspecific gland tends to elicit the largest response (Schneider, 1962).

Recently Morita and Yamashita (1961) have been able to record directly from a simple large sensillum basiconicum on the antenna of the larva of *Bombyx mori.* This had been shown to be an olfactory organ innervated by approximately twenty neurons (Dethier, 1941). When odours of substances contained in the essential oil of mulberry leaves (e.g., βγ-hexanol and *n*-butylaldehyde) were applied to the sensillum a slow negative potential accompanied by an increase in action potential frequency occurred. Some compounds evoked a slow diphasic potential, from negative to positive, while anaesthetics evoked slow positive potentials accompanied by a decrease in impulse frequency. A complete interpretation of these results is rendered difficult by the fact that the sensillum is multiply innervated; however, the available evidence strongly suggests that the slow negative potential evoked by naturally occurring food substances is a true receptor potential.

Odour Qualities

It is clear from studies of attractants and repellents that for all insects there are at least two odour modalities, that is, 'acceptable' and 'unacceptable', but it is unlikely that these represent accurately the olfactory world of insects. For many insects that respond in a highly specific manner to one particular odour, as, for example, the male silkworm to female sex-attractant, and many monophagous caterpillars to the odour of their one food-plant, it is possible that the olfactory receptors are tuned only to that odour. Electrophysiological recordings from the antennae of male *Bombyx mori* thus far have not revealed a sensitivity to any compound other than the natural and synthetic sex attractants of *Bombyx* and the natural attractants of closely related species (Schneider, 1962).

The honeybee, on the other hand, is obviously sensitive to many odours, but does it confuse them as one or can it discriminate? By training bees to associate a particular odour with food, von Frisch (1919) was able to show that a number of odours were discriminated. Furthermore, compounds with different structure, which to man possessed similar odours, were confused as one by the bee, whereas compounds with nearly identical structure but obviously different odours were easily distinguished. Within the following pairs the two members are easily distinguished by the bee: amyl acetate and methyl heptenone, bromstyrol and phenylacetaldehyde, isobutyl benzoate and salicylic acid amyl ester, *p*-cresol methyl ether and *m*-cresol methyl ether.

CONTACT CHEMORECEPTION

Sensitivity

Many behavioural studies have been conducted with numerous species of insects for the purpose of locating and mapping contact chemoreceptors, determining limits of qualities, and elucidating the nature of receptor action. These studies, centred for the most part around feeding behaviour, have usually been designed as measurements of acceptance and rejection thresholds. Extension of the proboscis, duration of feeding, and measurement of crop loads have been a few of the criteria employed (for details consult Dethier and Chadwick, 1948 a).

TABLE 4
(From Dethier and Chadwick, 1948 a)
Comparison of taste thresholds

Compound	*Threshold Concentrations*
Sucrose	Man, 0·02M; bee, 0·06–0·125M; butterfly (*Pyrameis*), average *ca.* 0·01M, in starvation as little as 8×10^{-5}M; *Danaus*, $9{\cdot}8 \times 10^{-6}$M; horsefly (*Tabanus*) 0·005–0·11M.
Sodium chloride	Man, 0·009M; bee, rejects *ca.* 0·24M in 0·5M sucrose; various caterpillars reject at 0·2M, whereas others accept over the full range up to and including 5·0M.
Hydrochloric acid	Man, 0·00125M; bee, rejects 0·001M in 1·0M sucrose; various caterpillars reject at 0·01–0·2M.
Quinine	Man, $1{\cdot}5 \times 10^{-7}$M; bee, rejects at 8×10^{-4} in 1·0M sucrose; various caterpillars reject at 0·002–0·033M; aquatic beetles were conditioned to respond to $1{\cdot}25 \times 10^{-6}$M.

Data on man are for specific thresholds, adapted from Moncrieff (1944); for the bee, from von Frisch (1934); for *Pyrameis*, from Minnich (1922); for *Danaus*, from Anderson (1932); for caterpillars, from Eger (1937); for aquatic beetles, from Bauer (1938). The figures for insects are thresholds of response.

Threshold studies have revealed many of the characteristics of the contact chemical sense. They have shown, for example, that the thresholds are frequently lower than those of man for similar substances (Table 4). They have revealed among individuals differences that follow a common pattern. For example, the scattering of thresholds in a population of *Phormia* is not significantly different from a normal distribution when plotted against the logarithm of concentration (Dethier and Chadwick, 1947). Where sufficient data have been reported a similar relationship can be shown to exist with other insects (e.g., Eger, 1937; Frings, 1946; von Frisch, 1935; Weis, 1930; Hodgson, 1951).

Threshold determinations have revealed that sensitivity of response varies with the receptor field stimulated. In the horsefly *Tabanus* the mean labellar threshold for sucrose is 0·021M; the tarsal threshold, 0·060M (Frings and O'Neal, 1946). In *Calliphora erythrocephala* the labella are generally more sensitive than the tarsi (Haslinger, 1935). In *C. vomitoria*, on the other hand, the tarsi are sixteen times more sensitive than the labellum to sucrose (Minnich, 1931), but lactose elicits a response only when applied to the labellum (Minnich, 1929 b). *Musca domestica*, *Cochliomyia americana*, and *Phormia regina* exhibit lower rejection thresholds following oral stimulation than tarsal stimulation (Deonier, 1938, 1939; Dethier, 1955 a). Similar results have been obtained with *Pieris* (Verlaine, 1927). The antennae of honeybees are more sensitive to solutions than the legs (Frings, 1944; Marshall, 1935; Minnich, 1932); the proboscis, more sensitive than the antennae (Kunze, 1933). In the beetle *Hydrous* the labial palpi are sensitive to hydrochloric acid and insensitive to sodium chloride and sugar, while the maxillary palpi are sensitive to sodium chloride and sugar (Ritter, 1936). In the related species *Laccophilus* the antennae are more sensitive than either pair of palpi to acids, salts, and alcohols (Hodgson, 1951).

The aforementioned studies do not reveal whether the differences in threshold reflect central phenomena, variations in the sensitivity of the receptors, summation, or differences in sensitivity due merely to the number of receptors stimulated.

Differences between acceptance thresholds following unilateral and bilateral tarsal stimulation had suggested that some relation does exist between sensitivity and the number of receptors stimulated (Imamura, 1938). An analysis of thresholds following stimulation of one tarus versus two tarsi in *Phormia* showed that the bilateral threshold for sugar is lower than the unilateral threshold (Dethier, 1953 b). This difference could be due, however, either to summation or to a simple statistical bias. In the analogous visual case where comparisons have been made between monocular and binocular vision, Pirenne (1943) and Bárány (1946 a, 1946 b) pointed out that the experimental procedure by its very nature assures that the two eyes will see more clearly than one. 'Let us assume that the visual acuities (or other thresholds) of both eyes fluctuate independently of one another . . . and that the instantaneous thresholds for monocular vision have the same distribution in both eyes, . . . then if the one eye alone has the chance of a of seeing the symbol, both eyes together have the chance $2a-a^2$. As a is smaller than 1, this expression will always be greater

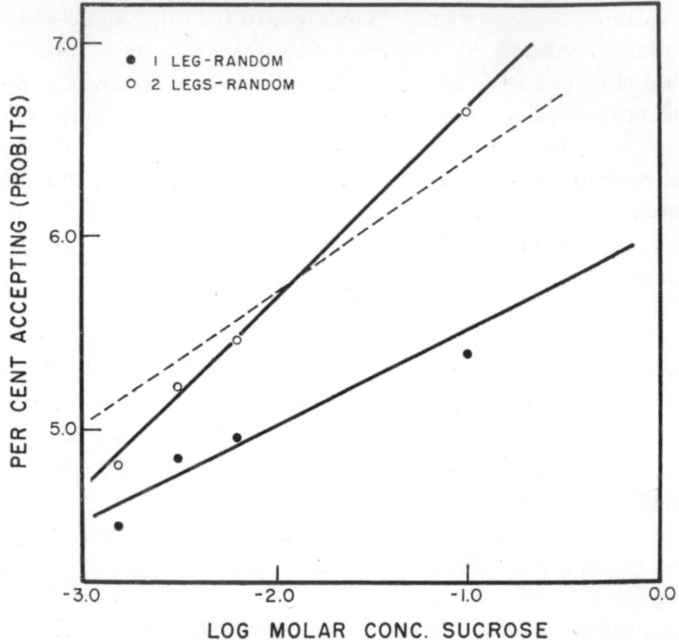

FIG. 76. Comparison of the distribution of acceptance thresholds for sucrose, as a function of concentration, for flies stimulated unilaterally or bilaterally. The broken line represents the theoretical distribution of bilateral thresholds (two-legged flies) calculated from the expression $1-q^2$, where q equals the fraction of the population of one-legged flies not responding. (From Dethier, 1953.)

than a – that is to say, two eyes will be able to see better than one solely as a result of random combination' (Bárány, 1946 b, p. 127). And as Smith and Licklider (1949) went on to state, the same source of bias is inherent in the procedure as applied to the determination of thresholds in other sense modalities.

The idea can be clarified still further by quoting from the study of hearing by these authors (p. 279). 'In order to estimate the magnitude of the bias, it is necessary to define the null condition under which we should say that there is no binaural summation. We can imagine, for this purpose, two monaural listeners, one with only a right ear, the other with only a left ear. The two listeners have no means whatsoever of communicating with each other, but both report to the same experimenter. To obtain measures of monaural and "binaural" sensitivity, the experimenter tests the two listeners separately (successively), then together, in the latter instance recording a positive response whenever *either* listener reports hearing the stimulus tone.' The case of unilateral versus bilateral tarsal stimulation of *Phormia* is similar. The results show that the bilateral threshold for sucrose is lower than the unilateral threshold by a factor that is never greater than can be satisfactorily accounted for on a simple probability basis, that is, the greater the number of available receptors, the greater that chance that the number required for a threshold response will be stimulated (Fig. 76) (Dethier, 1953 b).

Discrimination

Threshold measurements do not permit evaluation of intensity discrimination over the complete effective concentration range of a compound. Von Frisch (1935) had demonstrated that honeybees responded differently to 0·125M and 0·156M sucrose and to 0·25M and 0·3125M

TABLE 5

(From Dethier and Rhoades, 1954)

Intensity discrimination of sucrose

Intensity	*Nearest conc. which can be distinguished*	$\Delta I/I$	$\Delta I/I$ *(geometric mean)*
0·001	0·000007	0·99	2·4
0·001	0·007	6·0	
0·01	0·007	0·3	0·387
0·01	0·015	0·5	
0·1	0·088	0·12	0·12
0·1	0·112	0·12	
1·0	0·70	0·3	0·346
1·0	1·40	0·4	
2·0	1·0	0·5	0·418
2·0	2·7	0·35	

sucrose, a ratio of 1 : 1·24 ($\Delta S/S = 0{\cdot}25$). Frings (1946) and Frings and O'Neal (1946) had found that *Periplaneta americana* and *Tabanus sulcifrons* could also discriminate at this level. On the basis of tests with two specimens Verlaine (1927) claimed a slightly greater sensitivity for *Pieris*.

A technique permitting the measurement of $\Delta I/I$ for the complete effective concentration range of a compound was developed by Dethier and Rhoades (1954) and employed with *Phormia*. The smallest ratio found (0·12) indicates better discrimination than that obtained in earlier studies. An examination of the results tabulated in Table 5 shows that discrimination is best over the middle ranges of concentration and is optimum at about the same concentration for which there is a maximum preference. The discrimination factor for the chemical senses of man is about 0·3 according to Moncrieff (1944) but earlier Lemberger (1908) had recorded optimum values of 0·15 for sucrose and 0·11 for sodium–saccharin and higher values at both extremes of the concentration range (cf. also Dahlberg and Penczek, 1941; Schutz and Pilgrim, 1957).

Rejection Thresholds – Electrolytes

The number of compounds that can be detected by insects is very great. From a behavioural point of view the only manifestation of stimulation by the majority of them is the rejection of acceptable solutions (e.g., sugar or water) to which they have been added. Rejection thresholds, therefore, represent the concentration of substances necessary to prevent responses to sugar or water. Because the test solutions are always mixtures, the thresholds involve: the sensitivity of two different receptors, possible interactions at the receptor level, and demonstrated interaction at the central level. Despite these complications, it has been possible to establish rather precise relationships between the stimulating effectiveness of many compounds and their molecular properties.

Electrolytes were among the first compounds studied. Tests conducted with the mouth-parts of the cockroach *Periplaneta americana* showed that for several series of salts with a common union (acetates, bromides, chlorides, iodides, nitrates, and sulphates) the stimulative efficiency could be correlated directly with ionic mobilities (Frings, 1946). Similar results had been obtained earlier with the oral receptors of *cecropia* moth larvae (Frings, 1945). Extensions of these studies to the tarsal receptors of the horsefly *Tabanus sulcifrons* (Frings and O'Neal, 1946), the ovipositors of parasitic Hymenoptera (Dethier, 1947c), oral receptors of the beetle *Laccophilus* (Hodgson, 1951), the labellar receptors of *Phormia* (Dethier, 1955 a), and the receptors of a number of other species (Frings, 1948) showed that the same general relationships held. According to Frings, the data are in substantial agreement with most of the data reported in the literature for chemical stimulation of other animals by the series of cations employed, namely, in decreasing order of thresholds: $Li^+ > Na^+ > Mg^{++} > Ca^{++} = Sr^{++} > K^+ = Cs^+ = Rb^+ > NH4^+ >>> H^+$. As pointed out by Frings, the order of effectiveness is also that of partition coefficients, which parallels that of ionic mobilities (Osterhout *et al.*, 1934). The arrangement for anions is less clear. The work of Frings (1946) established the following order of thresholds: $PO_4^{---} > Ac^- > SO_4^{--} = Cl^- \geq Br^- > I^- > NO_3^- >>> OH^-$.

The situation is actually much more complex than these generalizations imply. For example, the activity of divalent cations is anomalous in that they do not fit any of these series. Furthermore, the behaviour of insects towards divalent ions is noticeably different from their behaviour towards monovalent ions (cf. Hodgson, 1951). In addition, there are species differences. It is possible that these may reflect differences in the molecular structure of the receptors, as has been proposed for mammals (Beidler, 1953, 1954, 1960; Beidler, Fishman, and Hardiman, 1955).

Rejection Thresholds – Non-electrolytes

The rejection thresholds of over two hundred aliphatic organic compounds have been measured by employing flies that had been rendered anosmic by removal of the antennae and labella (Dethier and Chadwick, 1947, 1948 b, 1950; Chadwick and Dethier, 1947, 1949). A number of significant relationships were revealed by these data.

Within any homologous series exceptionally high correlations were found between the stimulating power of the compounds and such properties as boiling point, molecular area, oil–water partition coefficients, molecular moments, vapour pressures, and activity coefficients. Molecular weight, number of carbon atoms, and osmotic pressure were eliminated from consideration in part by the use of isomers, which proved usually to have different thresholds, and the correlation with vapour pressures was inverse. Because of the paucity of data relating to the various chemical and physical properties enumerated above, it became convenient to plot stimulative efficiency against the chain length of the molecule. Graphs so constructed (Fig. 77) show clearly that for all series of homologous aliphatic compounds studied the members of the series are rejected at logarithmically decreasing concentrations as the carbon chain length is increased. It is apparent from Fig. 77 that this relation is not a continuous one. For each series the curve shows a sharp break in the region of a definite chain-length characteristic for each series.

Taking a saturated straight-chain hydrocarbon as a starting-point, one may, without altering appreciably the arrangement of the carbon

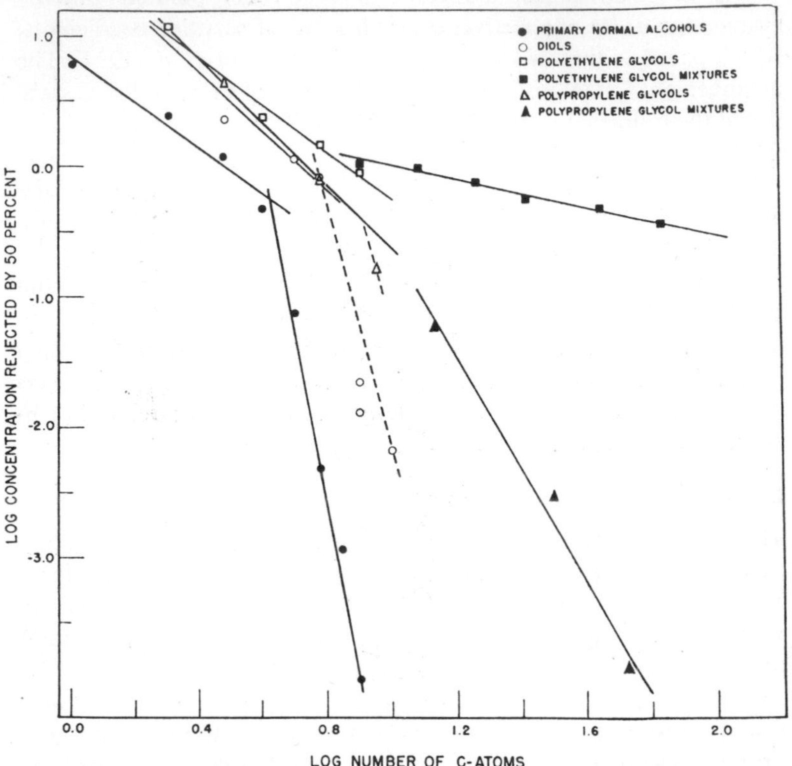

FIG. 77. Rejection thresholds of glycols and alcohols by *Phormia*. (From Dethier and Chadwick, 1948 b.)

linkages, substitute various kinds of polar groups for one or more of the hydrogen atoms. Whereas all such substitutions raise the molecular weight and the boiling point, the effect on solubility is variable. The different polar groups may be arranged in increasing order of solubility as follows: $Br < Cl < CH_3 < CHO < C{=}O < OH$. The CH_3 radical represents the unsubstituted compound. This series also represents in reverse order the relative stimulating efficiencies of these polar groups. When the number of substitutions of the groups to the right of the CH_3 (in the above representation) is increased the stimulating efficiency decreases. Thus, glycols are less effective than alcohols, and diketones are as a rule less effective than ketones. Increase of the number of substitutions of those polar groups to the left of the CH_3 tends to increase stimulating effectiveness. Thus, dibromo compounds are more effective than monobromo homologues.

The effects of thc positions of the functional groups are illustrated by experiments with the glycols. The following rules are found to hold:

(1) juxtaposition of two hydroxyl groups in a short molecule (e.g., 1, 2-butanediol) makes for a high threshold; this effect is reduced as chains become longer;

(2) in a chain with no terminal OH groups, i.e., subterminal but not adjacent (e.g., 1, 3-butanediol) the thresholds are low;

(3) if both OH groups are terminal thresholds are intermediate;

(4) branching tends to raise the threshold, other factors being equal.

Taken all together, the foregoing results state essentially that the length of the free alkyl group largely determines the stimulating effectiveness and that its power is modified to varying degrees by the nature of the attached polar groups. The length of the alkyl group is

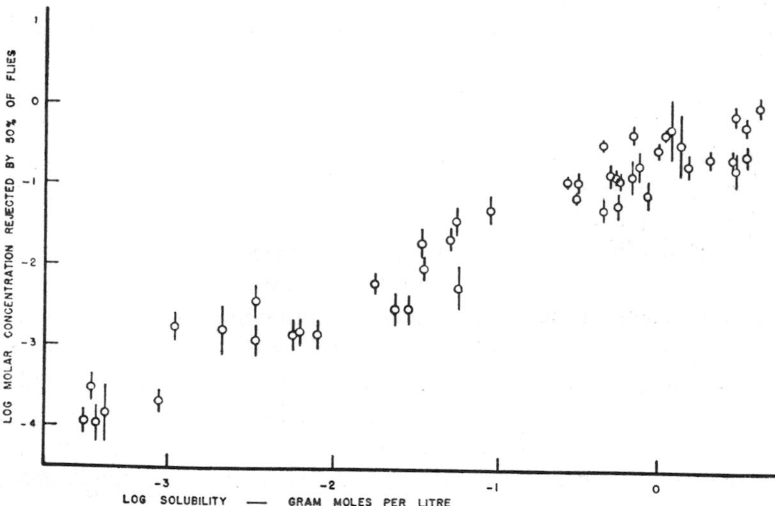

FIG. 78. Correlation between concentration required for stimulation and the solubility of compounds at 25–27 degrees C. in water. Each of the forty-six points represents a different aliphatic compound. (From Dethier and Chadwick, 1950.)

also of prime importance in determining the solubility characteristics of compounds of this type; hence the same structural characteristics that decrease water solubility likewise decrease threshold.

There is then only one molecular property, for which data are available, which brings all the data from the different series into a single homogeneous system. This is water solubility (Fig. 78). The order of stimulative efficiencies follows the inverse of the order of water solubilities with fewer contradictions than appear in most of the other comparisons attempted. Additional evidence that solubility is of importance in this connexion has been presented by the work of Dethier (1951 a), which showed that the thresholds of alcohols are altered as the alcohol is presented as an aqueous solution, a glycol solution, or a mineral oil solution (Fig. 79).

When threshold values are expressed as thermodynamic activities rather than as moles the differences between successive homologues of a series are not so marked, but a plot of the logarithm of these values against the logarithm of activity coefficients (Fig. 74) does not produce a straight line of the sort that one is accustomed to expect from parallel experiments on narcosis (for a complete discussion consult Ferguson, 1951; Brink and Posternak, 1948; Dethier, 1954 b).

In spite of the generally good correspondence between low solubility in water and high stimulating power, it seems likely, from the data on oil–water partition coefficients, that plots of threshold values against water solubilities would also yield a smaller slope for the lower than for the higher range of compounds in each series if such an analysis could be made. This type of relationship seems to have no conterpart in any of the tabulated values for the physical properties, and its consistent recurrence prompted Chadwick and Dethier (1949) to consider the possibility that different forces may be of primary importance in stimulation by the lower and higher members of each of the types investigated. This amounts to postulating at least a two-phase system for the limiting mechanism in contact chemoreception. The hypothesis that small molecules gain access to the receptors in part through an aqueous phase, whereas the larger aliphatic molecules penetrate chiefly through (or accumulate in) a lipoid phase, would appear to offer a basis for reconciling most of the contradictions encountered when it is attempted to fit the facts into a single-phase system.

Movement of the smaller molecules through an aqueous medium should occur at rates related inversely to the molecular weight, which would help to account for their being more stimulating than is anticipated from the relationship found for the higher members of the series, although it is doubtful that the entire difference can be explained in this way. It may be noted also (Fig. 80) that the inflections in the curves relating thresholds to molecular size occur at increasing chain

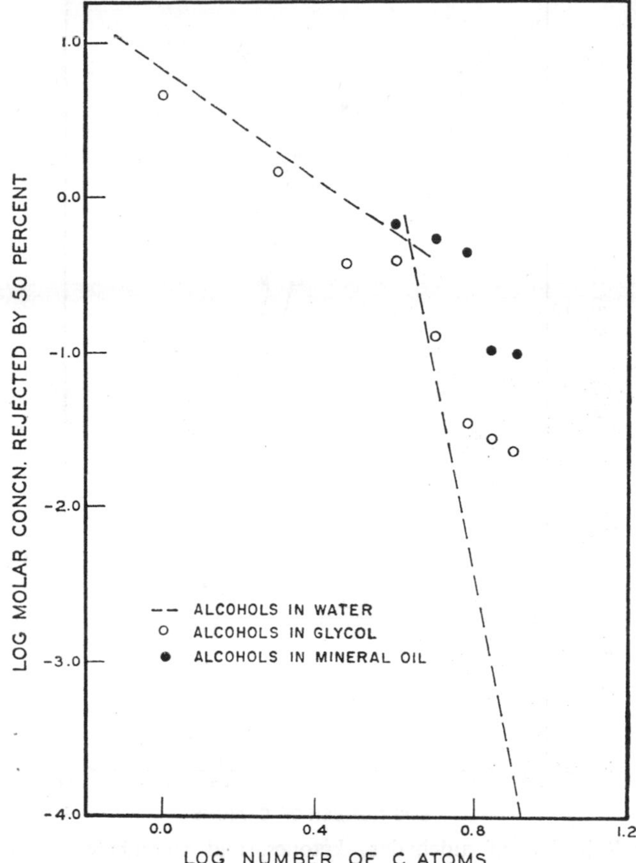

FIG. 79. Rejection thresholds of aqueous, glycol, and oil solutions of primary alcohols by *Phormia*. (From Dethier, 1951.)

lengths in passing from the less to the more water-soluble species. At the same time the predominant importance of lipoid affinity is suggested by the logarithmically increasing stimulating power of both lower and higher members of all series, as well as by the inverse relationship between water solubility and stimulating effectiveness in comparisons of the several series with each other.

Further analyses of the date of Dethier and Chadwick (1948 b, 1950) suggest that the important factor in stimulation by non-electrolytes is adsorption (Davies and Taylor, 1959). When the logarithm of rejection thresholds (molar concentration) is plotted against the logarithm

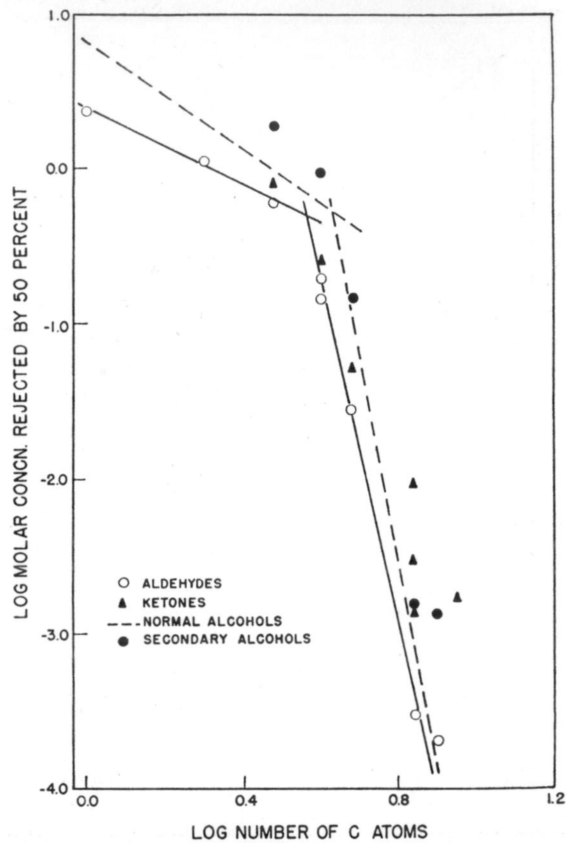

FIG. 80. Rejection of aldehydes, ketones, and secondary alcohols by *Phormia*. (From Chadwick and Dethier, 1949.)

of the adsorption constant for an oil/water interface the slope of the resulting line is very near that expected for adsorption from solution on to a pure lipid membrane (Fig. 75).

Rejection Thresholds – Organic Electrolytes

The situation with regard to organic electrolytes is less clear than that for the non-electrolytes. Tests with a number of fatty acids indicated that while the H ion is the principal factor in stimulation with compounds of this type, a contribution is made also by the anion or undissociated acid, which is effective in inverse proportion to the hydrophile nature of the molecule. The relationship is thus very similar to that found with the same class of compounds for human taste (cf., e.g., Taylor *et al.*, 1930).

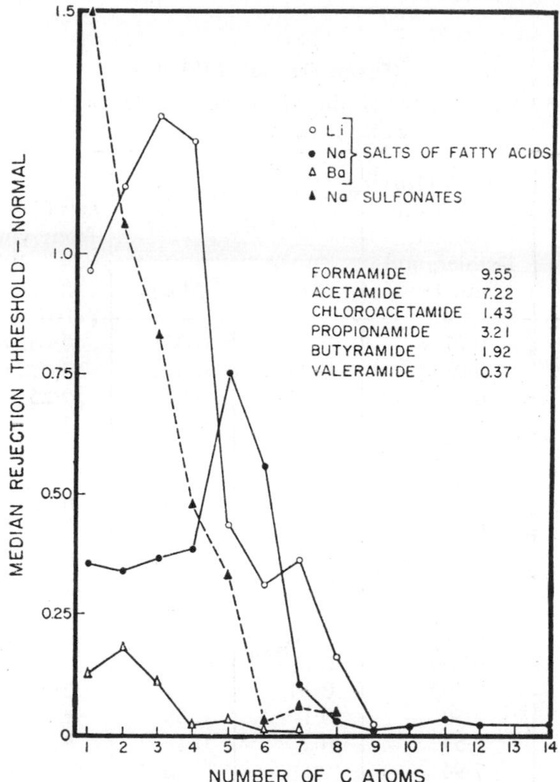

FIG. 81. Relation between the stimulating efficiency of organic salts and chain lengths of the anion. (From Dethier, 1956.)

Tests with homologous organic salts show that beginning with the five-carbon compound there is a logarithmic decrease similar in all respects to that observed with non-polar homologues (Fig. 81) (Dethier, 1956).

Acceptance Thresholds

Among compounds acceptable to insects carbohydrates are the most usual and important. Comparisons of the acceptability of various carbohydrates have been undertaken with the honeybee (Vogel, 1931; von Frisch, 1934), *Calliphora* (Haslinger, 1935), water beetles (Bauer, 1938), the ants *Lasius niger*, *Myrmica rubra*, and *M. rubida* (Schmidt, 1938), wireworms (Thorpe *et al.*, 1947), the butterfly *Pyrameis atalanta* (Weis, 1930), the blowfly *Phormia* (Hassett, Dethier, and Gans, 1950; Dethier, 1955). The number of sugars acceptable to these

TABLE 6
(From Dethier, 1953 a)
Acceptance thresholds of various insects for sugars
(Molar concentrations)

Sugar	PHORMIA (*Tarsi*) (Data from Hassett, Dethier, and Gans, 1950)	CALLIPHORA (Data from Haslinger, 1935)		APIS (*Mouth*) (Data from von Frisch, 1930)
		Tarsi	*Mouth*	
Sucrose	0·01	0·0006	0·0035	0·0625–0·125
Maltose	0·0148	0·00125	0·002	0·0125
Trehalose	0·126	0·14	0·02	0·25
Lactose	*	*	0·1	*
Cellobiose	5·01	0·05	0·03	*
Melibiose	*	*	*	*
Melezitose	0·063	0·07	0·01	0·125–0·25
Raffinose	0·275	0·1	0·0071	*
Fructose	0·0076	0·0033	0·004	0·25
Fucose	0·087	0·02	0·01	1·0
Glucose	0·114	0·125	0·04	0·25
Sorbose	0·218	...	...	...
Xylose	0·400	0·2	0·14	*
Galactose	0·502	0·14	0·09	2·0
Arabinose	0·50	0·1	0·08	*
Mannose	7·59	0·2	0·1	*
Ribose	7·94	...	...	...
Lyxose	33·1	...	...	...
Rhamnose	*	*	1·0	*

* Non-stimulating at all concentrations.
... Not tested.

species varies, the blowflies being more catholic than either the honeybee or the ants. However, if the data of von Frisch, Haslinger, and Hassett *et al.* are compared (Table 6), allowances made for statistical variance, and the sugars divided into three categories (mono-, di-, and tri-saccharides), certain general relationships appear. For bees the order of effectiveness is: (dissaccharides) sucrose = maltose >

trehalose; (monosaccharides) fructose = glucose > fucose > galactose. All other sugars fail to stimulate. For *Calliphora* legs the order is: (disaccharides) sucrose = maltose > trehalose = cellobiose > lactose; (monosaccharides) fructose > fucose > glucose = xylose = galactose = arabinose = mannose. For *Calliphora* mouth-parts the order is: (disaccharides) sucrose = maltose > trehalose = cellobiose > lactose; (monosaccharides) fructose ≥ fucose > glucose ≥ arabinose = xylose = galactose = mannose. For *Phormia* legs the order is: (disaccharides) sucrose = maltose > trehalose > cellobiose > lactose; (monosaccharides) fructose > fucose = glucose ≥ sorbose ≥ xylose = galactose = arabinose > mannose = ribose > lyxose.

For these three species of insects it is true in general that the most stimulating disaccharides are the α-glucosides and the most stimulating monosaccharides are fructose, glucose, and fucose. From studies with *Phormia*, in which 75 carbohydrates, 8 polyhydric alcohols, 53 amino acids, and 18 monobasic and dibasic acids have been applied to individual labellar hairs, some of the limiting factors in stimulation have been revealed (Table 7) (Dethier, 1955 a). For example, trioses, tetroses, heptoses, and octoses are uneffective. This finding indicates that there is an optimum chain length. The size of the molecule as a whole appears to be critical only within certain limits. Thus, at the smaller extreme some pentoses stimulate while at the other extreme certain trisaccharides stimulate. However, polysaccharides are uneffective. For additional details the work of Dethier (1955 a) should be consulted.

Categories of Receptors

Ultimately, an understanding of the mechanism of action of the receptors themselves had to await the application of electrophysiological techniques. Studies of this sort have been confined to a few carefully selected species: the flies *Phormia regina*, *Lucilia caeser*, and *Calliphora vomitoria*; the butterfly *Vanessa indica*; and the Colorado Potato Beetle, *Leptinotarsa decemlineata*.

The most intensively investigated and well-known receptors are those occurring on the tarsi and labellum of the black blowfly, *Phormia regina*. They have been the subject of co-ordinated behavioural, histological, and physiological study and may be taken as a model for discussion. The multiplicity of neurons associated with these hairs complicated for a while studies of the mechanism of chemoreception. Because of the specificity of the neurons, however, it was originally possible to arrive at a considerable understanding of

Table 7

(From Dethier, 1955 b)

Effectiveness of various carbohydrates in stimulating single labellar hairs and groups of tarsal hairs in *Phormia regina*.

Compounds which elicit proboscis extension when applied to single hairs are designated (+). For compounds which are effective on entire tarsi the molar concentration which causes 50 per cent of the flies to accept is given when known. Starred values are from Hassett, Dethier, and Gans (1950). Compounds designated with (−) are non-stimulating at all concentrations; those designated with (†) are effective on groups of labellar hairs but not on single hairs.

Compound	*Single hair*	*Tarsi*	*Compound*	*Single hair*	*Tarsi*
Triose			m-Erythritol	−	−
DL-glyceraldehyde	−	−	Penta-erythritol	−	−
Tetroses			Mannitol	−	−
D-erythrose	−	−	*L*-Arabitol	−	−
L-erythrose	−	−	Inositol	+	0·194*
Pentoses			Glycosides		
L-Fucose	+	0·087*	α-D-methyl glucoside	+	0·069*
D-Arabinose	+	0·144*	β-D-methyl glucoside	−	−
L-Arabinose	+	0·536*	NO_2-benzyl glucoside	−	−
D-Xylose	+	0·440*	*p*-Aminophenyl glucoside	+	
L-Xylose	+	0·337*	Monoacetyl NO_2-β-glucoside	−	−
D-Ribose	−	8·99*			
D-Lyxose†	−	42·27*	Phenyl β-glucoside		
Ribulose	−	−	tetraacetate	−	−
L-Rhamnose	−	−	α-*D*-Methyl mannoside	+	
2-Desoxyribose	−	−	*p*-Aminophenyl		
Hexoses			β-maltoside	+	
D-Fructose	+	0·0058*	Nitrophenyl maltoside	+	
D-Glucose	+	0·132*	7-Acetyl *p*-nitrophenol		
L-Sorbose	+	0·140*	cellobioside	−	−
D-Galactose	+	0·50*	Substituted sugars		
D-Mannose†	−	7·59*	*n*-Acetyl glucosamine	−	−

D-Tagatose	—	—	Glusosamine hydrochloride	+	0·204
D-Glucose	—	—	NO_2-α-glucose	+	
Idose	—	—	NO_2-β-glucose	±	
D-Altrose	—	—	Diacetone glucose	+	
Heptoses			α-Pentaacetyl glucose	—	—
D-α-Glucoheptose	—	—	Diacetone nitrobenzoyl		
D-Gluco-*D*-guloheptose	—	—	glucose	—	—
Octose			1, 2, 3, 4-Acetyl-6-trimethyl		
D-Gluco-*L*-gala-octose	—	—	glucose	—	—
Disaccharides			β-NO_2-tetraacetyl		
Sucrose	+	0·0098*	glucose	—	—
Turanose	+	0·011	α-*D*-Glucose-1-phosphate		
D-Maltose	+	0·0043*	(dipotassium)	—	0·101
D-Trehalose	+	0·133*	α-*D*-Fructose-6-phosphate		
Cellobiose†	—	5·01*	(barium salt)	—	—
Lactose	—	—	Glucose-6-phosphate		
Melibiose	—	—	(barium)	—	0·083
Invert sugar	+	0·0062	α-*D*-Fructose-1, 6-diphosphate	—	—
Equimolar glucose-fructose					
mixture	+	0·0078	(Calcium)	—	—
Trisaccharides			(Barium)	—	—
Melezitose	+	0·064*	(Magnesium)	—	—
Raffinose	+	0·20*	NO_2-maltose	+	
Polysaccharides			NO_2-7-acetyl maltose	—	—
Levo-glucosan	—	—	NO_2-cellobiose	?	?
Xylan	—	—	Diacetyl glucuron	—	—
Glycogen	—	—	Sucrose octaacetate	—	—
Hydroxycellulose	—	—	β-Triacetyl glucuron	—	—
Polyhydric alcohols			Glycuronic acid monobenzoate	—	—
Sorbitol	—	—			
Glycerol	—	—	Gulonic lactone	—	—
Dulcitol	—	—	α-Glucoheptonic lactone	—	—

chemoreceptor activity by behavioural techniques. It was shown, for example, that a single labellar hair responded to touch, water, certain sugars, and a wide variety of electrolytes and non-carbohydrate organic compounds. In a hungry, thirsty fly bending a hair, applying water, or stimulating with certain sugars elicited a reflex proboscis extension. The application of such compounds as salts, acids, alcohols, aldehydes, ketones, glycols, ethers, etc., to the same hair prevented extension or elicited retraction if the proboscis was already extended.

By adapting the hair successively to bending, to water, and to carbohydrate, and by noting that removing the tip of the hair prevented response to chemicals but not to bending, Dethier (1955 a) concluded that the neuron whose process terminated at the base of the hair was a mechanoreceptor. He concluded further that of the remaining neurons one was concerned with acceptance (exclusive of mechanoreception) while another was concerned with rejection. In other words, one neuron was conceived of as being sensitive to water and certain sugars while the other was considered to be sensitive to all of those compounds that caused rejection. Later behavioural experiments (Dethier, Evans, and Rhoades, 1956) indicated, however, that rejection was in reality not a simple modality because it could be initiated either by stimulation of the rejection receptor or inhibition of the acceptance receptor. Sugars such as mannose, rhamnose, and sorbose, which of themselves do not cause rejection, are able to interfere with stimulation by certain other sugars that alone are acceptable. For example, mannose inhibits fructose (but not glucose), rhamnose inhibits glucose (but not fructose or sucrose), sorbose probably inhibits glucose and fructose. Furthermore, certain rejected salts, notably $HgCl_2$ and $CuCl_2$, render sugar receptors reversibly insensitive.

Still more recently, behavioural investigations into the mechanisms controlling thirst and water satiation suggested that acceptance was not a simple modality either and that there must be a water receptor distinct from the carbohydrate receptor (Evans, 1961 a; Dethier and Evans, 1961). In female flies at certain stages of the reproductive cycle acceptance is further broken down into carbohydrate acceptance and protein acceptance (Dethier, 1961).

Conclusions drawn from behavioural studies were borne out to a very satisfactory degree when success finally attended attempts to record electrically from chemoreceptive hairs. After many people had tried and failed to record action potentials by standard techniques, Hodgson, Lettvin, and Roeder (1955) and Morita, Doira, Takeda, and Kuwabara (1957) independently developed a novel technique. It consisted of placing a fluid-filled micropipette over the tip of a hair and employing it both as a recording electrode and as a source of chemical stimulation. More recently a greatly improved technique was developed by Morita (1959). It involved puncturing the side wall of the hair and recording with the pipette electrode from this point. The tip of the hair was thus left free for stimulation by any kind of material whether electrolyte or not. The indifferent electrode was inserted into the crushed head.

Originally the potentials from only two neurons were recognized in the records obtained from the fly (Hodgson *et al.* 1955; Hodgson and Roeder, 1956). One neuron, designated the *L* (for large spike) fibre by

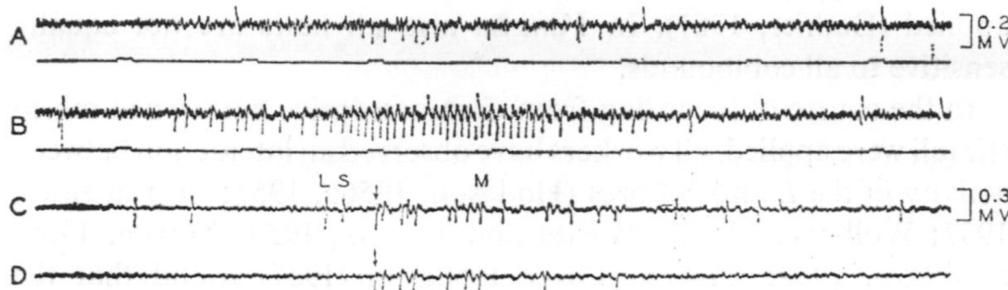

FIG. 82. Electrical response of a labellar hair of *Phormia* to stimulation by salt, sucrose, and bending. A, intact hair stimulated with 0·01M NaCl and motion. B, same hair with tip removed. C, cut hair stimulated by 0·01M NaCl + 0·1M *D*-fructose. The hair is bent at arrow. D, same hair responding to motion after adaptation to chemicals. Time, 0·2 sec. Positive potential at recording electrode is down. (From Wolbarsht and Dethier, 1958.)

Hodgson and Roeder (1956), clearly responded to salts, while the other, designated as the *S* (for small spike) fibre, responded to sugars. Subsequently, Wolbarsht and Dethier (1958) were able to detect the spikes of a third neuron (designated *M* for mechanoreceptor) which responded only to bending of the hair (Fig. 82). Mellon and Evans (1961) have now detected spikes from a fourth neuron which responds to water. The function of the fifth neuron, present in some hairs, is not known.

Since it is now known that certain hairs contain four distinct receptors, conclusions drawn from earlier studies of electrophysiological records must be re-evaluated, specifically the conclusions that: low concentrations of salt sometimes stimulate both *L* and *S* fibres (Hodgson and Roeder, 1956), that acids and alcohols stimulate the *L* fibre (Hodgson and Roeder, 1956), that water stimulates *L* and *S* fibres

(Wolbarsht, 1957), that fructose stimulates *L* and *S* (Hodgson, 1957; Wolbarsht, 1957; Evans, 1958), that sucrose stimulates two fibres in *Calliphora vomitoria* (Morita, 1959), that bending stimulates *L* and *S* (Hodgson *et al.* 1955; but see also Hodgson and Barton Browne, 1960), that the primary receptor cell is responsive to chemical, tactile, and thermal stimuli within the normal physiological range and hence is at variance with the usual concept of single specificities of receptor cells (Hodgson and Roeder, 1956; Hodgson, 1958 a, 1958 b).

Another variable that must be considered is the possible differences among hairs. Some hairs clearly respond more vigorously to bending or to water than others. Some hairs in the female fly show discharge of one fibre when protein such as crystalline haemoglobin or brain-heart extract is applied, but in other hairs all fibres are silent when protein is applied (Dethier, 1961). In *Vanessa* also all hairs are not equally sensitive to all compounds.

In the course of recording from chemoreceptive hairs when mixed stimuli were applied, all workers have observed an interaction between activity in the *L* and *S* fibres (Hodgson, 1956a, 1957; Morita *et al.*, 1957; Wolbarsht, 1958; Morita and Takeda, 1959; Morita, 1959; Stürckow, 1959; Takeda, 1961). Hodgson (1957) found that the presence of *S* impulses is characteristically accompanied by a decrease in *L* impulses and conversely that the stimulation of the *L* fibre is associated with a decrease of *S* spikes. Since the inverse relationship between the frequencies of *S* and *L* impulses is not constant, it does not appear that the facts can be explained simply as a result of partial depolarization of one receptor unit by electrotonic spread from the more active adjacent unit. Wolbarsht (1958) also noticed this situation and decided that the activity of the *L* fibre is not related to the activity of the *S* fibre but depends only on the character of the stimulating solution. He believed that such properties of the salt as thermodynamic activity and the diffusivity of the salt can account in part for the change in activity reported by Hodgson. On the other hand, Takeda (1961) has concluded that the depression of the frequency of impulses from the sugar receptor of *Vanessa* in the presence of NaCl represents a direct inhibitory effect.

At the present time the picture in the blowfly appears to be as follows: one neuron is specifically sensitive to sugars; one neuron is specifically sensitive to monovalent salts; the neuron whose process terminates at the base of the hair is sensitive to mechanical stimulation; a fourth neuron, whose exact location has not yet been established histologically, has as its adequate stimulus water.

The situation in the butterfly *Vanessa indica* is not yet so clear. Kuwabara (1951, 1952, 1953) has shown that water, sugar, and sometimes sodium chloride elicit proboscis extension. Both sodium chloride and quinine inhibit. There is no behavioural response to acids. Morita *et al.* (1957) concluded that there were more than three kinds of impulses from this chemoreceptive hair; one neuron responded to sodium chloride, one to sugar; probably there were also fibres responding to quinine and water. A later work (Morita and Takeda, 1959) concluded that there were four sensory neurons responding as follows: (1) one responding to concentrations of sodium chloride which were less than M/4; (2) one responding to sodium chloride in the range 1M to M/64; (3) one responding to sodium chloride concentrations greater than M/64; (4) one responding to sugar. Presumably there is also a mechanoreceptor. A further analysis of the situation in this insect has yielded the conclusion that the tarsal hairs contain a mechanoreceptor, a sugar receptor, and, in some cases, a sugar–NaCl receptor (Takeda, 1961). In 50 per cent of the hairs tested there was no response to NaCl. No sensitivity to quinine or acetic acid could be detected nor were any other kinds of chemoreceptors found. The only histological evidence bearing on this question is the description by Eltringham (1933) of the chemoreceptive hairs of *Vanessa atalanta*. No statement is made in this work of the number of neurons associated with each hair.

In *Leptinotarsa* there are apparently five receptor cells associated with each hair, but the electrical picture is still unclear. Sodium chloride evokes impulses designated by Stürckow (1959) as *h* and *n*; potassium, impulses designated as *h′* and *n′*. Stürckow suggested that *h* and *h′* originate in anion receptors and *n* and *n′* in cation receptors. Water gives isolated low potentials; a sugar receptor is inferred; bending the hair provokes no clear spikes attributable to a mechanoreceptor, although there is an unruly pattern of activity; alkaloids associated with plants that are unacceptable as food provoke salvos of spikes from two cells.

Electrical Events Following Stimulation

It is clear in all cases thus far studied in detail that the hairs subserving contact chemoreception are compound organs containing a number of chemoreceptors and usually a mechanoreceptor. In the fly at least each chemoreceptor is specifically different with regard to the chemicals to which it is sensitive. In all cases each receptor performs the dual function of reacting to the stimulus and generating nerve impulses. Each of these functions is currently the subject of intensive study.

The suggestion was made by Dethier (1956) that chemicals depolarize the membrane of the distal process of the neuron at the tip of the hair, that this depolarization travels down the nerve fibre to the cell body at the base of the hair, and that the action potential is generated in this region. Studies of the effects of temperature on thresholds and on frequency of impulse discharge lent some support to this idea. When the temperature of the tip of the hair, and hence the receptor surface, was altered in the range 2°–41° C., no change in behavioural threshold occurred (Dethier, 1956), nor was there any change in the frequency of impulses (Hodgson, 1956 b; Dethier and Arab, 1958). When the temperature of the whole preparation, and hence the cell bodies, was altered, however, marked changes in frequency occurred (Hodgson and Roeder, 1956; Hodgson, 1956 b). According to Hodgson (1956 b), the fibres in some hairs increased their frequency with warming while others decreased with warming.

The most conclusive evidence bearing on the matter came, as might be expected, from electrophysiological work. Wolbarsht (1958), seeking evidence for a slow potential associated with stimulation, discovered when he placed one electrode on the tip of a hair and the other in the crushed head or labellum that there was a resting potential of the order of 60 mV. Strangely enough, however, this remained unaltered when the hair was stimulated. He concluded that the potential represented a difference across the basement membrane which separates the general body cavity and the area containing the neurons, associated cells, and hypodermis. Later, working exclusively with the mechanoreceptor component of the chemoreceptive hair (and with simple mechanoreceptors), he recorded a graded slow potential which occurred when the hair was stimulated by bending. It was always an increase in negativity at the recording electrode. It varied directly with the magnitude of the stimulus and showed no overshoot when returning to the baseline. This is a receptor potential in that it occurs prior to the initiation of any impulses, varies smoothly, and must attain a critical level before any impulses are generated. It is also either the generator potential itself or is associated with it. Evidence was produced that suggests that the receptor potential originates at a site that is not invaded by the propagated impulses and that this site is distad of the site of impulse generation. The geometry of the hair and the mechanoreceptor indicates that this must be in the distal process of the cell.

Morita (1959), recording through the side wall of the chemoreceptor hair, detected a slow d.c. potential occurring when the tip of the hair was stimulated (Fig. 83). When the stimulus was either sugar or sodium chloride the potential was negative at the recording point with reference to the base of the hair; when the stimulus was quinine the potential was positive. The closer the recording electrode was placed to the tip of the hair, the greater the negativity when sugar or sodium chloride was applied. On the basis of these recordings Morita has concluded that this slow potential is indeed a generator potential

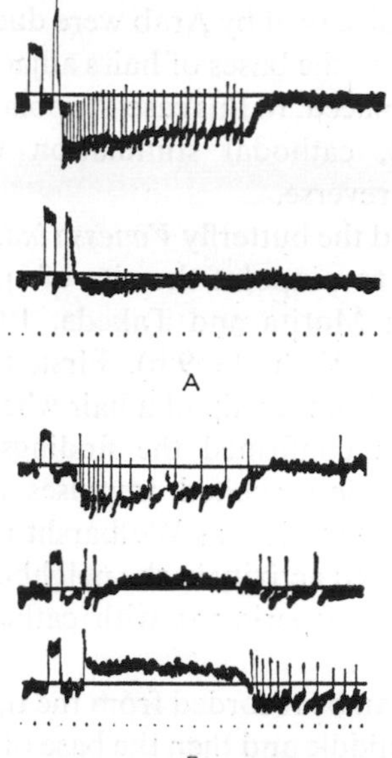

FIG. 83. A. Response of labellar chemosensory hair of *Calliphora* to 0·25M sucrose before (top) and after (bottom) crushing. B. Response of a hair to 0·25M sucrose (top), 0·25M sucrose plus 0·05M $CaCl_2$ (middle), and 0·05M $CaCl_2$ (bottom). Time, $\frac{1}{60}$ sec. (Redrawn from Morita and Yamashita, 1959.)

arising at the point of stimulation and initiating impulses at the base of the hair. He makes no distinction between receptor potential and generator potential, and the presumption is that they are one and the same in this hair.

The electrical sign of the impulses arising from stimulation proved puzzling, and an attack on this problem threw some light on the question of the site of impulse generation. All workers now agree that the initial component of the spike is positive (Morita *et al.*, 1957; Wolbarsht, 1958; Hodgson, 1958 b). Wolbarsht (1958) interpreted this condition as indicating that the distal processes of the chemoreceptive cells act as somewhat poorly insulated extensions of the recording pipette into the interior of the cell. The spikes of the mechanoreceptors are conceived of as being recorded by electrotonic spread up through the contents of the hair, which would be analogous to an external electrode opposite a part of the cell membrane that is not involved in the propagated impulse. This conception is supported by the results of polarization experiments. Anodal polarization produces stimulation; cathodal stimulation produces depression, as has been seen with intracellular electrodes in the eye of *Limulus*.

Arab (1958) found that behavioural responses were evoked by cathodal stimulation and would not occur with anodal stimulation. Wolbarsht (1958) was able to reconcile this apparent discrepancy. He showed that the behavioural responses observed by Arab were due to the action of the current on the neurons at the bases of hairs adjacent to the one on which the electrodes were placed. In this case the polarizing current was extracellular; hence, cathodal stimulation was excitatory and anodal stimulation, the reverse.

Working with the fly *Lucilia caeser* and the butterfly *Vanessa indica*, Morita and his co-workers attempted to pinpoint the site of spike generation (Tateda and Morita, 1959; Morita and Takeda, 1959; Morita, 1959; Morita and Yamashita, 1959 a, 1959 b). First, they showed that spikes were never recorded from the tip of a hair when it was severed from its base. They then confirmed the findings of Wolbarsht (1958) that anodal stimulation elicited impulses and cathodal current blocked them. They found also, as Wolbarsht had, that anodal stimulation of one hair blocked activity in the neighbouring hair, but they did not do a similar experiment with cathodal stimulation as Wolbarsht had.

In an attempt to explain how spikes can be recorded from the tip of the hair, Morita (1959) cooled first the middle and then the base of the hair, recorded in each case from the tip, and analysed the shape of the spike. According to his records, cooling the middle affected predominantly the falling phase of the spike, while cooling at the base affected both the rising and falling phases. On the basis of this evidence he claimed that spikes originate at the base of the hair and fire in both directions, that is, back along the distal process to the tip, as well as centripetally along the axon to the central nervous system. If this condition occurs, it would mean that spikes invade the area of the generator potential contrary to the situation found in mechanoreceptors.

Morita and Yamashita (1959 b) recorded simultaneously from the tip and the base and found that the spike at the tip is generally larger than the spike recorded from a hole in the side wall. They observed that the side-wall spike peaked more quickly, and they took this to mean that the differences in height were not due to a gradient of electrotonic spread. They also concluded from this result that there is back firing, and they argued that impulses are recorded extracellularly and not intracellularly as Wolbarsht (1958) concluded.

Hanson and Wolbarsht (1962) re-examined the situation in *Phormia* and found that the impulse is indeed conducted some distance down the dendrite, that distance being a large fraction, if not the entire length, of the short ones, but only a small fraction of the length of longer ones. Electrodes located at various places along the dendrite all showed an initially positive phase of the impulse sometimes followed by a longer negative phase. The following interpretation was proposed: the action potential is generated at a considerable distance from the recording electrode and is recorded as a positive swing. As the action potential invades the dendrite, the active region comes beneath the recording electrode and appears as a negative deflection. Simultaneous records from several electrodes placed along the dendrite show that the active region of the membrane proceeds from the cell body toward the trip. The record resulting from an algebraic sum of the two phases shows the positive phase being abruptly terminated by the longer lasting negative phase. Cocaine, xylocaine, procaline, and chloral hydrate reversibly depress or abolish this negative phase with a correspondingly longer lasting positive phase. Continuous chemical stimulation or injury accentuates and/or speeds up the onset of the negative phase.

The Sugar Receptor

Since different receptor cells in a contact chemoreceptive hair respond specifically to different chemicals, the question of mechanism of stimulation, that is, how the chemicals depolarize the dendrite membrane, should be investigated separately in the various types. The types are most clearly delineated in the blowfly. In this insect, as already pointed out, there is one cell specifically sensitive to sugars and one to monovalent salts. A modestly detailed story of the operation of the sugar receptor has been constructed from behavioural studies. The task now presented to electrophysiology is that of proof-reading the story, filling in the details, and revising where necessary.

Carbohydrates are the most effective, if not the only, stimuli; however, this cell is highly specific and unequally sensitive to the various compounds. Behavioural tests in which eighty-two different carbohydrates were applied to the chemoreceptive hair housing the receptor revealed a spectrum of activity from complete unresponsiveness to extreme sensitivity (Dethier, 1955 a). The most effective compounds are certain pentoses, hexoses, and compound sugars possessing an α-*D*-glucopyranoside link. In general, the α-form of a sugar is more stimulating than the β-form. Among effective pentoses *D*-arabinose is more stimulating than *L*-arabinose. It is clear from these tests that the structural configuration of a sugar is its most important determinant as an effective stimulus. On the other hand, no sense can be made of the situation on the assumption that there is one key molecular structure for stimulation.

The first intimation that there are multiple and different sites of action on the sugar receptor cell arose from a series of studies in which mixtures of sugars were found not to be effective at concentrations predicted from the threshold values of the individual constituents. There were instances of synergism and of competitive inhibition. The inhibitory effect of a given sugar varied, however, depending upon which other sugar it was mixed with at the time. For example, mannose, a weakly stimulating sugar, inhibited fructose, but not glucose; rhamnose inhibited glucose but not fructose. There was some evidence that sorbose inhibited both fructose and glucose (Dethier *et al.*, 1956).

Supporting evidence for the idea of multiple sites came from an entirely different kind of study. Evans (1961 b) found that feeding blowfly larvae on a medium containing a specific sugar depressed the sensitivity of the adult to that sugar. Relative sensitivity to glucose or fructose could be enhanced or depressed by rearing in the presence of the appropriate sugar. Evans interpreted these results as indicating that the sugar reduced either the number or the affinity of sites on the receptor cell for that particular sugar.

The nature of the combining action of sugars, while not understood, can be narrowed down somewhat by a process of elimination. An outstanding feature of stimulation by sugars is that no change in threshold can be demonstrated to take place as the temperature of the stimulus is changed. Nor is any change in threshold observed when the pH of the sugar solution is changed (Dethier, 1956). Another feature of stimulation by sugars is that there is no inhibition by any of the following metabolic inhibitors: phlorizin, fluoride, azide, idoacetate, cyanide (Dethier, 1955 a). This finding indicates that the first step in stimulation probably does not involve any steps in the glycolytic cycle below those blocked by the compounds listed. The absence of a marked temperature and pH change argues against an enzymatic reaction being involved. It was proposed tentatively (Dethier, 1956) that stimulation by sugars involves combination of the sugar molecules with a specific receptor site or substance by weak forces, such as van der Waal, to form a complex which depolarizes the membrane, after which (or simultaneously) sugar is removed passively by a shift in concentration gradient.

At this point current knowledge of the sugar receptor ends. Few electrophysiological investigations of stimulation by carbohydrates have been reported thus far. Hodgson (1957) examined the effects of twenty-three carbohydrates. At that time the existence of a water fibre was not suspected, and the lack of this information complicated the interpretation of records. It appears, nevertheless, that all acceptable sugars stimulate one neuron, while unacceptable sugars either fail to stimulate or actually inhibit.

In *Vanessa indica* the sugar receptor responds to *D*-glucose, *D*-fructose, and sucrose in increasing order of effectiveness. Lactose, *D*-galactose, inositol, trehalose, and *L*-sorbitol are non-stimulating (Takeda, 1961). Maltose and turanose elicit small deformed spikes which have been interpreted by Takeda as indicative of a combined stimulatory and inhibitory action. The sugar receptor is sensitive to concentrations of sucrose as low as 2^{-7} M. In addition to this receptor there is one that responds in identical fashion to sucrose and to NaCl.

The Salt Receptor

It was originally believed that rejection of a solution was triggered solely by activity in one neuron, and since so many compounds elicited rejection, it was assumed that the single neuron was grossly non-specific. Studies on competitive inhibition and on the action of heavy metal salts, however, hinted that rejection was not a single modality. As a consequence, it was no longer possible to assume that every compound that was rejected acted on the same receptor cell.

Electrophysiological studies, while only just beginning, have partially answered the question of the adequacy of stimuli for rejection. They indicate that many rejected compounds block activity in all fibres of the chemoreceptive hairs, but that monovalent salts stimulate one cell actively (Hodgson, 1956 a; Morita, 1959). It has been possible to come to some understanding of the mechanism of action of this salt fibre by acquiring enough data to make the same kind of theoretical analysis which Beidler (1954) made of mammalian salt receptors (Evans and Mellon, 1962 b).

Beidler assumed that the stimulus reacts with some receptor substance and that the reaction obeys the mass action law. His second assumption was that the magnitude of response is directly related to the number of ions or molecules that have reacted with the receptors. He derived an equation which related magnitude of response to the concentration of the applied chemical stimulus. This is $c/R = (c/R_m) + (1/KR_m)$, where c = concentration, R = magnitude of response, R_m = magnitude of maximum response, and K = the equilibrium constant. The validity of the equation can be tested by measuring c and R. Beidler found the agreement to be excellent. Now, knowing the equilibrium constant, he calculated the free energies of reaction from the expression $\Delta F = RT \ln K$, where ΔF = change of free energy, R = the gas constant, and T = the absolute temperature. The low value which he found for ΔF (from $-1{\cdot}22$ to $-1{\cdot}37$ Cal./mole) for a series of sodium salts was taken to indicate that physical rather than chemical forces are involved in the interaction between the chemical stimulus and the receptors. This conclusion raised the question of what the receptor substance may be.

Beidler argued that the small temperature dependence and the low values for ΔF suggest a reaction similar to those that occur with ion binding by proteins and natural polyelectrolytes. Some properties of the reacting groups of the receptor substance can be determined from a study of the effect of changing pH. Since no effect could be demonstrated over the range 3·0–11·0, one might conclude that the molecules of the receptor substance are strong acidic radicals. The relatively weak carboxyl radical of a protein, for example, cannot be considered as the reacting group. The phosphate and sulphate radicals of such natural polyelectrolytes as nucleic acids and certain polysaccharides are able to bind cations in a manner consistent with the properties of the receptors described by Beidler.

The many complexities of the mammalian taste organs, as, for example, the receptor cell being non-neural and synaptically connected to a neuron, the multiple innervation of a receptor cell, and the innervation of more than one cell by a single neuron, obstructed further analyses of the nature of the receptor sites and the process of stimulation. None of these handicaps are associated with the salt receptor of the insect. A quantitative study of the repetitive response of the labellar hair receptor to NaCl has shown that Beidler's theory applies equally well to this receptor (Evans and Mellon, 1962 b). The calculated relative free energy change of the reaction between salt and receptor site in this case is the range 0 to -1 kcal./mole. This value suggests that weak physical forces are involved, and evidence has been obtained that the salt-combining sites are anionic and strongly acidic. As a consequence, the cation of a salt largely dominates stimulation.

The Water Receptor

The water receptor discovered by Evans and Mellon (1962a) is the only cell in the chemoreceptive hair of *Phormia* that is activated by water. The most effective stimulus tested thus far is pure water. Aqueous solutions of sucrose appear to depress the activity of the cell as a linear function of the logarithm of osmotic pressure. At 5M sucrose the frequency of impulses decreases to less than half of the maximum. Other non-electrolytes (e.g., glycerol and mannose) also inhibit, but no simple relation was found between parameters of the solution and the degree of inhibition. Inorganic electrolytes also inhibit water response, but in a more specific manner. Aqueous solutions of NaCl begin to inhibit at 0·1M. Inhibition appears to be complete at about 0·3M. Calcium chloride solutions inhibit at about 0·01M. The inhibition of water response is unrelated to spike activity in other fibres.

Modalities

For the blowfly it is clear that water, sugars, protein, and unacceptable compounds can be distinguished as different. To what extent these four taste categories can be subdivided into other taste modalities is not clear. Although there is evidence that different sugars act upon different sites at the molecular level, they none the less stimulate the same receptor. In the case of unacceptable compounds, that is, salts, acids, alkaloids, alcohols, etc., it is probable that different sensory input results from stimulation by the different compounds. If this suggestion is confirmed it provides a peripheral mechanism for discriminating among a number of compounds and indicates that the modality 'unacceptable' is not a homogeneous one.

Aside from incomplete electrophysiological data obtained with *Phormia*, evidence for taste modalities has been derived principally from the following sources: (1) observations of the behaviour of individuals conditioned to respond to a given chemical; (2) determinations of the additive or non-additive capacity of diverse stimuli; (3) measurement of the amount of sucrose drunk by honeybees after contamination with subliminal concentrations of different chemicals; (4) comparison of the threshold changes for different compounds during starvation; (5) localization of specific kinds of receptors. Much of the information derived from these kinds of experiments is suggestive rather than conclusive; nevertheless, considering all of the available evidence, it is highly probable that insects can do better than discriminating simply between acceptable and unacceptable.

Bauer (1938) trained *Dytiscus marginalis* and *Hydrous piceus* to respond positively to sucrose; these animals could not be trained simultaneously to avoid glucose, and also reacted positively in the majority of cases to some fifteen or twenty other sugars and sugar derivatives. As in the experiments of Schaller (1926) and Ritter (1936) with the same or related species, the beetles learned readily to distinguish between pairs chosen from sucrose, sodium chloride, acids (hydrochloric and acetic), and quinine, and could even be trained to accept quinine and avoid sodium chloride. But specimens that had learned to avoid hydrochloric acid also avoided acetic and could not be taught to respond differently to the two; the same result was obtained when quinine was matched against salicin or aloin. Bauer concluded that the sweet substances (with the possible exception of mannose, which was avoided by some individuals) constitute a single homogeneous grouping; salts, acids, and bitter substances, normally avoided, are distinguished from sweet and from each other, so that taste substances can be classified into the same four qualities for these beetles as for man.

As mentioned above in the discussion of methods, von Frisch (1935) found additive the stimulatory effects of all sugars acceptable to the bee. Summation was noted also between sodium chloride and lithium bromide, ammonium bromide, or hydrochloric acid, but the repellent effect of quinine was lessened rather than enhanced by the addition of acids (hydrochloric, acetic, sulphuric, citric, lactic). When sucrose solutions, one containing sodium chloride and another quinine hydrochloride, were prepared and were accepted by equal proportions of the bees they were drunk in different amounts. Almost as much of the quinine was taken as of the control, but considerably less of the solution containing salt. The results would indicate three taste qualities: sweet, acid–salt, and bitter. But in other experiments von Frisch found that starved bees show no better acceptance of sodium chloride than those fully fed, although the threshold for rejection of quinine rises eight times and that for hydrochloric acid by a factor of five. He concluded therefore that salt represents a quality different from either acid or bitter. Furthermore, although there is no summation of repellency between quinine and acids, other bitter substances, such as aloin, arbutin, colocynthin, and salicin, are rendered more repugnant by the addition of hydrochloric acid, so that the category bitter is not homogeneous for the bee. It is possible that investigations of this kind would reveal similarly complex relationships in man.

Other evidence as to the separation of the taste qualities in insects was provided by Ritter (1936), who found that after amputation of the maxillary palpi specimens of *Hydrous piceus* would still react to 0·007M hydrochloric acid but not to salt, sugar, or quinine. Removal of the tips of the labial palpi then abolished the response to acid, although animals lacking both sets of palpi and the antennae still reacted positively to meat juice, presumably via receptors in the mouth. These observations would seem to set the acids apart from the other taste substances, but are at variance with the findings of Bauer (1938) with the same and related species, and of Hodgson (1951) with *Laccophilus*. Bauer found that amputation of the maxillary palpi left the gustatory response to sucrose, etc., unaltered except for an increase in threshold. Hodgson found by ablation experiments that all the head appendages could mediate responses to acids, salts, and alcohols. Thresholds were increased considerably when the antennae were removed, but less so when either pair of palpi were extirpated.

CHAPTER VI

Response to Humidity

The behavioural responses of insects to water vapour mixed with the permanent gases of the atmosphere indicate that these organisms somehow perceive the water or differences resulting from changes in the concentration of the vapour. A unique feature of water is its presence both in the organism and in the environment. The existence of water on both sides of the integument poses problems that are not encountered in the case of other stimuli. Conceivably water may act on the organism independently of what is within (as do, for example, odour molecules), or it may cause outward movement of internal water so that the insect does not respond directly to a change in external environment but rather to a change induced in its own internal environment. For these reasons, and because all attempts to understand the mechanism of hygroreception have been based upon experiments which correlate the degree of activity or direction of movement with the amount of water in the air, decisions must be reached as to which relationship of water vapour to atmosphere gases is to be measured. If humidity receptors are conceived of as responding to the concentration of water molecules, then the absolute concentration of water to which they are exposed should be measured. On the other hand, if the humidity reactions are conceived of as operating through the agency of evaporation or transpiration, then the drying power of the air is the variable to be measured.

Conventionally there are a number of humidity definitions (Humphreys, 1940). The *absolute humidity* is either the mass of water vapour per unit volume or the gas pressure exerted by the water vapour per unit area. *Relative humidity* is the ratio of the actual mass of water vapour in a small volume to the maximum mass that can exist in the same volume at the same temperature. It is also defined as the ratio of the actual to the maximum pressure of water vapour per unit area that can exist in the presence of a flat surface of pure water at the same temperature. *Saturation deficit* may be defined as: (1) the amount of water vapour in addition to that already present, per unit volume, necessary to produce saturation at the existing temperature and pressure; (2) the difference between actual and saturation pressure; (3) the ratio of the vapour pressure deficit to the saturation pressure at the existing temperature.

Absolute humidity in mass per volume is difficult to measure. Conventionally one measures relative humidity. In an attempt to measure the drying power of the air many investigators measure saturation deficit (Anderson, 1936). Leighly (1937) and Thornthwaite (1940) have pointed out that evaporation is a physical process dependent upon a vapour pressure gradient between the evaporating surface and the air and is not directly related to relative humidity or to saturation deficit in the air. Hence, saturation deficit is of no value as an indicator of moisture losses by evaporation or transpiration (see also Ramsay, 1935; Wellington, 1949; Edney, 1957).

Responses to water vapour include: orientation from a distance to high concentrations of water vapour, proboscis responses to water vapour in the immediate vicinity, avoidance of regions of high and low humidities, and aggregation in zones of preferred humidity.

Just as the degree of hunger or satiation influences the response of insects to food, so also does the state of water balance (and starvation) influence the behavioural response to humidity. Desiccated flour beetles (*Tribolium castaneum*) reverse their preference for humid areas after water has been provided. The intensity of the reaction to dryness also increases with increased starvation (Willis and Roth, 1950). Similarly, the cockroach *Blatta orientalis*, which prefers lower humidities when its water balance is optimum, becomes hygropositive when desiccated (Gunn and Cosway, 1938). Comparable reversals have been demonstrated for the beetle *Ptinus tectus* (Bentley, 1944), *Drosophila* (Perttunen and Erkkila, 1952), *Aedes*, and *Tenebrio molitor* (Dodds and Ewer, 1952). It is clear from these and other studies not only that a water deficit in the body elicits a moist reaction but also that the presence of a maximum amount of water in the body elicits a dry reaction (Perttunen, 1951; Syrjämäki, 1962). Other factors that influence response to humidity are age (Perttunen and Ahonen, 1956; Perttunen and Salmi, 1956; Syrjämäki, 1962), diurnal rhythms (Perttunen, 1953), stage of the reproductive cycle (Perttunen, 1955 a), stage of development (Hafez, 1950, 1953), sex (Roth and Willis, 1951 c; Perttunen and Ahonen, 1956; Syrjämäki, 1962).

Most of our speculation regarding the physiology of hygroreceptors is based upon analyses of behavioural responses to humidity gradients. The following species have been studied in some detail: *Locusta migratoria migratorioides* (Kennedy, 1937), *Blatta orientalis* (Gunn and Cosway, 1938), *Culex fatigans* (Thomson, 1938), *Tenebrio molitor*

(Pielou, 1940; Pielou and Gunn, 1940), *Pediculus humanus corporis* (Wigglesworth, 1941), *Agriotes osbcurus* and *A. lineatus* (Lees, 1943), *Ptinus tectus* (Bentley, 1944), *Choristoneura fumiferana* (Wellington, 1949), *Tribolium* spp. and *Sitophilus* (Willis and Roth, 1950; Roth and Willis, 1951 a, 1951 b, 1951 c), *Aedes gracilis* and *Blethisa multipunctata* (Perttunen, 1951), *Blatella germanica* and *Aedes aegypti* (Roth and Willis, 1952), *Drosophila* (Perttunen and Syrjämäki, 1958; Perttunen and Erkkila, 1952; Syrjämäki, 1962), *Neodiprion americanus banksianae* and *N. lecontei* (Green, 1954), *Oncopeltus fasciatus* (Andersen and Ball, 1959), *Melanoplus bivittatus* (Riegert, 1958, 1959, 1960), *Schistocerca gregaria* (Aziz, 1957 a, 1957 b). The strength of reaction and the ability to discriminate differences in humidity varies among the species. With *Locusta migratoria migratorioides*, which aggregates in dry microclimates, more individuals respond as the gradient becomes steeper. With *Culex fatigans*, *Tenebrio molitor*, which avoid high humidities, and *Agriotes* spp., which avoid low humidities, the intensity of the reaction is related to the highest humidity. *Ptinus tectus* reacts most intensely at low humidities. *Culex* discriminates 1 per cent differences in the range near 100 per cent relative humidity, but reacts only to 50 per cent differences in the range of relative humidity from 30 to 85. *Tribolium castaneum* discriminates between humidities differing by 15 per cent over the entire range. Reactions to differences of 5 per cent are weak between R.H. 0 and 5, absent between R.H. 40 and 45, 45 and 50, and 50 and 55, but strong between R.H. 95 and 100. The louse also discriminates better at higher humidities. Wireworms detect the difference between R.H. 100 and 95·5. Normal undesiccated *Drosophila melanogaster* of both sexes exhibit an intensity of reaction that is correlated with the degree of the higher alternative rather than with the difference. When alternate humidities lie between 100 and 87 per cent R.H., the drier is preferred; when they lie between 77 and 20 per cent the wetter is preferred (Perttunen and Syrjämäki, 1958).

The reactions of some species to a given relative humidity have been studied at different temperatures. The results have been interpreted as indicating that the reactions of *Culex* and *Tenebrio* are more in accord with relative humidity than with saturation deficiencies, while the reverse is true of *Agriotes*. What this may mean is difficult to know. Although the results are interpreted by some as indicating that the receptors act as evaporimeters, the lack of correlation between saturation deficit and evaporation weakens the argument (cf. Thornthwaite, 1940). On the other hand, in studies conducted with spruce budworm larvae (*C. fumiferana*) and sawfly larvae of the genus *Neodiprion* a

TABLE [illegible]

(From Syrjämäki, 1962)

Sites of humidity receptors or receptive areas found in insects

h = receptors supposed to function hygrometrically, *e* = receptors or receptive areas supposed to function evaporimetrically, *i* = receptors identified.

Species	Site of Receptors				Author
	Antennae	Palps	Legs	Other parts	
Blatta orientalis	+	—	—	—	Gunn & Cosway, 1938
Tenebrio molitor	*i h*	—	—	—	Pielou, 1940
Pediculus humanus corporis	*i*	—	—	—	Wigglesworth, 1941
Phormia regina	+	—	—	—	Steiner, 1942
Agriotes-larvae	—	*e*	—	—	Lees, 1943
Ptinus tectus	+	—	—	—	Bentley, 1944
Musca domestica (larva)	+	—	—	*i*	Hafez, 1950
Oodes gracilis, *Blethisa multipunctata*	+	—	—	—	Perttunen, 1951
12 beetle species; larvae of 2 beetle species	*i*	—	—	—	Roth & Willis, 1951 a, 1951 b
Tribolium castaneum and *confusum*	*i*	*i*	—	—	Roth & Willis, 1951 a
Aedes aegypti ♂	*e*	—	—	—	Roth & Willis, 1952
Aedes aegypti ♀, *Blatella germanica*	*i*	—	—	—	Roth & Willis, 1952
Tenebrio molitor	+	—	—	+	Dodds & Ewer, 1952
Drosophila melanogaster (larva)	—	—	—	*i*	Benz, 1956
Lucilia sericata and *cuprina*	+	—	—	—	Cragg & Cole, 1956
Apis mellifica	*i*	—	—	—	Kuwabara & Takeda, 1956
Gryllus bimaculatus	+	—	—	—	Amouriq, 1957
Schistocerca gregaria	*i*	—	—	—	Aziz, 1957 b
Zootermopsis nevadensis (larva)	+	—	—	+	Ernst, 1957
Glossina morsitans	—	—	—	*i*	Bursell, 1957
Gryllus domesticus	*i h*	—	—	—	Amouriq, 1959
Melanoplus bivittatus	*i*	—	—	—	Riegert, 1960
Drosophila melanogaster	+	+	—	+	Syrjämäki, 1962

relation between locomotory behaviour and rate of evaporation has clearly been demonstrated (Wellington, 1949; Green, 1954). No information is available with regard to the receptors involved. It is possible that the response is mediated by rather general changes in the internal milieu rather than by specific sense organs.

The identity of humidity receptors is even less firmly established than that of olfactory receptors. In *Tenebrio* responses to humidity are abolished when the antennae are extirpated or completely covered. The most common sensilla are pits and pegs, the latter being confined to the seven distal segments. The intensity of response is greatly decreased when the seven distal segments are removed, but complete abolition requires removal of the additional segments which bear only pits. Asymmetrical amputation has shown that a threshold number of pits is required (Pielou, 1940). In *Tribolium* but not in *Sitophilus*, similar ablation experiments have shown that there is a correlation between the number of thin-walled sensilla and the intensity of response (Roth and Willis, 1951 b). The sensilla are simple or multiply branched pegs. On the antennae of the human louse there are humidity receptors which are distinct from the olfactory receptors (Wigglesworth, 1941). They are tufted sensilla; each consists of a minute cone bearing four delicate apical hairs. A number of neurons are associated with each sensillum. Similar sensilla are the humidity receptors of the larva of *Musca domestica* (Hafez, 1950, 1953) and of *Drosophila melanogaster* (Benz, 1956). In grasshoppers the sensilla coeloconica have been suggested as humidity receptors (Aziz, 1957 b; Riegert, 1960), but there is no supporting experimental evidence (Slifer, 1961). By studying antennaless mutants of *Drosophila* Begg and Hogben (1946) came to the conclusion that the antennal receptors mediated positive responses to wet and that responses to dry were mediated by receptors at other unknown locations on the body. Perttunen and Syrjämäki (1958) came to exactly the opposite conclusions and proposed an explanation of the discrepancy. Kuwabara and Takeda (1956) conditioned honeybees to extend the proboscis when water vapour was held near the antennae and then amputated various lengths of antennae. They concluded that the sensilla ampullacea were most probably the hygroceptors. Bursell (1957) found that the normal orthokinetic response of the tsetse fly *Glossina morsitans* was abolished when the branched hairs guarding the thoracic spiracles were removed.

How the hydroreceptors operate is still a mystery. They could respond directly to water molecules striking the surface; they could permit evaporation of internal water, with a consequent change in chemical composition or osmotic pressure in the milieu of the receptors or by mechanical deformation; they could respond to temperature changes due to evaporation; they could act as hygrometers, i.e., structures with special hygroscopic properties (Pielou, 1940). In some instances (e.g., spruce budworm) responses may not be mediated by special receptors at all but rather by means of general changes in the body fluids occasioned by evaporation through non-sensory areas. For a recent discussion of these matters, the paper of Syrjämäki (1962) should be consulted.

CHAPTER VII

Photoreception

The range of radiations in the electromagnetic spectrum extends from about 10^{12} to about 10^{-6} mμ. Only a very small segment of this spectrum, from about 253 to 700 mμ, can be detected by organisms. The prime requisite for receiving the radiant energy of this narrow band of the spectrum is a pigment or pigments that will absorb in these wavelengths. For the organism to derive useful information from this energy absorption, bioelectric potentials must be produced. In insects, cells capable of accomplishing these ends are grouped together in three organs: the compound eyes, the dorsal ocelli, the lateral ocelli. Of these the compound eyes, by virtue of their predominant role in behaviour and their extraordinarily large complement of cells, are by far the most important. These great sensitive spots on the surface of the head, with no lids to shield them, are in a continuous state of activity from the light impinging upon them during the lifetime of the insect.

THE COMPOUND EYE

Structure

The principal components of the compound eye are the monopolar neurons that absorb radiant energy and generate action potentials and the transparent areas of the cuticle and internal lenses overlying them. Since cuticle overlies all of the body surface, transparency, or at least translucency, is a *sine qua non* for the functioning of the photoreceptors. Further modification of the cuticle, however, in respect to shape has given it the added property of gathering light. Together with clear cellular bodies, the crystalline cones, it constitutes a lens system, the dioptric apparatus of the eye.

The compound eye is a collection of sensilla known as ommatidia (Fig. 6). Each ommatidium is constructed of a corneal lens, a crystalline cone, a number of primary neurons, and enveloping cells. In primitive insects (e.g., *Machilis*, one of the Thysanura) the two cells which secreted the cornea lie immediately beneath it, that is, between the cornea and the crystalline cone. In most insects these cells withdraw to a position on either side of the crystalline cone where, having become pigmented, they are called corneal pigment cells.

Beneath the corneal lens lies the crystalline cone. There are three types of cones. In one, four cells undergo changes in which a fused intracellular body consisting of protoplasmic ground substance and glycogen is formed (Fyg, 1960). The nuclei are located at the outer or basal border of the cone (eucone type). In another type the cone cells secrete a transparent material while themselves remaining distinct (pseudocone type). In still other eyes no vitreous body is formed, the cone cells being the only occupants of the area (acone type).

The primitive number of retinula cells in an ommatidium is probably eight (Snodgrass, 1926), but one is usually rudimentary or eccentrically placed. The arrangement of the remaining seven varies greatly from one species to another. Sometimes one occupies a basal position so that only six contribute to the formation of the rhabdom. Sometimes the cells are clearly arranged in two layers, three proximal and four distal. More commonly, all cells are in a single layer around a central axis.

The sensory cells appear like bipolar neurons early in their development (Fyg, 1960), but when fully developed are unipolar, dendrites being absent. In the place of dendrites the surfaces of the cells facing the central axis are modified into peculiar structures, the rhabdomeres (Fig. 6). These are the receptive surfaces of the cells (Schultze, 1868; Grenacher, 1879).

Together the rhabdomeres of all retinal cells form a rod, the rhabdom. Some workers had considered the rhabdom to be cuticular (Machatschke, 1936), but the specificity of the test upon which this claim is based is open to question and other tests for chitin have given negative results (Richards, 1951). Other students of the eye had considered the rhabdomeres to be modified neurofibrillae traversing the interior of the cell. The structure of the rhabdom as revealed by electron-microscopy is open to different interpretations. Information is now available on *Musca domestica, Apis mellifera,* the phalaenid moth *Erebus odora,* a species of skipper *Epargyreus,* two grasshoppers, *Dissosteira* spp. and *Schistocerca* spp. (Fernández-Morán, 1956, 1958), *Drosophila melanogaster* (Fernández-Morán, 1956, 1958; Wolken, Capenos, and Turano, 1957), *Sarcophaga bullata,* and *Anax junius* (Goldsmith and Philpott, 1957).

The ommatidia of *Musca, Sarcophaga, Drosophila,* and *Apis* are similar. Each is of the apposition type. Of the eight retinal cells only seven contribute to the rhabdom, the eighth being shorter. In cross-section each cell is roughly wedge-shaped. The rhabdomere appears as a rod or beading extending the length of the medial surface (Fig. 87).

It is 60–70 μ long and about 1·5 μ in diameter (*Musca*). A longitudinal section of a rhabdomere reveals that it consists of closely packed parallel tubules aligned at right angles to the long axis of the cell (Fig. 84). Each is about 400 Å. in diameter and 1,000–15,000 Å. long. The most reasonable interpretation of these tubules is that they are microvilli, that is, finger-like evaginations of the retinal cell; consequently, their boundaries are part of the cell membrane and their contents are extensions of the cytoplasm (Miller, 1957; Goldsmith and Philpott, 1957; Fernández-Morán, 1958; Slifer, 1961). A fine particulate component appears in the microvilli in fixed material. Except for the small one, the rhabdomeres appear to occur as pairs, one

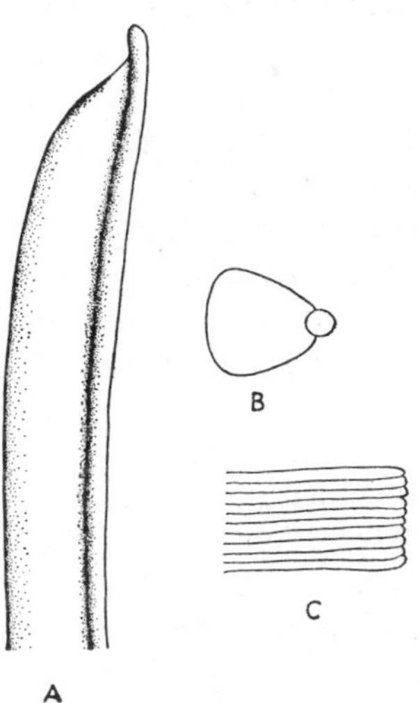

FIG. 84. A. Distal tip of retinal cell from the compound eye of *Musca domestica* as reconstructed by Slifer (1961) from electron-micrographs of Fernández-Morán (1958). B. Cross-section of cell with rhabdomer at right. C. Section through that part of rhabdomer containing microvilli. (Redrawn from Slifer, 1961.)

member of which lies opposite its twin on the far side of the ommatidium. The longitudinal axes of the microvilli in both members of a pair are parallel but in a different plane from those of other pairs. The core separating the rhabdomeres is a loose network of fine filaments in fixed materials. In the eye of the grasshoppers *Dissosteira* and *Schistocerca* the fine filaments in the matrix are closely packed and run lengthwise in orderly courses. Distally this core disappears as the rhabdomeres come together just below the crystalline cone. Here the microvillar structure is replaced by an electron-dense structure. In the eye of the dragonfly *Anax junius* and in the superposition eye of the moth *Erebus odora* there is no central matrix, since the rhabdomeres meet axially. The rhabdom of the skipper consists of eight fused rhabdomeres. Most workers believe that the visual pigment is located in the rhabdomeres, that is, in the lumina of the microvilli. In *Erebus* there is an extensive underlying structure, the tapetum, composed of tracheoles which are highly reflective (Fernández-Morán, 1958).

The retinal cells may occupy one of the two positions with respect to the crystalline cone (Fig. 6). In apposition eyes the retinal cells lie immediately beneath the crystalline cone; in superposition eyes the retinal cells are situated some distance proximad of the crystalline cone. The intervening space is transparent. In all eyes each ommatidium is enclosed in pigment cells. The number of pigment cells is not constant, but usually there is a distal set (iris pigment cells) surrounding the crystalline cone and another set (retinal pigment cells) surrounding the retinal cells.

At the base of the ommatidia, and marking the proximal limit of the retina, is a fenestrated basement membrane. Through the fenestrae pass the proximal processes, the axons, of the retinal cells. There is usually one axon for each cell. In *Erebus*, however, there are sometimes nine axons from a single ommatidium. This occurrence indicates that sometimes the axons begin to branch close to the cell body. Some synapse almost immediately with neurons of the optic lobe; others extend a considerable distance into the lobe before synapsing. The presence of two kinds of retinal fibres, long and short, has been known for some time. Hanström (1927) had speculated upon the possible physiological differences between the two and likened them to the rods and cones of the vertebrate eye.

The optic lobes are in fact a part of the brain, but since so many physiological studies of the eye treat them as part of the eye rather than as the central nervous system, a brief description at this point will be helpful. Most of our knowledge of these complicated structures stems from the classical studies of Zawarzin (1914) on the larva of the dragonfly *Aeschna*, Cajal (1909, 1918) and Cajal and Sanchez (1915) on the house fly and the blowfly. In addition, there are the accounts of Günther (1912) and Holste (1923) on *Dytiscus*, Bretschneider (1921) on the moth *Deilephila euphorbiae*, and Power (1943) on *Drosophila*. The general works of Hanström (1928) and Snodgrass (1935) should also be consulted.

The optic lobe (Fig. 85) is divided into three areas: the lamina ganglionaris, usually in immediate contact with the basement membrane of the retina; the medulla externa; the medulla interna.

The lamina ganglionaris is the first or most distal synaptic layer of the optic lobe. It consists of giant monopolar cells, small monopolar cells, short retinal fibres, long retinal fibres, and centrifugal fibres.

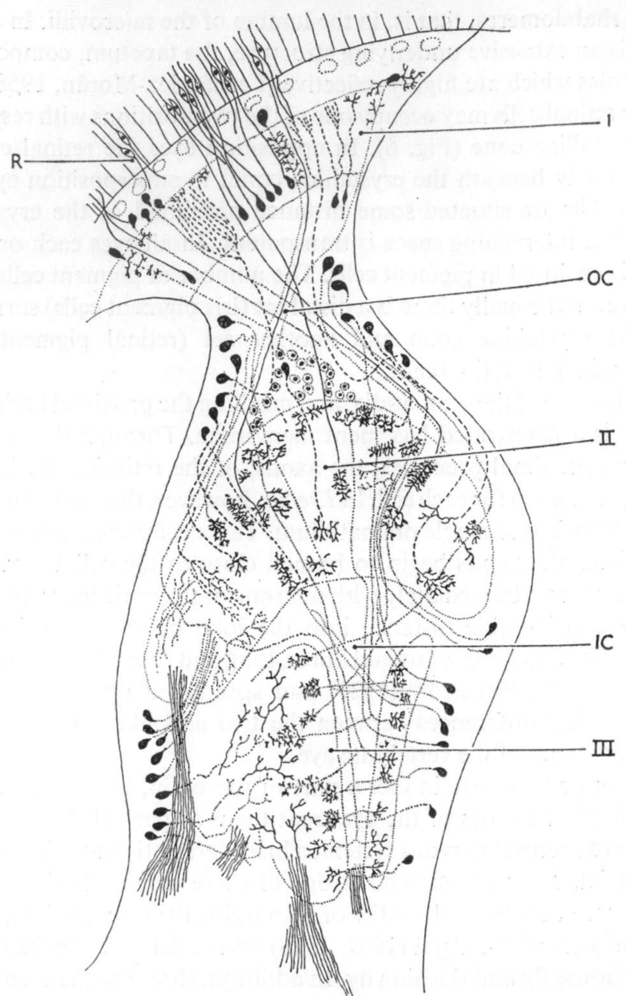

FIG. 85. Simplified diagram of the neural pathways within the optic lobe of *Calliphora*. R, retina; I, lamina ganglionaris; II, medulla externa; III, medulla interna; OC, outer chiasma; IC, inner chiasma. (Redrawn from Cajal and Sanchez, 1915.)

After the axons of the retinal cells traverse the basement membrane about one from each ommatidium passes directly to the lamina, while its five or six companions turn immediately at right angles, forming local chiasmata with those of other ommatidia. The axons then enter the lamina in groups or bundles, each bundle consisting of axons from several ommatidia. Each bundle in the lamina becomes associated with the axon of a giant monopolar cell, with which most of the retinal fibres synapse, and the axon of the centrifugal cell whose cell body lies in the medulla externa. The units ('optic cartridges' of Power) in the lamina thus consist of a long retinal fibre, a number of short retinal fibres, a giant monopolar fibre, and a centrifugal fibre. These fibres now enter the outer chiasma. Fibres from the anterior ommatidia cross to the posterior region of the medulla externa; fibres from the posterior ommatidia cross to the anterior area of the medulla externa; fibres from the middle ommatidia pass directly through the chiasma without crossing. All fibres from the lamina ganglionaris end in the medulla externa. At the present state of our knowledge of the eye there is little point in pursuing the complexities of the optic lobe beyond this level.

The Function of the Retinal Cells

It is generally assumed that the photosensitive pigment is located in the retina cells. As yet there is no direct evidence for this. Prior to 1957 all attempts to isolate a visual pigment failed (Goodwin and Srisukh, 1949; Wald and Burg, 1957; Wolken, 1957; Wolken, Mellon, and Contis, 1957), but Goldsmith (1958 a) was finally able to isolate retinene from the heads of honeybees. It had the specific absorption peak 664 mμ. Since no retinene was obtained from parts of the body other than the head and since retinene previously has been found only in eye tissues, Goldsmith concluded that it is the chromophore of a visual pigment located in the compound eyes and/or ocelli. He found a pigment that possesses a wavelength maximum at about 440 mμ. On bleaching in light the maximum moves to 370 mμ, probably representing the formation of retinene (Goldsmith, 1958 b). Spectral sensitivity measurements of the eyes of honeybees reveal several peaks at different wavelengths, one at 440 mμ (compound eye of drone). This is the only light-sensitive pigment containing retinene that has been extracted from insect eyes thus far. Bowness and Wolken (1959) isolated from the house fly a yellow pigment with a spectral absorption maximum at 437 mμ when unbleached and at 440–446 and 350–360 mμ when bleached, but neither vitamin A nor retinene was detected in this pigment. The work on colour vision suggests that there are others with maxima at different wave lengths.

Electrical Events

An electrophysiological attack on the action of retinal cells has been pushed with more vigour than the biochemical, but, for reasons that will become apparent, the results so far have a high degree of ambiguity.

It has been known for nearly a century that retinae give an electrical response to light. This response, the electroretinogram, is usually detected by placing one electrode on the surface of the cornea and the other at any point on the body. Considering the neural complexity of the eye, this is a relatively crude measurement to make. It should be apparent that the electroretinogram (ERG) is a mass effect dependent, as Granit (1955) has pointed out, upon the favourable orientation of certain retinal structures which conduct currents in one direction. Furthermore, the second electrode, the so-called indifferent electrode, is not necessarily indifferent (cf. Granit, 1955).

For these reasons and also because the profile of the potential changes recorded from the eye differs in form and magnitude with the location of the electrodes, the intensity of illumination, the duration of illumination, the degree of light or dark adaptation, the time of day (Jahn and Wulff, 1941a, 1941b, 1943), the temperature (Ishikawa and Hirao, 1960c), the age of the preparation (Hassenstein, 1957; Naka and Kuwabara, 1959), the amount of blood lost (Ruck and Jahn, 1954), the amount of pressure applied to the body (Autrum and Hoffmann, 1960), the species of insect, the individual (Hartline, 1928), and the characteristics of the recording apparatus, it is understandable that there is great difficulty in interpreting ERGs and reconciling the results reported by one laboratory with those reported by another. These difficulties will become apparent below. None the less, hidden in the ERG is the code to some of the primary events that occur in photoreceptors when they are stimulated by light, and ERGs have been studied intensively in the hope that they will yield bits of this information.

ERGs have been recorded from a large number of insects. The first ever obtained (from *Melanoplus differentialis*, *M. femur-rubrum*, *Chortophaga viridisfasciata*, *Vanessa atalanta*, *Bombus pennsylvanicus*, *Musca domestica*) were described by Hartline (1928) as being essentially similar to one another and consisting exclusively of negative components. These included a rapidly rising wave (which he designated as *A* and later workers as *b*) whose decay was interrupted by a slowly rising wave (his *B* and the *c* of others). The off-effect was merely a decay of the *c* wave. Up to 0·08 seconds the Bunsen–Roscoe law held. The many differences in the profiles of the ERGs were interpreted as being due to differences in the form and magnitude of the two negative waves.

Melanoplus was again studied ten years later (Jahn and Crescitelli, 1938; Crescitelli and Jahn, 1939) as were the grasshoppers *Trimerotropis citrina* and *T. maritima* (Jahn and Wulff, 1942). The ERG was essentially similar to that reported by Hartline; however, this time it was reported as beginning with a weak positive wave (*a*) prominent in some eyes, absent in others, and abolished by light adaptation. In addition, a negative off-effect (*d* wave) occurred in the form of a small hump on the *c* wave. The moth *Samia cecripoa* was reported to have a similar ERG except that a *d* wave was never seen (Jahn and Crescitelli, 1939). But for *Galleria mellonella* Taylor and Nickerson (1943) reported *a*, *b*, *c*, and occasionally *d* waves.

The ERG of the water beetle *Hydrous triangularis* showed in its most complicated form (high intensity, night eye) a simple negative profile consisting of *b* and *c* waves only, while *Dytiscus fasciventris* in similar circumstances showed *a*, *b*, and *c* waves (Wulff and Jahn, 1943). On the other hand, Bernhard (1942) described the ERG of *Dytiscus* as being a simple *b* and *c* wave.

In the grasshopper *Dissosteira carolina* the profile obtained was totally negative, consisting of *b* and *c* waves and only occasionally a *d* wave (Taylor and Crescitelli, 1944). The most marked departure from form encountered was an occasional ERG, in which, after the initial negative response to illumination, there was a long, slow, positive swing. A similar ERG had been reported by Hartline (1928) for *Chortophaga viridisfasciata*. The ERG of the cockroach *Periplaneta americana* was reported as a simple negative wave (Ruck, 1958 a; Walther, 1958 a, 1958 b), as were also the ERGs of *Tachycines*, *Dixippus*, and the nymph of *Aeschna* (Autrum, 1948 a, 1948 b, 1950).

For all of the species mentioned thus far everyone agrees that the *usual* ERG is essentially a cornea-negative swing. Depending on conditions and species, it may or may not have an initial *a* wave and a final *d* wave. There may be negative and positive after-effects.

Disagreement arises when the ERGs for Diptera and Hymenoptera from different laboratories are compared. For *Musca domestica* Hartline (1928) stated that the ERG was similar to that of the other species he studied, i.e., a negative potential consisting of components *b* and *c*, but in a later record (Hartline, Wagner, and MacNichol, 1952) the ERG appeared with a small positive *a* wave at the on-point and a small short negative *d* wave at the off. For *Eristalis* and *Sarcophaga* Hassenstein (1957) recorded an ERG with a very pronounced positive on-effect followed by a slower negative wave and terminated at the end of stimulation with a sharp negative off-effect. These on- and off-effects have the sign and position of the *a* and *d* waves respectively. For *Lucilia* Kuwabara and Naka (1957) and Naka and Kuwabara (1959) showed a simple positive monophasic wave at low stimulus intensities. For *Phormia regina* the records of Ruck (1958 b) showed at high intensities a small positive *a* wave and complex multiphasic waves with prominent negative components. The ERGs for *Apis mellifera* and the dragonfly *Pachydiplax longipennis* were similar. In his original papers Autrum (1948 a, 1948 b) described the ERG of *Calliphora* as a diphasic response consisting of a spike-like positive on-effect and a similar but negative off-effect (in these reports the potential sign was incorrectly reversed but corrected in later papers). With short flashes of light the wave was smoothly diphasic; with a stimulus of long duration the positive wave returned to a line of zero potential which continued until the off-effect. At high stimulus intensities Autrum reported a 'negatives Zwischenpotential', and in a later paper (Autrum and Hoffmann, 1960) figured the 'normal' ERG as having a pronounced negative wave between the on- and off-effect. The positive on-effect is sometimes preceded by a small negative wave (Autrum, 1950; Kirschfeld, 1959). Similar ERGs have been described for *Apis*, *Bombus*, *Vespa*, and the adult of *Aeschna* (Autrum and Stoecker, 1950; Autrum and Gallwitz, 1951).

Autrum decided that there are two fundamentally distinct kinds of ERGs in insect eyes, the one, the *Dixippus*-type, purely negative and monophasic, the other, the *Calliphora*-type, diphasic. In the first category ('slow') he placed all of the slow-flying, night-flying, and aquatic species (e.g., most Orthoptera, Blatteria, Lepidoptera, aquatic Coleoptera, and dragonfly nymphs); in the second category ('fast'), the rapidly flying species (Diptera and Hymenoptera).

The wave forms of 'slow' and 'fast' eyes do not appear so radically different in the records of most workers as they do in the records of Autrum, Hassenstein, and Kirschfeld. Whereas the on- and off-effects are the prominent features of the 'fast' eye as described and the slow negative potential is negligible, the reverse is generally true in records from other laboratories. Autrum has maintained that carefully handled, fresh preparations are required to give reliable ERGs, and both Hassenstein (1957) and Naka and Kuwabara (1959) have shown that the ERGs of flies become monophasic as the preparation ages (about three hours). In all of the earlier work the preparations were intentionally allowed to stand for approximately three hours in the dark to stabilize. On the other hand, it is clear from all records that the ERGs of Diptera and Hymenoptera are more complicated than those of Orthoptera. Autrum (1950) suggested that those of Lepidoptera, with their small *a* waves, may represent an intermediate form.

According to Autrum, there are fundamental physiological differences, other than wave form, between 'slow' and 'fast' eyes. The 'slow' ERG increases in magnitude with increase in stimulus intensity, it changes markedly with light and dark adaptation, it responds poorly to flickering light. Above frequencies of forty–fifty flashes per second it fails to follow the stimulus. For stimuli of durations up to about 0·08 seconds, the magnitude of response is related to energy (intensity × time). The 'fast' ERG increases in magnitude with an increase of stimulus intensity, it is unaffected by light and dark adaptation, its absolute sensitivity is less than that of 'slow' eyes (*Tachycines* is approximately 140 times more sensitive than *Calliphora*), it follows flicker up to about 300 flashes per second, the rate depending upon stimulus intensity and temperature. The on-effect for all stimuli longer than 5 msec. is dependent only upon intensity; the off-effect in the range 5–200 msec. is dependent upon the total energy (i.e., intensity × time). Ruck (1958 a, 1958 b), on the other hand, maintained that 'slow' and 'fast' eyes differ only in their flicker fusion frequency and that the wave form of the ERG, absolute sensitivity, and rate of dark adaptation are independent visual functions not necessarily related to each other, to the flicker fusion frequency, or to the form of the ERG. In contesting these conclusions, Autrum and Hoffmann (1960) demonstrated that subjecting the eye of *Calliphora* to oxygen lack (0·1 per cent O_2 plus 99·9 per cent N_2) caused the ERG to revert to a monophasic negative type until reoxygenated. The flicker fusion frequency of this negative ERG drops to 60 per second; it is very sensitive to light adaptation. It was also pointed out that damage to the eye and long use of preparations leads to the conversion of the diphasic potential into a slow monophasic potential. The observations of Hassenstein (1957) and Naka and Kuwabara (1959) confirm this. It is noteworthy that in practically all of the work reported prior to 1948 preparations were held for a period of one to four hours in the dark in order to stabilize.

The shape of even the simple 'slow' type ERG has suggested to all workers that it is the summation of several components. Even the ERG of *Limulus*, the simplest of them all, is now believed to be dual

(Wulff, 1950). Hartline (1928) considered that there were two negative waves in the ERGs of insects (his A and B). Bernhard (1942) also believed that in *Dytiscus* the ERG is made up of two negative waves, a slow (S) and a rapid (R). In the dark-adapted state and at low intensities R predominates; in the light-adapted state and high intensities, S. He believed that R represents receptor activity and S is in some way related to adaptation. Jahn and Wulff (1942) believed that the ERGs of the grasshoppers *Trimerotropis citrina* and *T. maritima* represent the sum of a positive and a negative wave. Taylor and Crescitelli (1944) also assumed two components of opposite sign in the ERG of *Dissosteira*, but did not completely abandon the idea that the negative component itself might in fact consist of two waves. In *Galleria* the *a* wave of the ERG was considered by Taylor and Nickerson (1943) to result from the interaction of two components. For the more complicated, i.e., the 'fast' type ERG, Autrum (1950) considered that the negative off-effect is the homologue of the R component of the 'slow' type ERG and that the R component is a constant feature of all ERGs.

The compound nature of ERGs suggested that different components have different origins. Roeder (1940) had found that extirpation of the optic ganglion of *Melanoplus* did not abolish the slow wave of negativity characteristic of the ERG. For *Dytiscus*, neither removal of the ganglion nor its cocainization altered the ERG other than to remove the small spikes (nerve action potentials) that had been superimposed on the slow wave (Bernhard, 1942). This smooth monophasic wave is identical to that recorded when the electrodes are placed on the outer and inner surfaces of the retina, and its size decreases as the leads are removed proximally away from the retina. In some cases Bernhard was able to record from a cornea from which the basement membrane and all structures below it had been removed. In these cases the usual large negative wave was obtained. This is clear evidence, at least for *Dytiscus*, that the negative potential originates in the retinal cells and not in the giant monopolar cells. Working with *Trimerotropis*, Jahn and Wulff (1942) compared the ERGs of normal and deganglionated eyes and concluded that the retina contributes a negative component and the optic ganglion, a positive component.

The origin of some of the components in 'fast' eyes has been elucidated by two very ingenious experiments of Autrum and Gallwitz (1951). Successive portions of the optic ganglia of *Calliphora* were removed and the ERGs recorded. As more and more of the ganglionic mass (medulla interna and medulla externa) was extirpated, the negativity of the ERG increased. When the medulla interna, medulla externa, and all or part of the lamina ganglionaris were removed the ERG became a negative monophasic curve resembling that of *Limulus* (Fig. 86).

In the dragonfly *Aeschna cyanea* the optic ganglia of the young nymph are remote from the retinal layer. As the nymph develops, the distance between the ganglia and the retina decreases, until in the adult eye the usual situation obtains (Fig. 87) (Viallanes, 1884). The ERGs of nymph and adult are distinct – that of the nymph is

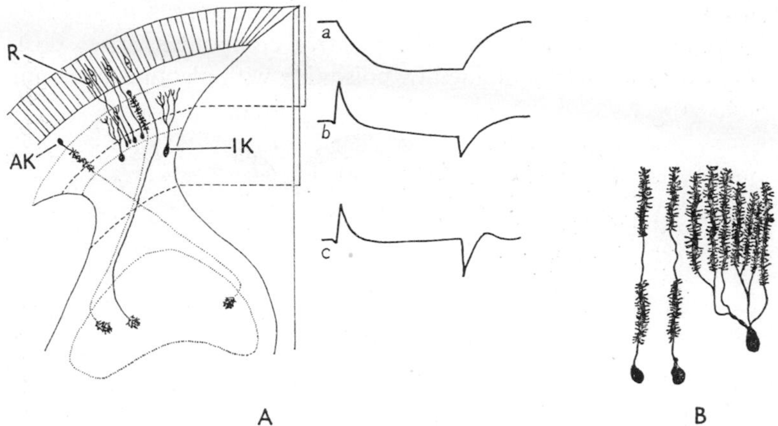

FIG. 86. A. Simplified scheme of the optic lobe of *Calliphora*. AK, centripetal cells; IK, centrifugal cells; R, retinal cells; a, ERG from isolated retina; b, ERG from retina plus lamina ganglionaris; c, ERG from intact lobe. B. Detail of centrifugal cells. (Redrawn from Autrum, 1959 after Cajal and Sanchez, 1915.)

the 'slow' type, that of the adult, the 'fast' type. The ERG of the deganglionated retina of the adult is the 'slow' type.

As a result of these experiments, Autrum (1958) has concluded that there is a negative component of the ERG of all insects assignable to the retina; it is the receptor potential. He has pointed out that in *Calliphora* under certain conditions (e.g., green or blue light) the positive on-wave is preceded by a negative deflexion. This negative wave, assignable to the retinal cells, triggers a positive electrical response in the centrifugal cells of the lamina ganglionaris. This positive wave is considered to be of great importance in connexion with adaptation. Dark adaptation has been measured for intact insects (e.g., the honeybee) by behavioural criteria, such as optomotor responses, and has been found to require up to thirty-five minutes for completion (Wolf and Zerrahn-Wolf, 1935 a). In the intact eye of *Calliphora*, as measured electrophysiologically, it has been found to require from minutes to hours. In the isolated retina, however, adaptation is complete within fractions of a second. It is proposed (Autrum, 1950, 1952, 1958) that the positive potential from the centrifugal cells acts as a 'bucking potential' preventing sustained depolarization of the retinal cells. As a corollary of this, resolution of faster rates of flicker becomes possible. When the ganglia are removed the resulting monophasic ERG is unable to follow flicker at the same high rates as the intact eyes.

Support for the idea that the positive component arises post-synaptically has been obtained by poisoning with nicotine, a specific

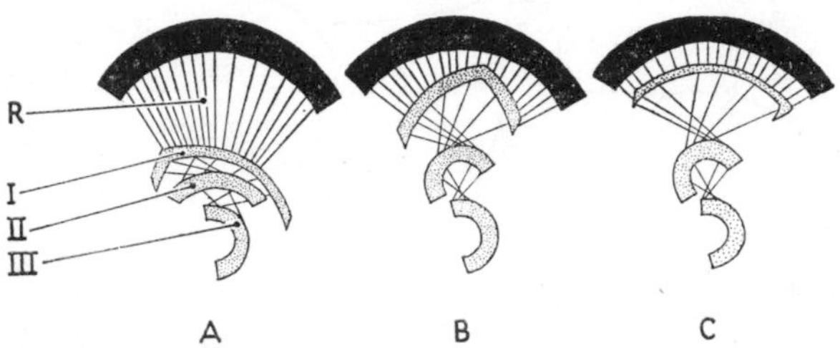

FIG. 87. Position of the retina (R) in relation to the optic lobe (I, II, III) in the developing dragonfly. A, young larva; B, older larva; C, imago. (Redrawn from Autrum, 1958 after Viallanes, 1884.)

synaptic poison. This treatment abolishes the positive components of 'fast' ERGs, leaving the negative portions unchanged, and has no influence on 'slow' ERGs, as in *Dixippus* (Autrum, 1958).

Ruck (1958 a, 1958 b) has not been able to confirm the relation between wave form of the ERG, flicker, and adaptation in the eyes of *Apis mellifera*, the dragonfly *Pachydiplax longipennis*, and *Phormia regina*. He suggested that the lowering of flicker fusion frequency in Autrum's experiments is due to injury and that actually the flicker fusion characteristics of an eye are determined by the retinal elements themselves.

Other ideas on the subject of ERG components include Hassenstein's (1957) analysis of the ERG of *Sarcophaga* and *Eristalis* into a diphasic component and a negative component and Naka's and Kuwabara's (1959) conclusion that the ERG of *Lucilia* is composed of a negative and a positive component, both of which originate in the receptor layer. Burtt and Catton (1958), on the basis of an observed reversal of polarity of potentials (also noted by Naka and Kuwabara) at a critical depth in the eye (retina plus optic lobes) corresponding to the superficial part of the lamina ganglionaris, concluded that cells in this layer, probably the giant monopolar cells, are the source of the major part of the potential observed when the eye is illuminated. This conclusion is in disagreement with the results of Bernhard (1942) from *Dytiscus*, and has been criticized by Autrum (1958) as representing pecularities of the recording technique. Ruck (1957) has argued that an interpretation of these data in a manner consistent with the distribution of current in a volume conductor would in fact localize the site of the origin of the ERG to the ommatidia.

Still another electrical phenomenon observed in the optic tract of insects is rhythmic spontaneous activity first found in *Dytiscus* (Adrian, 1937) and subsequently in all eyes in which it was sought (Roeder, 1939, 1940; Crescitelli and Jahn, 1942; Jahn and Wulff, 1942; Bernhard, 1942; Massera, 1952; Autrum, 1951, 1952; Burkhardt, 1954; Burtt and Catton, 1958). It is clearly of ganglionic origin, since extirpation of the optic ganglion abolishes it (Roeder, 1940; Burkhardt, 1954). 'Fast' eyes produce faster rhythms than 'slow' eyes (Autrum, 1951, 1952; Burtt and Catton, 1958). In *Dytiscus* there are differences between the day and night eye, the former having a higher flicker fusion frequency than the latter; furthermore, the dark-adapted night eye is more than 1,000 times more sensitive than the dark-adapted eye, and the light-adapted day eye more sensitive than the light-adapted night eye (Jahn and Wulff, 1941). The differences are unrelated to pigment migration in the eye. In *Dytiscus* there are actually two rhythms: a dark rhythm and a bright (fast) rhythm. The latter occurs only under maximum illumination, and was visualized by Adrian (1937) as representing firing of all neurons. By contrast, rhythms in butterflies and grasshoppers are found under any intermediate conditions (Crescitelli and Jahn, 1942). They occur at high temperatures as an after-discharge to a single flash of light and also as a result of repetitive stimulation. The dark rhythm in *Dytiscus* was explained by Adrian (1937) as the resting potential of all neurons in the system being favoured by injury. In *Mantis religiosa* and *Romalea microptera* there is also a light and a dark rhythm (Roeder, 1939, 1940). The light rhythm is somewhat similar to that found in *Dytiscus* and unlike that described by Crescitelli and Jahn (1942). Burkhardt (1954) has localized the bright rhythm as originating in the medulla externa. This rhythmic excitation is related to the stimulus in its amplitude but not in its frequency. The frequency lies between 100 and 250 per second. The amplitude is related to the number of illuminated ommatidia, the light intensity, and the state of adaptation of the eye. As illumination continues the amplitude gradually decreases. If illumination is interrupted before the amplitude has dropped to zero the rhythm is abruptly terminated. The likelihood is great that these rhythms are an important link in the causal chain of central processes which occur when an eye is illuminated.

One conclusion that can be drawn with certainty from all of the electrical data obtained from the compound eye is that the ERG, even in its simplest form, is the algebraic sum of potentials originating at a number of loci. Some of these loci are non-retinal; nevertheless, it is now doubtful that even retinal potentials are as simple as once believed (cf. Wulff, 1950). The most elegant approach to the whole problem has been made in *Limulus*. As the classical work of Hartline (1928) showed, this is a rather simple monophasic cornea-negative wave. When a micro-electrode is placed intracellularly in an ommatidium in the dark (Hartline, Wagner, and MacNichol, 1952; MacNichol, Wagner, and Hartline, 1953) there is a resting potential, negative at the recording electrode, of about 50 mV. When the ommatidium is stimulated there is a change in the positive direction (with intracellular recording the recording electrode goes positive when the cell is depolarized). Superimposed on this slow wave are spikes that are related linearly to the magnitude of depolarization. These spikes are synchronized with spikes recorded simultaneously from the axons of the ommatidium. Curiously enough, the only cell in the ommatidium which appears to be active is the eccentric cell; the others invariably are electrically silent. There is little doubt that the slow negative wave characterizing the ERG of the *Limulus* eye is the generator potential (and probably also the receptor potential) giving rise to the action potential in the nerves. There are now two reports of similar recordings having been made in insects. Burkhardt and Wendler (1960) have recorded with intracellular electrodes the ERG from individual retinal cells of *Calliphora*. The ERG is a simple negative monophasic wave nearly identical in appearance to that of *Limulus*. Naka and Eguchi (1962) have made similar recordings from the drone honeybee (see also Ishikawa, 1962).

Many attempts have been made to deduce from ERGs some of the characteristics of the photoreceptors themselves, but as the previous discussion has indicated, the ERGs have been much too complicated and too poorly understood to have contributed greatly to this end. Such attempts have been made by Wulff (1943) and Wulff and Jahn

(1943) and vigorously criticized by Granit (1947). More recently Autrum (1953, 1958) has proposed a hypothesis which can be summarized as follows: Light is absorbed by a photosensitive substance, as a result of which the substance is altered and stimulates the retinal cells. In 'slow' eyes it decomposes, and the photosensitive substance is regenerated. Since these processes require time, adaptation is slow. In 'fast' eyes, however, decomposition and regeneration is blocked during illumination, but when illumination ceases the process proceeds very rapidly. In other words, adaptation is very rapid. The blocking is accomplished by the positive potential from the centrifugal cells. This is a very high potential (20 mV as compared with 1 mV in the frog).

Wulff and his associates (Wulff, Fry, and Linde, 1955; Fry, Wulff, and Brust, 1955) have made a different analysis. Following illumination of the eye there is always a latency before the first wave of the ERG arises. It is assumed that this is the period required for photolysis to initiate the retinal action potential. The coupling processes connecting these two events is obscure. According to the hypothesis of Wulff *et al.*, there are two processes involved in the sense cells: an electrical process generating the retinal action potential and an *auto*-catalytic rate process which controls the latent period. Light acting on a photosensitive substance generates another substance (C) whose concentration manifests itself as a retinal e.m.f. C is presumed to be generated at a rate proportional to the intensity of light. The retinal e.m.f. is proportional to log conc. C. The latency for a flash of light is a linear function of log I over most of the intensity range tested and is relatively insensitive to time. Wulff *et al.* suggested that the failure of 'slow' eyes to obey the Bunsen–Roscoe law after 30 msec. may be attributed to decay of an electrically active substance rather than to a recovery process as Autrum (1950) suggested.

COLOUR VISION

From the observations of Plateau (1888) to the present time there have been literally hundreds of recorded observations about insects showing preferences for one colour or another. Consequently, there is not the slightest doubt that insects can distinguish among the various coloured objects in nature and that their eyes are sensitive to wavelengths from about 253 mμ (the near ultra-violet) to about 700 mμ (the infra-red). Lubbock (1886) had shown that ants were less apt to move their pupae out of sunlight from which the ultra-violet had been filtered than out of normal sunlight. At the opposite end of the spectrum Buck (1937) had observed that the firefly *Photinus pyralis* could respond to red flashes (approximately 560–690 mμ) emitted by other individuals. What has not always been clear is whether or not the eye is equally sensitive to all wavelengths and can distinguish one wavelength from another when the energies of the various coloured lights are equalized; in other words, whether insects possess colour vision.

A large number of experiments designed to provide information on these points have been undertaken. They fall into two categories: behavioural and electrophysiological. In both instances some selected response is measured at different wavelengths of light whose spectral purity and intensity had been controlled with various degrees of rigor. In so far as response to different wavelengths is concerned, the results of the majority of tests, regardless of their sophistication, agree in a general way in showing that insects as a class are especially sensitive to ultra-violet and to blue-green light (Fig. 88).

Behavioural experiments have been based on phototactic responses (Peterson and Haeussler, 1928; Bertholf, 1931 a, 1931 b; Sander, 1932, 1933; Cameron, 1938; Weiss, Soraci, and McCoy, 1941, 1942, 1943; Weiss, 1943 a, 1943 b, 1944, 1946; Weiss, McCoy, and Boyd, 1944; Milne and Milne, 1945; Fingerman, 1952; Fingerman and Brown, 1953; Wolken, 1957; Wolken, Mellon, and Contis, 1957; Heintz, 1959; Goldsmith, 1960), optomotor responses (Schlegtendal, 1934; Rokohl, 1942; Moller-Racke, 1952; Autrum and Stumpf, 1953; Schöne, 1953; Resch, 1954; Schneider, 1956), training (von Frisch, 1914; Koehler, 1924; Kühn, 1927; Kühn and Pohl, 1921; Bertholf, 1931 a; Ilse, 1949; Kuwabara, 1957; Hertz, 1939; Daumer, 1956, 1958), and simple observation (Lubbock, 1886; Hamilton, 1922; Ilse, 1928, 1937, 1949; Buck, 1937). Phototactic responses have been employed exclusively for studying spectral sensitivity, while other behavioural techniques have been employed in the search for evidence of colour vision.

The relative efficiency of different wavelengths in eliciting phototactic responses has been measured for a number of species. Bertholf presented to *Drosophila* and *Apis* two sources of light, one of which was the test wavelength and the other, a white standard. In one series of tests the intensity of the test colour was kept constant and that of the standard varied until both sources were equally attractive. In another series of tests each coloured light was matched with a white light of fixed intensity. After the ratio of attractiveness had been found a white

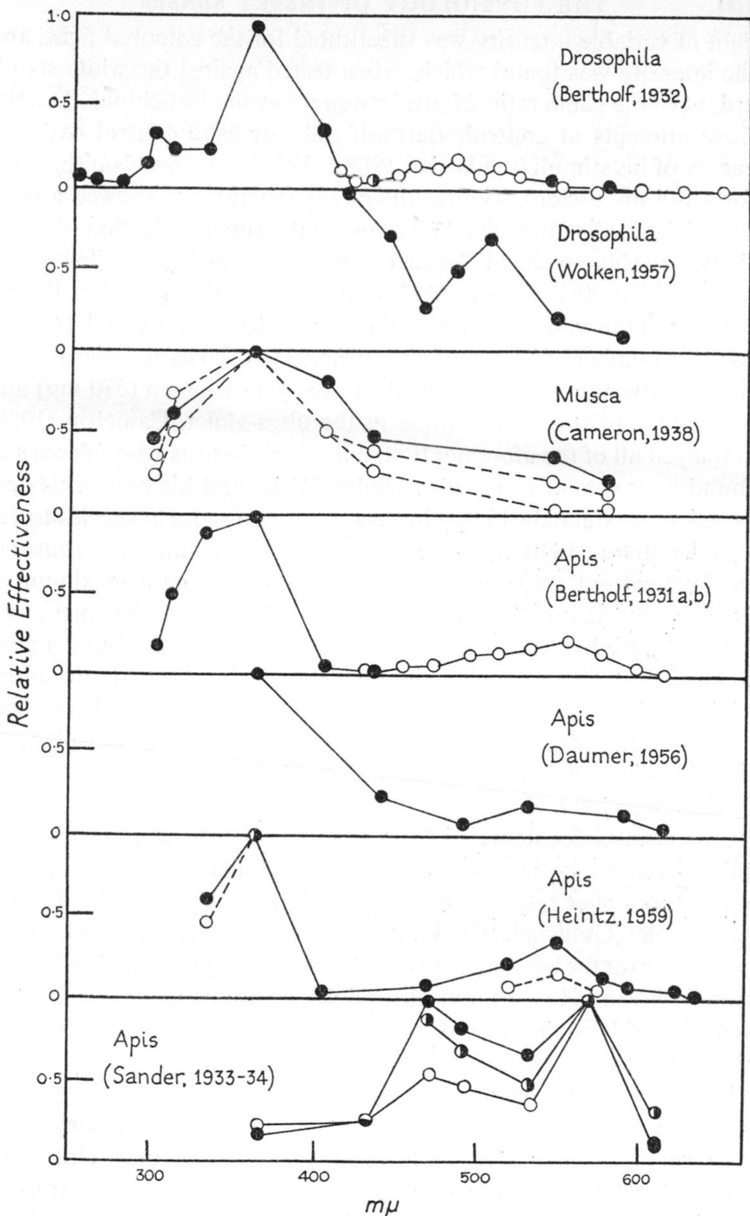

FIG. 88. Relative effectiveness of different wavelengths of light in evoking positive phototaxis and similar responses of adult insects. In each case, open circles indicate one set of experiments and the closed circles, another. (Redrawn from Goldsmith, 1961.)

light of variable intensity was substituted for the coloured light, and the intensity was found which, when tested against the white standard, gave the same ratio of attractiveness as the test colour. Despite these attempts at control, Bertholf did not have control over the energy of his stimuli (see Weiss, 1943 a, 1943 b, and Goldsmith, 1961, for a full discussion). The results of his experiments showed a peak sensitivity in the ultra-violet (365 mμ) and a slight indication of sensitivity in the blue-green (487 mμ) for *Drosophila* and in the yellow-green (553 mμ) for *Apis*. Sander (1933) adjusted his lights so that the intensities of the white standard and the test colours were equal. He then used the number of insects (*Apis*) attracted to each as an index of relative effectiveness and found peaks in the yellow-green (570 mμ) and in the blue (470 mμ), but none in the ultra-violet. Cameron (1938) employed all of the aforementioned methods in tests with *Musca* and found a maximum in the ultra-violet. Weiss and his co-workers exposed approximately 15,000 insects representing forty species to ten wavelengths of light of equal intensities. The composite group behaviour pattern consisted of a peak at 492 mμ and a maximum at 365 mμ. Wolken determined for *Drosophila* the relative energy required to produce a constant phototactic response and found a peak in the blue-green and a maximum commencing towards the ultra-violet. Heintz measured, as a function of intensity, the number of bees that crawled per unit time over a slit in a box illuminated by different wavelengths and found a small peak in the green and the maximum in the ultra-violet. He suggested that Sander's failure to detect a peak in the ultra-violet stemmed from the very high light intensities employed. Since these intensities elicited maximum responses in the blue-green, no higher response could possibly have been obtained in the ultra-violet. Goldsmith (1960), perturbed by Sander's failure to find a maximum for the bee in the ultra-violet, tested the phottoactic effectiveness of green (546 mμ) and ultra-violet (365 mμ) lights of equal intensities and did find a peak at 365 mμ. In short, whether the curves describing the relative effectiveness of different wavelengths in eliciting phototactic responses are true action spectra (relative energy for a constant effect) or not, all show that the most effective part of the spectrum for *Musca*, *Apis*, and *Drosophila* is the near ultra-violet and, to a lesser degree, the blue-green. This finding has been confirmed in whole or in part for so many species by Weiss and his associates that it is probably of general occurrence.

The danger, of course, in interpreting these behavioural tests without caution as indicative of spectral sensitivity is that the response of an insect to specific wavelengths may vary with the physiological state. Ilse (1928) has observed, for example, that cabbage butterflies (*Pieris brassicae*) normally land preferentially on blue or yellow flowers or paper models of the same colours, while gravid females ready to oviposit shift their preference to green and blue-green (1937). On the other hand, electrophysiological studies have confirmed the more general behavioural findings (Crescitelli and Jahn, 1939; Jahn and Crescitelli, 1939; Jahn, 1946; Jahn and Wulff, 1948; Donner and Kriszat, 1950; Autrum and Stumpf, 1953; Goldsmith, 1958 a, 1958 b; Goldsmith and Ruck, 1958; Walther, 1958 a, 1958 b; Walther and Dodt, 1957, 1959). Spectral sensitivity curves were obtained in these cases by relating the magnitude of some selected components of the ERG to the wavelength of light or, more accurately, by plotting some function of the quanta necessary to produce a given response against wavelength. For the moth *Samia cecropia* (Crescitelli and Jahn, 1939) and the grasshopper *Melanoplus differentialis* (Jahn and Crescitelli, 1939) the greatest sensitivity, exclusive of ultra-violet, which was not tested, is in the blue-green (from about 460–530 mμ). The curve for night and day eyes of *Dytiscus fasciventris* also shows a maximum in the blue-green (about 520–575 mμ). It is based upon the magnitude of the *a* wave. This was plotted against intensity. From the family of curves (one for each colour) obtained, a constant response magnitude was selected and plotted against wavelength (Jahn and Wulff, 1948). Curves for *Musca domestica, Lucilia caesar, Calliphora vomitoria, Pollenia rudis*, and *Drosophila melanogaster* based upon measurements of the on-effect of the ERG at wavelengths of equivalent quantum intensity show maxima in the green and in the near ultra-violet (Donner and Kriszat, 1950).

A spectral effectiveness curve for *Calliphora erythrocephala* shows a peak at 540 mμ (blue-green) and one at 630 mμ (red) (Autrum and Stumpf, 1953) (Fig. 89). This curve is based on the amplitude of the on-effect of the ERG, or the height of the flicker potential occurring as a reaction to twenty-seven flashes, produced by stimulation by light of different wavelengths but equal quantal value. No tests were made with ultra-violet, but the rising curve at the shorter wavelength suggested ultra-violet sensitivity. This expectation was realized in tests subsequently conducted by Walther (1957) and Walther and Dodt (1957, 1959). A spectral sensitivity curve (reciprocal of the quanta necessary to generate a constant magnitude of on-effect plotted as a percentage of the maximum of 507 mμ against the wavelength) for *Calliphora* shows maxima in the red (about 630 mμ), the blue-green

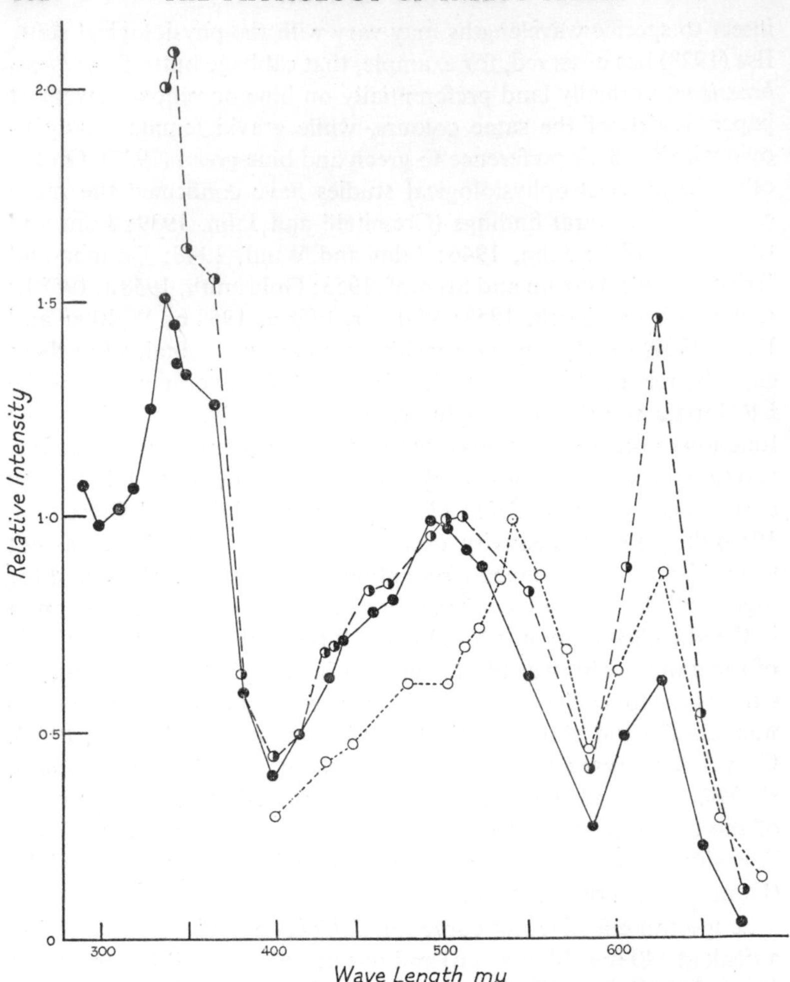

FIG. 89. The spectral sensitivity of the compound eye of *Calliphora*. Data from Autrum and Stumpf (1952) (open circles), Walther and Dodt (1957) (half-filled circles), and Walther and Dodt (1959) (solid circles). (Drawn from Goldsmith, 1961.)

(540 mμ), and the ultra-violet (341–369 mμ). The curve for *Periplaneta* is similar, but lacks the peak in the red.

A spectral sensitivity curve for the drone honeybee shows a maximum at 400 mμ for the compound eye and maxima at 335–340 mμ and 490 mμ for the median ocellus (Goldsmith, 1958 a, 1958 b; Goldsmith and Ruck, 1958). The dorsal ocelli of the cockroaches *Periplaneta americana* and *Blaberus craniifer* show a peak at 500 mμ (Goldsmith and Ruck, 1958).

One of the more interesting aspects of all of these descriptions of spectral sensitivity is the great stimulating effectiveness of the near ultra-violet. Hess (1920) had questioned the sensitivity of the insect retina to ultra-violet and suggested the possibility of stimulation actually occurring as a result of fluorescence set up in various tissues of the eye. Fluorescence may occur (Walther and Dodt, 1959), but Merker (1929) and Lutz and Grisewood (1934) showed that crushed eyes of *Drosophila* did not fluoresce in ultra-violet of the wavelength to which flies respond. They showed, furthermore, that the cornea of *Apis* and *Sarcophaga* can transmit in the 253-mμ band of the spectrum. Additional reasons for rejecting Hess's hypothesis are mentioned by Walther and Dodt (1959) and discussed by Goldsmith (1961).

Taken at face value, the spectral sensitivity data indicate what may constitute brilliance for an insect, and a number of studies bear this out wholly or in part (Moller-Racke, 1952, with *Dytiscus*, but compare Schöne, 1953; Rokohl, 1942; Lüdtke, 1953, and Resch, 1954, with *Notonecta*). Demonstration of true colour vision has been technically more difficult. There is now evidence for colour vision in thirty-three genera of insects in six orders. The evidence has been derived principally from training experiments, optomotor responses, and electrophysiological analyses.

Von Frisch (1914) trained honeybees to collect food from a dish placed on a card of a particular colour. This card was then placed in one square of a checkerboard of greys (white to black) of different intensities. The position of the coloured card was changed constantly. Under these conditions the bees could always pick out a blue or yellow card from the checkerboard of greys. Thus, it was demonstrated that bees conditioned to blue confused blue-violet and purple, while those conditioned to yellow confused yellow, orange, and yellow-green. None could distinguish red. Later tests of the papers used by von Frisch showed that some of the blues and greens reflected ultra-violet, whereas some of the yellows and greens reflected red and blue (Lutz, 1924). Similar experiments employing spectral colours projected on a white background demonstrated that bees could distinguish four regions of the spectrum: yellow-green and orange (510–650 mμ), blue-green (480–500 mμ), blue and violet (400–480 mμ), and the near ultra-violet (300–400 mμ) (Kühn and Pohl, 1921; Kühn, 1927). These results were confirmed by the training experiments of

Kuwabara (1957) and of Daumer (1956, 1958), who also demonstrated that bees can even discriminate between wavelengths within these bands, but with less precision.

Colour vision can also be investigated by colour-matching tests. Daumer (1956, 1958) applied these with outstanding success to honeybees by training them to come to a particular colour. The training colour was then paired with a colour produced by mixing wavelengths. Various mixtures were tested until one was found which was as acceptable to the bees as the training colour. For example, bees can distinguish between white light containing ultra-violet and that lacking ultra-violet. White light with ultra-violet ('bee white') can be matched by a mixture of 15 per cent ultra-violet (360 mμ) and 85 per cent blue-green (490 mμ). The complementariness of ultra-violet and blue-green had already been suggested by Hertz (1939), and Ilse (1937) had shown that purple adjacent to white sets up a green colour contrast in the white. Similarly, 'bee purple' can be matched by mixtures of yellow and ultra-violet. Goldsmith (1961) has summarized Daumer's results in a preliminary chromaticity diagram which is explained in Fig. 90.

From the results of all of his matching experiments, Daumer concluded that the eye of the honeybee possesses a receptor maximally sensitive to ultra-violet, one for blue-violet, and one for green-yellow. The existence of two of these has been confirmed by the electrophysiological analyses of Goldsmith (1958 a, 1958 b, 1959, 1961). The wave form of the ERG in the early studies with grasshoppers and *Dytiscus* had shown no change as the wavelength of the stimulus was changed, provided the intensities were matched (Crescitelli and Jahn, 1939; Jahn, 1946; Jahn and Wulff, 1948). On the other hand, as Walther (1958 a) found in the cockroach eye, there are some areas of the eye where differences in the form of the ERG arising from differences in the colour of the stimulus cannot be matched by adjusting intensity. Goldsmith and Ruck (1958) also found that the ERG of the ocellus of the bee had at low stimulus intensities a different contour for ultra-violet than for green.

By adapting with lights of different wavelengths it is possible to demonstrate the existence of different receptors (Hamilton, 1922; Fingerman and Brown, 1953). The dark-adapted eye of the worker honeybee shows a peak of sensitivity in the green (535 mμ) and a smaller peak in the ultra-violet (Goldsmith, 1960). If the eye is adapted with red or yellow light the peak at 535 mμ diminishes and the peak at 340–345 mμ increases (Fig. 91). The complementary experi-

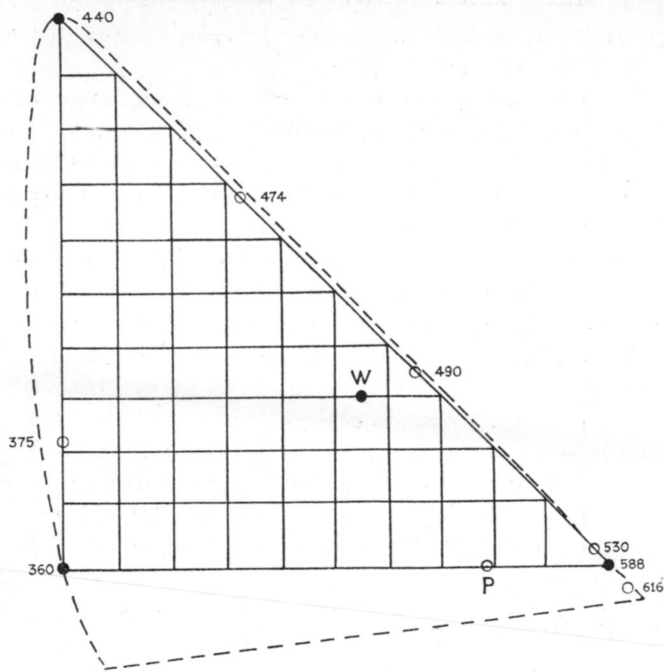

FIG. 90. Tentative chromaticity diagram for the honeybee based on the work of Daumer (1956). The behavioural experiments of Daumer led to the prediction that any colour can be matched for bees by an appropriate mixture of three monochromatic reference stimuli, e.g., ultraviolet (360 mμ), blue-violet (440 mμ), and yellow (588 mμ). Any light, therefore, can be represented in Fig. 90 by a point; for example, 'W' is the white of the xenon emission spectrum. The proportions, in fractions of the total energy – the chromaticity co-ordinates – of the yellow and blue reference stimuli required for a colourimetric match of the light represented by the point are given by the co-ordinates of the point, 588 mμ on the abscissa and 440 mμ on the ordinate. Since the sum of the three chromaticity co-ordinates is 1, the fraction of the energy at 360 mμ can be calculated by difference. The locus of the spectrum is given by the experimental points; however, as is suggested by the dashed line, it may actually lie somewhat outside the triangle, for it is questionable whether this kind of experiment is sufficiently precise to reveal the necessity for small negative values of one of the chromaticity co-ordinates. The complementary to 360 mμ is 490 mμ, for both wavelengths lie on a straight line passing through the white point. Similarly, the point 'p' is the 'bee-purple' complementary to 440 mμ and is composed of 79 per cent 588 mμ and 21 per cent 360 mμ. (Redrawn from Goldsmith, 1961.)

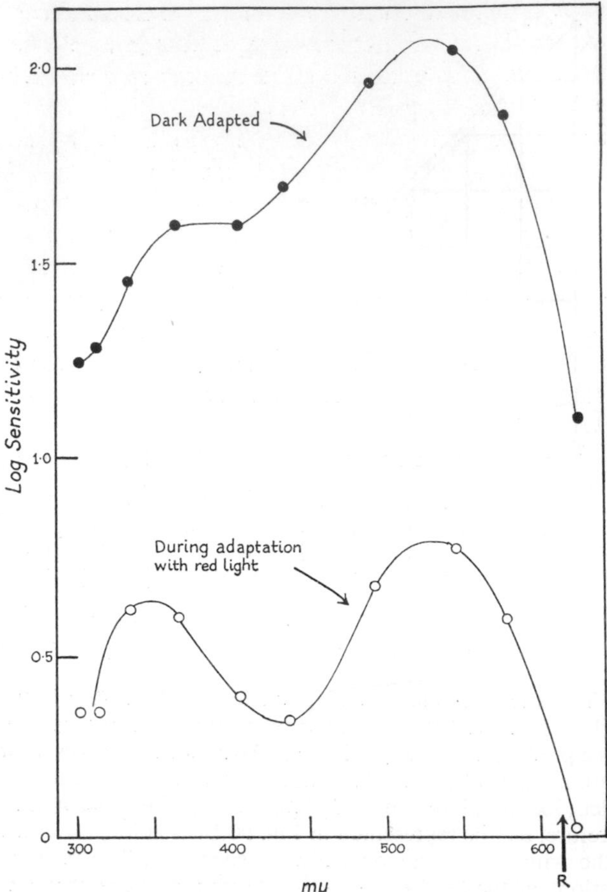

FIG. 91. Alteration of the shape of the spectral sensitivity of the worker honeybee by selective light adaptation. During a constant level of adaptation brought about by red light the ultra-violet receptor system contributes more prominently to the spectral sensitivity function (open circles) than it does in the dark-adapted eye (filled circles). Ordinate: logarithm of the reciprocal of the relative number of quanta required to produce a retinal action potential of constant size. (Redrawn from Goldsmith, 1961.)

ment is less striking because the ultra-violet receptor system contributes less to the ERG than the green system and because the sensitivities of the two systems behave differently to different coloured adapting lights. Nevertheless, these experiments confirm the existence in the bee of two of Daumer's postulated receptor types. The existence of a receptor maximally sensitive at about 440 mμ has been demonstrated in the drone (Goldsmith, 1958 b). Furthermore, Goldsmith (1958 a) has found a retinene-containing pigment with a maximum absorption in the blue-violet (440 mμ).

Studies of the cockroach eye have also revealed the existence of more than one type of receptor (Walther and Dodt, 1957, 1959; Walther, 1958 a, 1958 b). In the dorsal area of the eye the sensitivity maximum to ultra-violet is higher than that to blue-green; in the ventral part of the eye it is lower. Whereas the ventral area shows a single-peaked (507 mμ) sensitivity curve that is unaltered by the state of adaptation, the dorsal area shows indication of another peak in the ultra-violet. Adaptation with monochromatic lights changes the relative spectral sensitivities, and colour specific differences occur in the shape of the ERG.

For *Drosophila* Hamilton (1922) had produced evidence for the existence of a system sensitive to blue-violet and one sensitive to blue-green by specific wavelength adaptation. Fingerman and Brown (1953), employing a similar technique, concluded that *Drosophila* also possesses sensitivity in the red (650–675 mμ).

The blowfly *Calliphora* is unique among the insects studied in that the spectral sensitivity curve of its eye, as measured electrophysiologically, exhibits three maxima: ultra-violet, blue-green, and red (Autrum and Stumpf, 1953; Walther and Dodt, 1958 a, 1958 b). There is a discrepancy of about 30 mμ between the positions of the green maximum reported by the two papers.

In their search for evidence of colour vision, Autrum and Stumpf combined electrophysiological and flicker fusion techniques. After adjusting the intensities of two monochromatic lights they flickered them alternately. Thus during the period of stimulation there was constant intensity of illumination but flickering wavelengths. If the ERG showed with heterochromatic flicker ripple that could not be removed by adjustment of intensities, then one could conclude that the eye discriminated between the two wavelengths. The findings were as follows: In the region 690–620 mμ discrimination is slight, but this region is sharply distinguished from all other regions; yellow to blue-green (620–650 mμ) is distinguished from all other regions and discrimination in this band is sharp (a restricted region between 570 and 590 mμ cannot be distinguished from colourless light); blue-green (480 mμ) is distinguished from all other colours; on both sides of 480 mμ there is a region (450–500 mμ and 500–560 mμ) which is distinguished from all colours between 560 and 690 mμ. Autrum and

Stumpf concluded that there need be only two receptor systems to account for the data, a blue-green receptor and a red receptor. The maximum for the blue-green receptor lies between 500 and 550 mμ. Its sensitivity extends from the region of the near ultra-violet up to about 660 mμ. The maximum for the red receptor lies in the vicinity of 625 mμ. Its sensitivity extends from about 480 up to about 700 mμ. Several flies were found which were colour-blind when tested with flicker and whose spectral sensitivity curves were abnormal. The spectral sensitivity curve of one possessed the usual peak in the red but none in the blue-green. This fly possessed no colour discrimination in the region 400–500 mμ as judged by flicker. Another fly lacked the peak in the red (630 mμ) and was *totally* colour blind. This fly possessed the usual red eye-pigments in the pigment cells of the ommatidium. Later Autrum (1955 a) described the spectral sensitivity of a white-eyed mutant which lacked these pigments. Since this mutant also lacked a sensitivity peak in the red (630 mμ), Autrum concluded that the usual 630-mμ peak resulted from transmission of long wavelengths by the red shielding pigments.

Behavioural experiments conducted with a revolving drum and light of low intensities did not reveal a marked sensitivity in the red (Schneider, 1956). To reconcile the behavioural and electrophysiological results Schneider proposed that since the enveloping pigments of the ommatidia are partially transparent to red light, the ERG would be higher at red than at other wavelengths because the red would be stimulating a greater number of ommatidia. On the other hand, the failure of the screening pigments to isolate the ommatidia when the eye was illuminated with red light would lead to a loss in visual acuity and since the behaviour in a revolving drum depends upon visual acuity, it would fail to reveal a sensitivity to red. Autrum (1961) has reported, however, that even in a white-eyed mutant, which completely lacks screening pigment, the visual acuity equals that of wild-type flies.

Recently Burkhardt and Autrum (1960) have been able to record electrical events directly from single visual cells. The spectral sensitivity was determined for thirty-nine single retinal cells of the wild type of *Calliphora* and from the white-apricot mutant which lacks screening pigments (Autrum and Burkhardt, 1961). The red screening pigment does not absorb light in the region 616 mμ, and in weakly illuminated elements the amount of scattered red light is much greater than that amount of light coming through the lenses. Except in these weakly illuminated elements and in the far red, the screening pigments are not relevant to the shape of the sensitivity curves. All cells in the dorsal part of the eyes were found to have curves with a maximum at 489 mμ and one at 345 mμ. Three receptor types were found in the ventral region of the eye: a green receptor (maxima at 491 mμ and 345 mμ); a blue receptor (maxima at 468 mμ and 345 mμ); a yellow-green receptor (maxima at 524 mμ and 345 mμ). Some elements show a peak at 616 mμ. The numerical relationships among the green, blue, and yellow-green receptors is 18:4:3. This is almost the ratio to be expected if one assumed that of the seven retinula cells in an ommatidium five are green receptors, one blue, and the remaining one yellow-green. Since all have a peak at 345 mμ, corresponding to a stable position of the β-absorption in derivatives of vertebrate visual pigments, it is possible that the most common visual pigment in *Calliphora* is retinene with a maximum absorption at 490 mμ (Autrum and Burkhardt, 1961).

Some workers have been tempted to think of the insect eye as possessing analogues of rods and cones, especially since Hanström (1927) demonstrated retinal cells with short and long axons and suggested the analogy. But Wolf and Zerrahn-Wolf (1935 a), in discussing the relation between threshold intensities and time of dark adaptation for the honeybee, called attention to the fact that the curve describing this relation was, unlike that for the human eye, a smooth one. Nor do curves relating visual acuity and flicker fusion frequency to intensity exhibit any changes in slope that could be attributable to two populations of receptors of different sensitivities analogous to rods and cones (Hecht and Wolf, 1929; Wolf, 1933e; Hecht and Wald, 1934; Wolf and Zerrahn-Wolf, 1935 b). In *Drosophila*, however, Fingerman and Brown (1952, 1953) reported a 'Purkinje shift', that is, a shift of sensitivity of the eye towards shorter wavelengths as the light intensity is decreased. They interpreted this as indicating a shift from a photopic to a scotopic mechanism. According to their conclusions, *Drosophila* loses its ability to discriminate among wavelengths as intensity is lowered. No such change could be demonstrated in the cockroach (Walther, 1958 a, 1958 b), nor in the honeybee (Goldsmith, 1960, 1961). The data of Fingerman and Brown (1952, 1953) have been criticized by Goldsmith (1961). On the other hand, Weiss *et al.* (1942) reported that the order of attractiveness of 365 mμ and 470–528 mμ at low intensities was reversed at high intensities. With *Calliphora* Autrum (1955 a) found that the wavelength of maximum sensitivity was 540 mμ at high intensities but shifted to shorter wave lengths (480 mμ) as the intensity was dropped. Schneider (1955, 1956) reinvestigated this problem by comparing spectral sensitivity curves obtained in optomotor-type apparatus at high and at low intensities with the curve obtained electrophysiologically. The behaviourally determined curve obtained at low intensities showed a maximum at 480 mμ. The high-intensity curve shifted towards 540 mμ. This shift could, as Schneider pointed out, be due to the transparency of enveloping pigments to long wavelengths, but were this true, the white-eyed mutant should exhibit a maximum at 480 mμ, whereas it actually shows a maximum between 510 and 540 mμ (Autrum, 1955 a). The shift must be due to the participation of a receptor of low threshold, the 'receptor for twilight vision', whose maximum sensitivity lies at 480 mμ and a less-sensitive receptor whose maximum lies above 540 mμ (Schneider, 1956). Walther and Dodt (1957, 1959) have not reported any shift. In the back-swimmer (*Notonecta*) a shift in which red and yellow become darker to the animal with advancing dark adaptation (as measured by optomotor reactions) has been noted by Resch (1954) and Lüdtke (1953) and referred to as a 'Purkinje phenomenon'.

POLARIZED LIGHT

In 1948 von Frisch (1948, 1949) opened a new area of investigation in insect vision by demonstrating that honeybees could distinguish different quadrants of the sky in which the plane of polarization of sunlight differed. This conclusion was based on the fact that: (1) bees in the hive could orient their communication dances as long as they were able to see a patch of blue sky, and (2) the orientation of the dance could be altered by interposing a piece of polaroid between the bee and the sky. Bees act as though the sun is at right angles to the plane of polarization. Since then directional orientation in the presence of linearly polarized light has been demonstrated in many arthropods (for reviews see von Frisch and Lindauer, 1956; Waterman, 1960).

Polarized light may differ in degree, in type (linear, elliptical, or circular), or in orientation of major axis. Practically all polarized light in nature is linear (Jander and Waterman, 1960), and only this type is known to affect animals. Two basic explanations have been proposed to explain its perception. The most direct and obvious explanation is that the eye possesses a specific polarization analyser, that is, that animals see the direction of vibration of polarized light as distinct from such other characteristics as intensity and wavelength (von Frisch, 1949; von Frisch, Lindauer, and Daumer, 1960; Autrum and Stumpf, 1950; Vowles, 1950; Menzer and Stockhammer, 1951; Stockhammer, 1956, 1959; de Vries, 1956; Birukow and Busch, 1957; Jander, 1957;

Lüdtke, 1957; Jacobs-Jessen, 1959; Waterman, 1960; Jander and Waterman, 1960; and a number of investigators studying Crustacea). An alternative hypothesis suggests that differential responses to various planes of polarization of light depend only upon detection of different intensity patterns (Baylor and Smith, 1953; Stephens, Fingerman, and Brown, 1953; Bainbridge and Waterman, 1957, Baylor and Smith, 1958; Kalmus, 1958, 1959; de Vries and Kuiper, 1958; Baylor, 1959 a, 1959 b; Smith and Baylor, 1960). This later hypothesis is consonant to two basic facts: (1) differential reflection, refraction, and scattering of polarized light by environmental features or dioptric elements of the eye (Waterman, 1954) can produce quadrants of maximal and minimal intensities whose positions are determined by the direction of vibration; arthropods respond to light-intensity patterns. In further support of the hypothesis is the lack of convincing proof of the existence of a polarization analyser in the eye. No direct positive proof has been presented to contradict the opposing hypothesis.

Support for the idea that the animals do see the plane of polarization as distinct from intensity patterns has recently been summarized by Jander and Waterman (1960) in the following terms:

(1) In *Daphnia* and the beetle *Bidessus*, which could be made either positively or negatively phototactic, reversal of this sign caused a reversal of response to ordinary horizontal light intensity patterns, but had no effect on the response to the plane of polarization of a vertically directed beam. Therefore, polarized light orientation cannot be due to horizontal patterns due to scattering and reflection of polarized light.

(2) In all animals, responses to horizontal patterns of light intensity are of two sorts only, that is, towards or away, while four basic orientation directions have been observed in a vertical beam of linearly polarized light. Therefore, two different sensory mechanisms must be involved.

(3) Response to the direction of vibration of polarized light showed smaller deviations from the maximally preferred horizontal intensity patterns. Therefore, both reactions cannot be intensity responses.

(4) When the dark intensity patterns due to the scattering of polarized light are made artificially brighter, the crustacean *Mysidium*, *Daphnia*, and *Bidessus* still respond as before to the plane of polarization. Therefore response to polarized light is not simply a phototactic response to brightness.

(5) The crustacean *Mysidium* can distinguish between horizontal

light patterns and polarized light presented simultaneously by reacting to each as if it were alone. Therefore, polarized light and intensity patterns are distinct visual qualities.

(6) For *Daphnia* light contrast reaction deteriorates at low overall levels of illumination, while reactions to the plane of polarization do not.

(7) Honeybees orient at the same angle with respect to the plane of polarization under a polarizer as to that of corresponding quadrants of the blue sky, despite large differences in intensity in the two situations.

(8) 'Since bees know the regional distribution of polarized light in the sky (von Frisch, 1948, 1949), they must know the direction from which it is coming. Yet they cannot with ordinary image vision infer the direction of the original source from a light pattern established by reflection and refraction.'

(9) 'Under natural conditions reflection and refraction patterns due to polarized sky light must to a considerable extent cancel each other out because the plane of polarization is different in various parts of the sky. In addition such patterns as do arise will be confused by much more marked intensity patterns due to direct sunlight, which comprises up to 80 per cent of the total sky light, and to clouds and surface details of the earth. To claim that bees could learn sky polarization patterns from these reflection–refraction cues observed on their field trips seems highly unlikely in view of such conditions.'

(10) 'In this view, experiments with spiders (Papi, 1955; Görner, 1957), ants (Jander, 1957) and bees (Jacobs-Jessen, 1959), have shown in some instances that when the main intensity pattern is dislocated by transposing the sun 180° with a mirror, the animals nevertheless maintain their orientation direction relative to the blue sky.'

Additional evidence in support of this hypothesis is derived from the work of von Frisch (1960) and von Frisch, Lindauer, and Daumer (1960).

If insects do indeed possess a discrete polarized light vision it follows that there must be a mechanism in the eye for analysing the plane of polarization. This could be located either in the dioptric apparatus or in the retinal elements. It could depend on single refraction according to the Brewster–Fresnel law or upon double refraction. There is no convincing evidence for the existence of an analyser in the dioptric apparatus, and the proposition that analysis depends on simple reflection–refraction phenomenon at the corneal surface (Stephens *et al.*, 1953; Baylor and Smith, 1953) does not conform to a number of experimental facts. For one thing, the necessary properties would be realized only in an optically isotropic medium, and the corneal lenses of *Drosophila* are anisotropic (Stockhammer, 1959). Nor is a mechanism of double refraction present. When the dioptric apparatus is observed through a rotating polaroid no change in the pattern or intensity of transmitted light is observed (Autrum and Stumpf, 1950; de Vries and Kuiper, 1958; Stockhammer, 1959). Furthermore, analyses of the ERG have failed to support the hypothesis (Autrum and Stumpf, 1950; Baylor and Kennedy, 1958; de Vries and Kuiper, 1958).

The on-effect of the ERG is known to depend in its magnitude on the intensity of light. When the action potential resulting from the stimulation of a total of twelve–fifteen ommatidia by polarized light was measured there was no change in magnitude of response as the plane of polarization was rotated. It seems unlikely, therefore, that the eye as a whole acts as an analyser. Similar results obtained by stimulation of a single ommatidium also indicated that the single ommatidium does not act as an analyser. However, when the effects of polarized and non-polarized light of equal intensities were tested the polarized light always elicited the greater response (Autrum and Stumpf, 1950). From this it was concluded that each of the retinal cells (eight in the honeybee and seven in *Calliphora*) is maximally sensitive to light of a definite vibration direction, namely, that perpendicular to the radial direction of the cell within the ommatidium. With unpolarized light each cell receives less than maximal stimulation; with polarized light some receive maximal and some minimal. The net result in the ERG is a response of greater magnitude than to ordinary light because maximal and minimal effects do not cancel out. Thus, the unit of analyses seems to be the single retinal cell, and the central nervous system is presumed to integrate the pattern of light and dark from each ommatidium.

This hypothesis is supported by the electrophysiological work of Lüdtke (1957), Naka and Kuwabara (1959), and Burkhardt and Wendler (1960), as well as by field experiments of von Frisch (1950 a, 1950 b).

Von Frisch (1950 a, 1950 b) provided support for the hypothesis by comparing the actions of bees dancing under a polaroid material with the changes observed in the light-intensity pattern of the sky when viewed through an artificial ommatidium constructed of eight segments of polaroid material each oriented differently. When this model was held up to the blue sky a different pattern of intensity was seen for every part of the sky, depending on the position of the sun. When a sheet of polaroid was placed between the model and the sky in such an orientation as not to alter the pattern and another sheet was placed similarly over dancing bees the dances maintained proper orientation. When the covering sheets were rotated until that over the model altered the pattern the orientation of the dance changed. The artificial pattern produced in the model could usually be found in another part of the sky, and it was to this direction that the bees danced. When the pattern produced by interposing the polaroid between the model and the sky happened to have no normal counterpart in the sky the dance of the bees under the same polaroid became disorganized. If the pattern as seen through the model happened to occur simultaneously in two areas of the sky the bees also oriented their dances in two directions.

In so far as electrophysiological evidence is concerned not all workers have been able to confirm the findings of Autrum and Stumpf. Baylor and Kennedy (1958), employing especially refined control of intensity and wavelength, were unable to detect any difference in the ERG related to the presence or absence of polarization. Nor were de Vries and Kuiper (1958) able to detect changes in the ERG when the eye was subjected to flicker consisting alternately of vertically and horizontally polarized light. The insects themselves failed to show optomotor reactions in these circumstances. These results not only challenge the proposition that analysers are located in the retinal cells but also question even the ability of the eye to possess any analyser at all.

Contrary to these findings is the report of Burkhardt and Wendler (1960). By measuring the ERG of individual retinal cells of *Calliphora* with intracellular electrodes and controlling for adventitious polarization of oblique incident light at the corneal and crystalline cone boundaries, these workers were able to show that the amplitude of the ERG is dependent upon light intensity and the direction of vibration of linearly polarized light. A rotation of the plane of polarization from the most-effective position to the least-effective position changes the illumination potential of the cell quantitatively to the same degree as a 50 per cent reduction of light intensity.

If the retinal cells are indeed analysers it should be possible to find within them the necessary structural modification. Menzer and Stockhammer (1951) proposed that birefringence in the rhabdoms coupled with a mechanism for extinguishing one ray provided means of analysis. They suggested: (1) that the rhabdomeres consists of a doubly refracting central column and a surrounding cylinder of different refractive index, and (2) that the optical axis of each of the retinal cells is different. They reported that there was birefringence in the rhabdoms and that between crossed polarizers each rhabdomere extinguishes about four times during one complete rotation. Many objections to this hypothesis were raised by de Vries (1956), who also pointed out that the report of birefringence was based upon examinations of fixed material and that fresh material showed at best too little birefringence (less than 1 per cent) to meet the requirements of the hypothesis (de Vries, 1956; de Vries, Spoor, and Jielof, 1953; de Vries and Kuiper, 1958).

An alternative hypothesis to the effect that analysis is accomplished by means of dichroic molecules was advanced by de Vries (1956). Organic molecules tend to absorb light polarized in the direction of the long axis of the molecules. If all of the photosensitive molecules of a sense cell are arranged in parallel and different sense cells are oriented differently the visual organ possesses the necessary mechanism for analysing polarized light. Indeed, this mechanism works to a minor extent in the human eye, which can detect the polarization of light by Haidinger brushes. These are seen as a yellow shape (figure of eight) and are due to orientation (about 50 per cent) of the molecules of the yellow macular pigment. Nobody, however, has been able to demonstrate dichroism in the insect eye, even though evidence from electron-microscopy proves that the microvilli of each pair of rhabdomeres are oriented in a different horizontal direction and the visual pigment is presumed to be in the microvilli. De Vries (1956) concluded that if dichroism is present it must be less than 10 per cent; nevertheless, he did not consider that this negative finding disproved his hypothesis. Later, however, he concluded that the oriented structure of the rhabdomeres has nothing to do with the detection of polarized light and that insects do not 'see' polarization (de Vries and Kuiper, 1958). He and his co-worker were influenced in drawing these conclusions by failure to detect analysers and by the experiments of Baylor and Smith (1953, 1957). Stockhammer (1959), in discussing the dichroism hypothesis, advanced a number of arguments from structure which support the idea.

Baylor and Smith (1953, 1957) proposed that the responses of animals to the plane of polarization of light is in fact a response to a non-uniform distribution of intensities in the pattern of light reflected from a substratum (in the case of terrestrial animals) or scattered by various particles in water (Baylor, 1959 a, 1959 b; Smith and Baylor, 1960; Kalmus, 1958, 1959; Bainbridge and Waterman, 1957). Some of the evidence upon which this view is based has already been given. Additionally, it is claimed that the ability of insects to respond phototacticly to polarized light depends upon whether the substrate is black or white (e.g., Kalmus, 1958).

Evidence against the reflexion hypothesis has already been stated. In so far as bees are concerned, recent experiments by von Frisch, Lindauer, and Daumer (1960) emphasize the inadequacy of the hypothesis. With bees, direct analysis of the sky's light during the dance on a horizontal comb requires use of the dorsal areas of the eyes, while recognition of reflexion patterns of the substrate requires the ventral areas. Masking of the upper portions impairs orientation of the dance, but masking of the lower portions does not. Furthermore, walking bees orient as well on a white substratum as on a black, glossy one.

Whatever may be the mechanism, the fact remains that many invertebrates behave as though they can detect differences in the plane of polarization of light and utilize this ability in their economy of living.

FORM PERCEPTION

The intrinsic characteristics of the stimulus for a photoreceptor are intensity, wavelength, and plane of polarization, but the occurrence of stimuli also varies in space and time. In the visual field there is at any given time a definite spatial arrangement of the kinds and amounts of radiant energy. In other words, there are patterns of light. The fineness of form perception depends upon the accuracy with which photoreceptors can detect this pattern, that is, upon their resolving power, and ultimately upon the faithfulness with which the spatial and temporal relations are represented in the central nervous system.

The capacity of the dioptric apparatus to form images that are reasonably distinct by human standards is easily demonstrated by taking photographs in the focal plane of excised lens systems (Gottsche, 1852; Exner, 1891; and many others). In those eyes in which each ommatidium is optically isolated from its neighbours by enveloping pigment cells and in which the rhabdom lies immediately beneath the crystalline cone, a small inverted image is produced at the base of each cone. Eyes of this type are termed apposition eyes and are characteristic of diurnal insects (Fig. 6). Müller (1826) proposed that these minute images were physiologically unimportant as images. He visualized each ommatidium of the apposition eye as a device for gathering light from a narrow sector of the visual field and projecting it as a point on the retinal field. Since each ommatidium sampled, as it were, a mean intensity from a particular area, the point of light projected by all the ommatidia composed an erect mosaic image.

Nocturnal and crepuscular insects characteristically possess eyes in which the rhabdoms are situated at a considerable distance from the crystalline cone. The enveloping pigment migrates back and forth in their respective cells as the eye is light- or dark-adapted (Fig. 92).

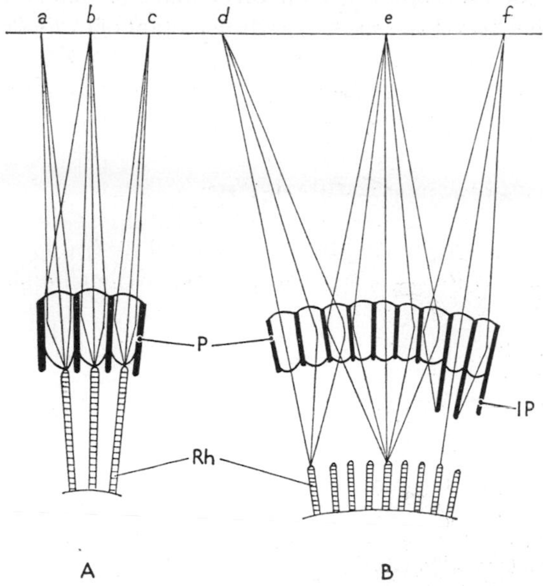

FIG. 92. Image formation in the apposition eye, A, and the superposition eye, B. a–f, paths of light rays; P, pigment; IP, position of pigment when eye is in the light adapted condition; Rh, rhabdom. (Redrawn from Wigglesworth, 1939 after Kühn.)

When this eye is dark-adapted the iris pigment moves distally into a position surrounding the cones. In this position each cone is isolated from its fellows, but the rhabdoms are now no longer shielded. Under these conditions light entering one ommatidium at an angle is not confined to that ommatidium as in the apposition eye, but may travel to neighbouring rhabdoms (Fig. 92). The image produced by a single ommatidium is an erect image which becomes larger the farther away from the crystalline cone it is projected. At the plane of the rhabdoms it is so large that it overlaps many rhabdoms where it is superimposed on the images similarly produced by the other lenses corresponding to those rhabdoms. Microscopic examination of the image at the level of the rhabdom reveals a large, somewhat fuzzy, erect image. As the microscope is brought to focus closer and closer to the crystalline cones, the rays of light forming the image are seen to retreat into each cone. The image at the level of the rhabdoms is a compound of superimposed images; hence, this type of eye is called a superposition eye. When the pigment in the superposition eye migrates proximally so that the rhabdoms are shielded from one another the eye functions like an apposition eye. It is noteworthy in this connexion that Autrum (1961) in measuring the visual acuity of a white mutant of *Calliphora* in which

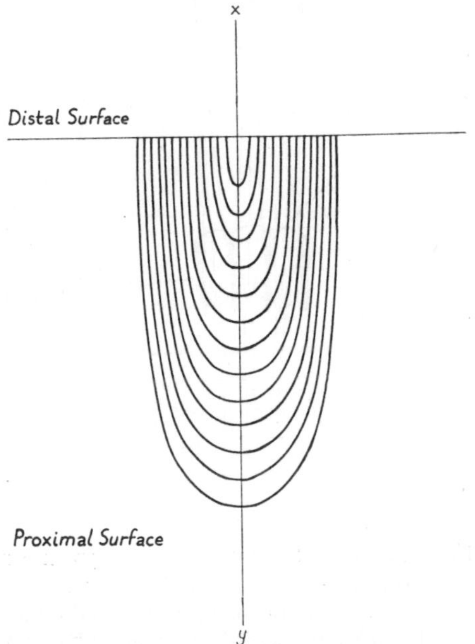

FIG. 93. Concentric lamellae of different refractive index in the dioptric apparatus of the ommatidium. The refractive index is greatest along the axis *xy*. (Redrawn from Exner, 1891.)

there was no screening pigment in the eye found no difference between the mutant and the wild type. Since the superposition is not total, that is, not all the images are congruent, it could be argued that the difference between the mosaic image and the superposition image is one of degree.

In order to explain image formation in the two types of eyes Exner (1891) proposed that the crystalline cone acted as a lens cylinder. If it were constructed of concentric lamellae of different refractive indices (Fig. 93), the refractive index would be greatest along the longitudinal axis and would decrease towards the periphery. The path of a ray of light in such a cylinder is diagrammed in Fig. 94. As a ray *xm* enters the cylinder it is refracted by the surface of each lamella *a* '*b*', but since the lamellae decrease in refractive index progressively from *xy* to *ab*, the ray is bent less and less until it re-enters regions of higher refractive index, where its path is now directed back towards *xy*. It finally emerges at *y*. If such a cylinder is as long as its focal length it will pro-

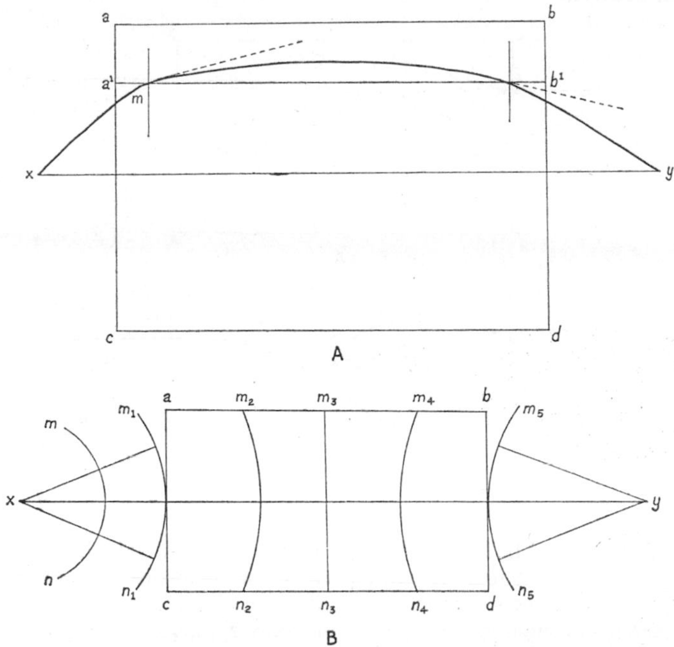

FIG. 94. Course followed by light through a cylinder abcd corresponding to the dioptric apparatus of the ommatidium. A, path of a ray of light. B, course of a spherical wave. a′–b′, layer of equal refringence; x, point of origin of wave; mm, m_1n_1, etc., successive positions of wave front indicating changes due to refraction accompanying passage through cylinder; y, focal point. (Redrawn from Exner, 1891.)

duce an inverted image at its base. If a cylinder is twice as long as its focal length it will produce an inverted image at its midpoint (Fig. 95). The rays will then diverge from the focal point and continue on straight paths. Rays that enter the cylinder obliquely (e.g., from the right) will emerge from the same side (i.e., the right).

If, in the apposition eye, the ommatidium is the optical unit, if it perceives light primarily from points on or near its axis, if there is minimal overlap of ommatidial visual fields and the image which has significance for the insect is a mosaic of point of light, then visual acuity should depend upon the number and spacing of luminous points received from the object in the visual field. There should be exact correspondence between the minimum angle subtended by adjacent ommatidia and the minimum angle subtended by two points that are perceived as separate (the reciprocal of the visual angle is termed the visual acuity).

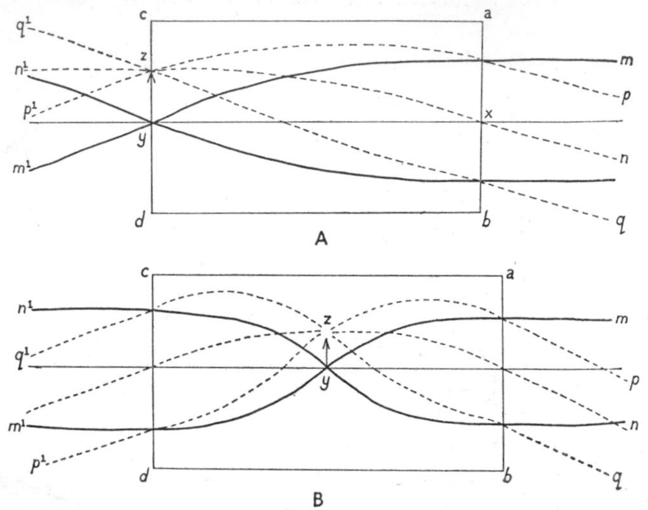

FIG. 95. Course of light rays through a lens cylinder abcd whose length is (A) equal to its focal length (B) twice the focal distance. m, p, n, q, rays from objects in the visual field; q′, n′, p′, m′, course of rays after passage through cylinder; xy, optic axis; zy, inverted image of object at base of cylinder. Note that in B an inverted image is produced at mid-point of cylinder. Rays continue through to produce an erect image at the rhabdoms. (Redrawn from Exner, 1891.)

Acuity does indeed depend upon the angle between adjacent directional elements, but reducing this angle to increase acuity has limitations. There is no improvement in acuity when the angle is so close that visual overlapping occurs, and there is now evidence that such overlapping is much greater than would be predicted from Müller's theory (de Vries, 1956; Burtt and Catton, 1954). Furthermore, as Barlow (1952) has pointed out, visual acuity is related to the resolving power of each ommatidial lens.

The resolving power of a lens is limited by its optical properties and the wave nature of light. The diameter of the ommatidium is critical, and diffraction must be taken into consideration. Because of diffraction, light coming through a small circular aperture produces an Airy pattern, a central point of maximum intensity with two concentric dark rings alternating with light rings. If two point sources are to be resolved they must be far enough separated so that the bright image centre of one falls no closer than within the first dark ring of the Airy pattern of the other. Müller (1826) had said that an apposition ommatidium was sensitive only to light from a point on or near its axis. It is maximally sensitive on its axis and minimally sensitive away from its axis, so the diameter determines how close two points can be if one is to stimulate maximally and the other minimally. In the honeybee, if the eye resolves points separated by twice the minimal ommatidial angle the performance of the ommatidia has approached the theoretical limit set by diffraction.

It is by no means certain, however, that the ommatidium is the optical unit of the eye. Refined techniques which permit illumination of single rhabdomers (in Diptera) have prompted the suggestion that it is the retinal cell which is the functional unit of the eye (de Vries, 1956; de Vries and Kuiper, 1958; see also Burkhardt and Wendler, 1960; Autrum and Burkhardt, 1961). By cutting transversely through an ommatidium in the region of the rhabdom and examining the cut end of the rhabdom as light is transmitted through the crystalline cone it can be seen that each rhabdom 'looks' at a different part of the visual field. Each visual field has a diameter of about 4 degrees, and the fields of neighbouring cells overlap so that the centre of one field lies approximately at the edge of the neighbouring field. The field of the whole ommatidium is about 8 degrees, and it overlaps with that of its neighbours. As with the entire ommatidium when it is analysed as a unit, the field of the individual cell is controlled by the diameter of the rhabdom and the diffraction of light. If a point source of light being viewed at the cut end of a rhabdomer is displaced more than 2 degrees from the optical axis of the retinal cell, it shines again, but more weakly, by reason of the diffracted light outside of the first dark ring of the Airy pattern. Once a beam has reached a rhabdomer it will, unless it deviates too far from the optical axis, be reflected repeatedly at the boundaries of the rhabdomer, since it has a higher refractive index than surrounding tissues. In this manner the rhabdomer acts as a wave-guide, and the cell captures light (see also Demoll, 1917). Since the internal reflexion decreases as the angle between the incident beam and the axis of the cell increases, there is a directional sensitivity in these cells, the Stiles–Crawford effect of human vision (de Vries and Kuiper, 1958).

If one recalls that the ommatidium is a multi-innervated sensillum and that the neurons of a sensillum may possess quite different characteristics (e.g., the chemoreceptive hair of flies), the independence of retinal cells is not unreasonable. On the other hand, the significance of the pattern of responses from single retinal cells cannot be simple because of the intricacy of synaptic connexions in the lamina ganglionaris. For every retinal cell whose axon traverses the area there are many that synapse together on giant monopolar neurons. Furthermore, there are many local chiasmata each involving several ommatidia. Some success towards understanding the extent to which an ommatidium is a functional unit of the eye has been achieved by the sophisticated functional analyses of movement perception by Hassenstein (1951, 1959) and Hassenstein and Reichardt (1956).

Behavioural measurements of visual acuity (usually derived from optomotor responses) have not always corresponded to the minimal ommatidial angle (Hecht and Wolf, 1929; Hecht and Wald, 1934; Wolf, 1933 a, 1933 b). Compared with man, whose visual acuity is from 2 to 2·5, the maximal visual acuity of the bee is 0·017 and of *Drosophila*, 0·0018. In the case of the bee, the value obtained corresponds exactly to the smallest ommatidial angle (0·90–1·00 degrees) measured by Baumgärtner (1928). In other cases, however, the correspondence has been less exact, the acuity being either greater or less.

Where the visual acuity has been less than expected in terms of ommatidial angles a number of explanations have been offered. Von Buddenbrock and Schulz (1933) proposed that ommatidia might be acting not as units but as pairs or groups. This hypothesis would also explain observed differences of visual acuity at high and low light intensities. As with man, the relation between visual acuity and the logarithm of intensity is described by a sigmoid curve (Fig. 96) (Hecht and Wald, 1934) which has been interpreted as an integral population curve denoting the number of retinal elements active at each intensity. In both the bee and *Drosophila* visual acuity and intensity discrimination, as measured by optomotor reactions, begin at approximately the same intensity and change rapidly within two log units (Wolf, 1933 a, 1933 b; Hecht and Wald, 1934).

It is also possible that visual-acuity measurements obtained from behavioural studies depend upon what part of the eye is being stimulated at the time. Viewed from the outside, the lens surface of a compound eye is an approximate and imperfect hemisphere. The relative area with respect to the head, and the number of ommatidia, vary from species to species and often between the sexes. Each of the ommatidia

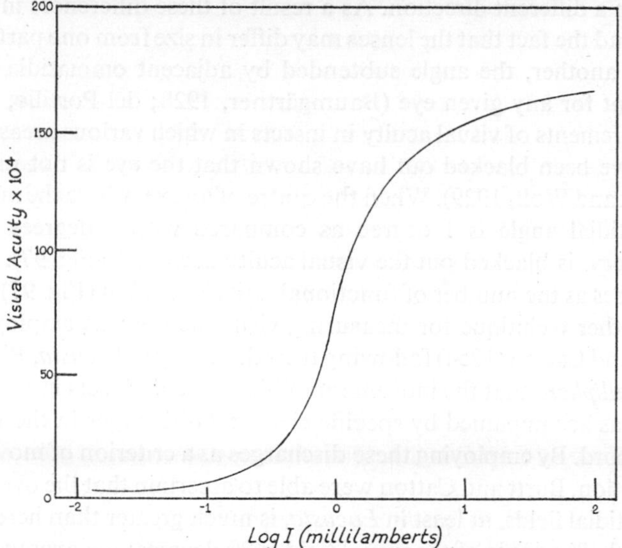

FIG. 96. Relation between visual acuity and intensity of illumination for the eye of the bee. (Redrawn from Hecht and Wolf, 1929.)

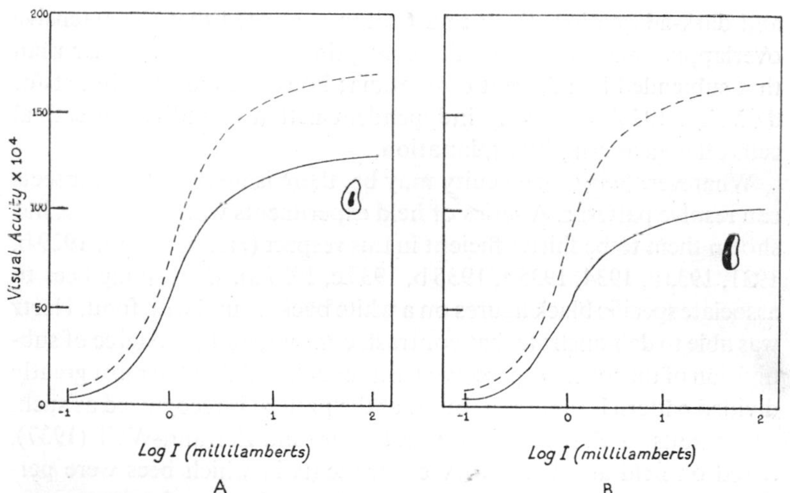

FIG. 97. Relation between visual acuity and illumination in bees in which A, the central area of the eye has been opaqued; B, the anterior region of the eye has been opaqued. The broken line represents the curve for normal individuals. (Redrawn from Hecht and Wolf, 1929.)

faces in a different direction. As a result of these differences in alignment and the fact that the lenses may differ in size from one part of the eye to another, the angle subtended by adjacent ommatidia is not constant for any given eye (Baumgärtner, 1928; del Portillo, 1936). Measurements of visual acuity in insects in which various areas of the eye have been blacked out have shown that the eye is not uniform (Hecht and Wolf, 1929). When the centre of an eye, where the minimal ommatidial angle is 1 degree as compared with 4 degrees at the periphery, is blacked out the visual acuity decreases (Fig. 97). It also decreases as the number of functional units is reduced (Fig. 97).

Another technique for measuring visual acuity was employed by Burtt and Catton (1954) following their discovery in *Locusta*, *Phormia*, and *Calliphora* that the movement of illuminated objects in the visual field was accompanied by specific electrical discharges in the ventral nerve cord. By employing these discharges as a criterion of movement perception, Burtt and Catton were able to ascertain that the overlap of ommatidial fields, at least in *Locusta*, is much greater than heretofore realized. The angle of the visual field is 20 degrees; the average angle subtended by adjacent ommatidia is about 2·4 degrees in the longitudinal and 1 degree in the vertical meridian. Responses to movement were obtained to angular displacements in the visual field as small as 0·16 degree of arc. The threshold of acuity was independent of light- and dark-adaptation. Burtt and Catton suggested that the extensive overlapping makes possible the perception of an angle smaller than that subtended by adjacent ommatidia; however, the experiments of de Vries (1956) suggesting independent action of individual retinal cells offer an alternative explanation.

Whatever their visual acuity may be, there is no doubt that insects can resolve patterns. A series of field experiments with honeybees has shown them to be fairly efficient in this respect (Hertz, 1929 a, 1929 b, 1931, 1933 a, 1934, 1935 a, 1935 b, 1935 c, 1937 a). By training bees to associate specific black figures on a white background with food, Hertz was able to demonstrate that contrast, contour, and the degree of subdivision of the form are perceived. She concluded that the most greatly divided pattern is preferred, but that the pattern is recognized as such. The results of Zerrahn (1933) and Wolf and Zerrahn-Wolf (1937), based on field and laboratory experiments in which bees were permitted to choose patterns spontaneously, are in essential agreement; however, these workers derived different conclusions. They contended that the pattern as such has no meaning. The number of choices of each pattern was proportional to the length of its contours, that is, the length of edges of black against white. This finding suggested that recognition and discrimination is based merely upon the degree of transitory stimulation produced in the compound eye. To test this hypothesis, Wolf and Zerrahn-Wolf mapped on translucent co-ordinate paper the points of intersection of the axes of the ommatidia with a place located at the same distance from the eye as were patterns used in testing. They then placed the co-ordinate paper over a pattern and counted the number of ommatidia whose visual fields would be black and the number whose fields would be white. They also counted the number of ommatidia in which there would be a black–white shift when the pattern was moved over a unit distance in any direction. Calculations could then be made of the relationships between the area of a pattern and the degree of subdivision necessary to provide a constant transition value. Predictions of discrimination based on these calculations were realized in field tests. Other lines of evidence were in agreement. For example, bees conditioned to flickering fields of equal size but different flicker frequencies exhibited choices that were directly proportional to the flicker frequency. These findings are in agreement with observations on the natural behaviour of bees in the field (Wolf, 1933 c). The honeybee reacts much more effectively to moving flowers than to stationary ones.

All of these experiments suggested that movement is of greater significance in form perception than the ability to resolve stationary patterns (cf. Exner, 1891). In its response to flicker the insect eye exhibits many of the characteristics of the human eye. It obeys Talbot's law (the brightness of a fused light produced by flashing it on and off is visually equivalent to the product of the actual source of illumination and the proportion of the time it is on) and the Ferry–Porter law (critical frequency, that is, the frequency at which a flashing light fuses, is proportional to the logarithm of intensity) as does the human eye (Wolf and Zerrahn-Wolf, 1935 b; Wolf, 1933 b). It is, however, more efficient at detecting flicker than is the eye of man. Some of the early values obtained for insects by optomotor methods were: 55 per second for the bee (Wolf, 1933 b); ± 60 per second for dragonfly larvae (Sälzle, 1932; Crozier, Wolf, and Zerrahn-Wolf, 1937). More highly developed behavioural techniques indicated that maximum values are actually much higher. The critical flicker frequency for *Calliphora* is about 265 per second, depending upon the number of ommatidia stimulated. The maximum of 265 per second drops to 60–165 per second when only one to four ommatidia are stimulated. A similar relationship holds for the honeybee (Autrum and Stoecker, 1950).

Studies of the electrical response (ERG) of the eye to flickering light agree beautifully with recent behavioural studies. As described earlier in this chapter, there are oscillations in the ERG which are synchronized with the stimulus flashes. In 'fast' eyes (e.g., *Calliphora*, *Apis*) the synchrony persists at even higher frequencies than those judged by optomotor responses to be fusing. In 'slow' eyes (e.g., *Dixippus*, *Tachycines*, *Periplaneta*) the responses, both behaviourally and electrophysiologically, are slower. These findings and the conclusions of others (Zerrahn, 1933; Wolf and Zerrahn-Wolf, 1937) that the decisive feature of pattern recognition is the transitory stimulation of ommatidia suggested to Autrum (1948 a, 1948 b, 1949, 1952, 1955 b) the idea of temporal resolution.

The concept is based upon the assumption that the ommatidium is the optical unit of the eye. In rapidly flying insects the angle subtended by ommatidia in the horizontal direction is approximately twice that in the vertical (del Portillo, 1936). During horizontal movement a point being observed remains in the visual field of a single ommatidium longer; consequently, the summation time for this stimulus is prolonged. Points of a pattern that succeed each other rapidly fuse less readily. Accordingly, the capacity for discrimination is improved through movement (Autrum, 1949). Studies of ERGs show that two points of light succeeding each other within a critical time fuse if they pass over the ommatidial grating vertically, but act as individual stimuli if they pass horizontally. The electrophysiological responses of 'fast' eyes reveal features which tend to favour reception of repetitive stimuli of short duration. The ERG shows that the on-effect for stimuli of $1-\frac{1}{200}$ second depends only upon intensity. It is independent of duration. The off-effect depends on the product of intensity and duration. Furthermore, in the 'fast' eyes, according to Autrum, a positive off-effect originating in the lamina ganglionaris prevents sustained depolarization as occurs in 'slow' eyes, and thus 'prepares' the eye for the next stimulus.

Insects also appear to be responsive to stroboscopic (apparent) motion. In contrast to the negative findings of Gaffron (1934), Autrum and Stöcker (1952) demonstrated that this phenomenon exists provided that certain critical conditions are met. For stroboscopic motion to be perceived the time sequences must be short for those insects ('fast') whose eyes possess high temporal resolution and long for those ('slow') species whose eyes possess low temporal resolution. A close relationship exists between the times that are important in motion perception, whether real or apparent, and the times for which the receptors can still separate separate stimuli. Motion is perceived as a vector without spatial connotations when two stimulated ommatidia are separated by an unstimulated one (Hassenstein, 1951).

OCELLI

Many insects possess dorsal ocelli in addition to compound eyes. The distribution of ocelli within the Class is erratic and is of no assistance in the problem of interpreting the role that these organs play.

The structure is basically similar in all ocelli. It consists of a transparent cornea which may be perfectly flat on both surfaces, biconvex, or plano-convex. Underlying the cornea there is frequently a transparent layer of corneagen cells and beneath this a layer of retinal cells very similar in structure to those of the compound eyes. In the more complex ocelli the corneagen cells may be thickened to form a auxiliary refractory organ. The retinal cells are grouped together in units of two, three, or four, and each cell of a unit contributes to a central rhabdom. In the lateral ocellus of *Sympetrum* there are about 675 photoreceptor cells. Beneath them lies a reflecting layer, the tapetum. As the sensory axons proceed proximally they soon form synaptic connexions with the intra-ocellar terminals of the ocellar nerve fibres (Cajal, 1918; Ruck, 1957). The ocellar nerve of the cockroach consists of about twenty-five fibres, of which four are very large – 6–10 μ. In the dragonfly (*Sympetrum*) there is one giant fibre (25–38 μ) and three or four ranging in diameter from 4–13 μ. The remainder are 1 μ or less. The neurocytes lie in the brain (Cajal, 1918; Satija, 1958 a, 1958 b).

Although the corneal lens is capable of forming fairly sharp images, everyone who has studied the optics of the system agrees that the image has little significance, since it falls a considerable distance behind the retina (Homann, 1924; Parry, 1947; Cornwall, 1955).

Electrical events have been studied in the ocelli of *Locusta migratoria migratoroides* (Parry, 1947; Hoyle, 1955; Burtt and Catton, 1958), *Periplaneta americana* (Ruck, 1957, 1958 a; Goldsmith and Ruck, 1958), *Blaberus craniifer* (Ruck, 1957, 1961 a), *Melanoplus bivittatus* (Ruck, 1957), *Apis mellifera* (Goldsmith and Ruck, 1958; Ruck, 1958 b). *Pachydiplax longipennis* and *Phormia regina* (Ruck, 1958 b), *Libellula luctuosa* (Ruck, 1961 a), *Libellula vibrans* (Ruck, 1961 b), *Anax junius*, *Aeschna* sp., and *Sympetrum ribicundulum* (Ruck, 1961 c). Because different workers employed different recording situations it is difficult to compare their results and to reconcile differences in the wave form and sign of the ERG. The most comprehensive analysis is that based upon extensive studies of the ocellus of the cockroach and dragonfly (Ruck, 1958 a, 1958 b, 1961 a, 1961 b). In these insects the total electrical response to light of high intensity

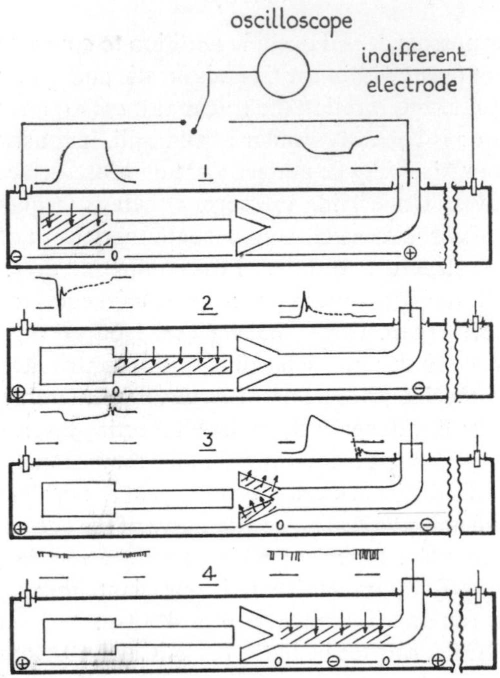

FIG. 98. Components of the ERG of the model ocellus. One photoreceptor cell (*left*) with an expanded sensory ending, and an axon which makes synaptic contact with one ocellar nerve fibre. The two units are contained in an electrolyte-filled compartment. A 'corneal' electrode enters at left; a 'nerve' electrode lifts the nerve into air; an indifferent electrode is placed far to the right. Four components of the ERG are shown, each in one repetition of the model. Active sites for each component are shaded. Current at active sites is indicated by arrows. Each component appears at corneal and nerve electrodes. (Redrawn from Ruck, 1961 a.)

consists of four components, of which two originate in the retinal cells and two in the ocellar nerve (Fig. 101). The first event is a generator potential arising in the distal end of the receptor. It evokes a depolarization in the axonal region of the receptor. This in turn evokes a hyperpolarizing postsynaptic potential in the fibres of the ocellar nerve. This component is easily discernible in the ocelli of dragonflies but rarely detected in cockroaches. Ruck (1961 b) has suggested that the postsynaptic potential is not induced directly by the electrical events in the receptor axon, but rather by the liberation of a transmitter substance at the end of the receptor axon. In the absence of the hyperpolarizing potential the fibres of the ocellar nerve discharge impulses (component 4). In the dragonfly the ocellar nerve in the dark discharges spontaneously, while the cockroach nerve usually discharges only at off. It is inferred that there is spontaneous receptor cell activity which modulates the rhythmic spontaneous discharges in the ocellar nerve.

The ocellus of the dragonfly is a very sensitive receptor. Corneal illumination as low as 10^{-5} ft.-candles produces an ERG (Ruck, 1958 b). Furthermore, it is to be expected that sensitivity is enhanced by the high degree of convergence of receptor axons on ocellar nerve fibres, multiple synapsing of single receptor axons with ocellar nerve fibres, and the presence of a white tapetum (Ruck, 1961 a).

The ability of the ocellus to respond to flickering light varies from species to species. The flicker fusion frequencies of *Apis*, *Pachydiplax*, and *Phormia* are very high, being, respectively, 250–265, 200, and +220 per second. For the cockroach maximum flicker fusion frequencies range from 45 to 60 per second (Ruck, 1958 a). Thus, the ocelli of those insects with 'fast' eyes are 'fast' and those with 'slow' eyes, 'slow'. As with the compound eyes, Ruck (1958 b) found that there is no general relation between flicker fusion frequency and sensitivity or rate of dark adaptation. Furthermore, since ocelli do not possess a lamina ganglionaris and since in the dragonfly the generator potential can respond to higher rates of flicker (220 per second) than can the receptor axon responses, the postsynaptic potential and the ocellar nerve impulses, the difference between 'fast' and 'slow' ocelli is a fundamental characteristic of the photoreceptor cell itself. The evidence of Autrum and Gallwitz (1951) that the ability of 'fast' compound eyes to follow high rates of flicker depends upon electrical interaction between the receptor cells and neurons of the optic ganglion cannot be extended to ocelli.

Dorsal ocelli are sensitive to the same spectrum of wavelengths as are compound eyes. The ocelli of *Periplaneta* have a single sensitivity peak at 500 mμ, while those of the honeybee show sensitivity maxima at 490 mμ and at 335–340 mμ (Goldsmith and Ruck, 1958). Because in the honeybee the ERG produced by ultra-violet stimulation is qualitatively different from that produced by stimulation of light of 490 mμ,

Goldsmith and Ruck (1958) believe that there are two types of receptor in this organ.

The exact nature of the contribution of dorsal ocelli to behaviour is still elusive. Alone they are insufficient for phototaxis (Homann, 1924; Bozler, 1926; Müller, 1931; Wellington, 1953; Cornwall, 1955; but compare Götze, 1927 and Wellington, 1953). They are not, however, totally without effect in light-directed behaviour. Elimination of ocelli may cause phototaxis to be temporarily reversed (Müller, 1931), reduce the speed of response to light (Bozler, 1926; Müller, 1931), or alter the direction of response to two light sources (Müller, 1931). In *Periplaneta* the characteristic persistent daily rhythm depends upon stimulation of the ocelli (Harker, 1956). As a consequence of these actions the ocelli are generally considered to be 'stimulatory' organs (Bozler, 1926; Wolsky, 1930, 1931, 1933).

STEMMATA

With the possible exception of dermal receptors sensitive to light, the lateral ocelli or stemmata are the sole visual organs possessed by many larval insects. Structurally they vary from forms similar to the dorsal ocelli of adults (e.g., larval ocelli of Tenthredinidae) to mere pigment spots equipped with refractive bodies. In blowfly larvae the photoreceptors are small groups of vacuolated cells pocketed among the hypodermal cells of the cephalic region (Bolwig, 1946).

The most thoroughly studied stemmata are those of lepidopterous larvae (Grenacher, 1897; Hesse, 1901; Dethier, 1942, 1943). Each resembles an individual ommatidium. It possesses two lenses, one corneal, the other analogous to the crystalline cone of compound eyes.

TABLE 9

(From Dethier, 1953 c)

Optical constants of the six ocelli of *Isia isabella*

Ocellus	*Minimum Angle of Resolution (Radians)*	*f value*	*Dioptric Value*	*Type of Image*	*Focal Distance*
1	$1{\cdot}1 \times 10^{-2}$	0·93	14,285	Triple	0·070
2	$1{\cdot}2 \times 10^{-2}$	0·89	14,084	Triple	0·071
3	$5{\cdot}3 \times 10^{-3}$	0·50	14,285	Single	0·070
4	$7{\cdot}1 \times 10^{-3}$	0·67	14,285	Single	0·070
5	$7{\cdot}8 \times 10^{-3}$	0·73	13,888	Single	0·072
6	$1{\cdot}0 \times 10^{-2}$	1·00	14,084	Triple	0·071

The first is a thick converging concavoconvex or biconvex meniscus lens.

If the secretion products of the three corneagen cells fuse incompletely during the formation of this lens, as is typical of certain ocelli, the cornea acts as a triple lens and forms three images (Pl. IV). The crystalline lens, like the cornea, is a thick, converging biconvex lens, either unitary or tripartite to correspond with the cornea. It also forms more or less distinct, real, inverted images. The receptive layer, like that of the ommatidium, consists of distal and proximal retinula cells. Some of the optical constants obtained from the lenses of the six ocelli of the caterpillar *Isia isabella* are given in Table 9. The peculiar optical properties of the lens system of ommatidia as described by Exner (1891) are not characteristic of these lenses.

Whether the ocellus acts as an eye or merely as a photoreceptor depends primarily on: (1) the ability of the dioptric apparatus to form images; (2) the location of the image plane with respect to the rhabdom; (3) the ability of the rhabdom to receive any images formed. By determining the image space (that region of space in which all possible positions of the image are situated) from the optical constants and by actual measurement of the length of the vertical retinal elements, Dethier has shown (Fig. 99) that regardless of the distance of an object from the ocellus, the image falls somewhere along the length of the rhabdom. In this manner a degree of accommodation is obtained which would otherwise be impossible with a fixed-lens system. The ocellus is analogous in this respect to a fixed-focus camera.

Vision in insects bearing simple eyes is the sum of the capacities of all units operating jointly. Hundertmark's (1936, 1937) experiments have shown that larvae which orient to black shapes on a white background are directed towards the black-and-white boundary. Dethier has postulated that the basic principles of mosaic vision apply equally well to lateral ocelli and compound eyes. Since each ocellus gathers light from the area at which it is directed and concentrates this light at some point along the vertical rhabdom, the six pairs of ocelli together form twelve points of light. The ocelli are so arranged on the head that little or no overlapping of the visual field exists, hence each spot represents the intensity from a different area. Combined they provide an exceedingly coarse mosaic of intensities. The paucity of units is compensated for in part by the habit, characteristic of many larvae, of moving the head from side to side while advancing. By this klinotactic-like behaviour a larger visual field is examined, and the recognition of changes in intensity, as at a black–white boundary, is

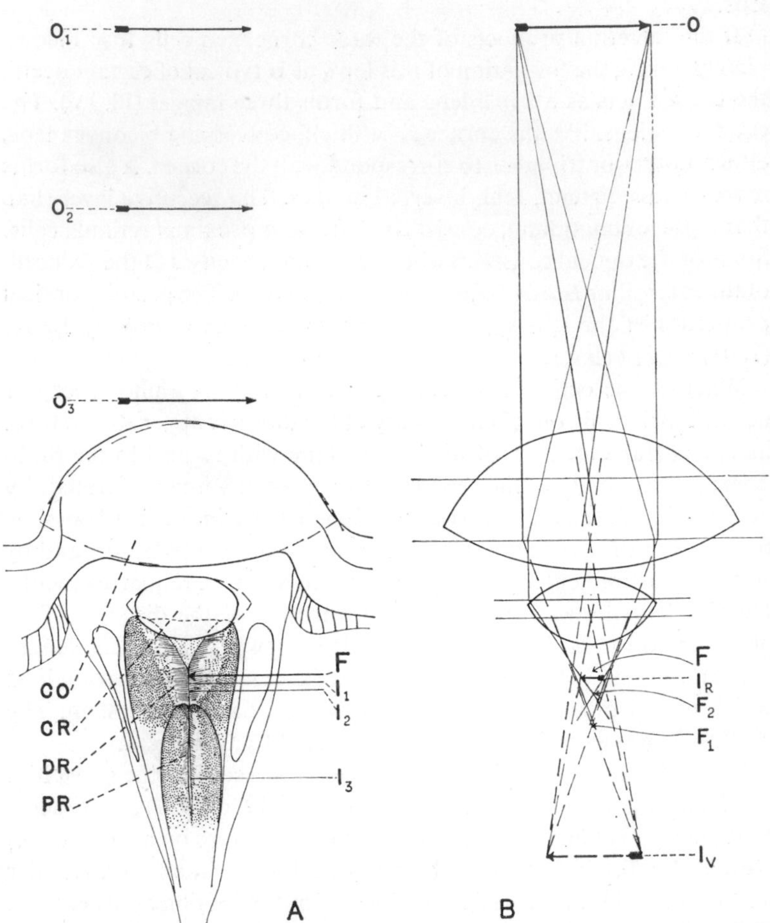

FIG. 99. A. Camera lucida drawing of an ocellus of the caterpillar of *Isia isabella* to illustrate the congruity of image space and retinal space and the kind of accommodation offered by a vertical rhabdom. O_1, O_2, O_3, representative objects; I_1, I_2, I_3, positions of resultant images; F, focal point; CO, cornea; CR, crystalline lens; DR, distal retinula; PR, proximal retinula. The broken line in the cornea represents the ideal lens curvature. B. Graphic construction of images formed. O, object; I_v, virtual image; I_r, real image; F_1, focal point of corneal lens; F_2, focal point of crystalline lens; F, focal point of entire lens system. (From Dethier, 1943.)

facilitated by this motion. Even in those species (e.g., *Cicindela*) where the ocellus consists of a larger number of retinal elements beneath each lens, it is believed that all ocelli function together as a unit.

Little is known about the parameters of the stimuli for stemmata. It has been demonstrated that larvae are sensitive to a wide band of the spectrum and seem to be able to respond to the plane of polarization (Wellington, Sullivan, and Green, 1957). Electrophysiological studies have only just been undertaken with these receptors. The ERG recorded with the active electrode on the ocellar nerve and the reference electrode in the abdomen is simple in appearance. It consists of a prominent positive wave followed at high intensities of stimulation by a slow negative wave. It is believed to consist of two components (Ishikawa and Hirao, 1960 a, 1960 b). The stemmata become completely dark-adapted in about one hour and completely light-adapted in about ten minutes. They follow flicker up to 25–30 per second.

References

ADAMS, J. R. (1961) The location and histology of the contact chemoreceptors of the stable fly, *Stomoxys calcitrans L.* Doctoral Dissertation, Rutgers Univ., New Brunswick, N.J.

ADRIAN, E. D. (1937) Synchronized reactions in the optic ganglion of *Dytiscus. J. Physiol.*, **91**, 66–89.

ALEXANDER, R. D. (1957) Sound production and associated behavior in insects. *Ohio J. Sci.*, **57**, 101–13.

ALEXANDROWICZ, J. S. (1951) Muscle receptor organs in the abdomen of *Homarus vulgaris* and *Palinurus vulgaris. Quart. J. Micr. Sci.*, **92**, 163–99.

ALEXANDROWICZ, J. S. (1952 a) Receptor elements in the thoracic muscles of *Homarus vulgaris* and *Palinurus vulgaris. Quart. J. Micr. Sci.*, **93**, 315–46.

ALEXANDROWICZ, J. S. (1952 b) Muscle receptor organs in the Paguridae. *J. Mar. Biol. Assoc. U.K.*, **31**, 277–86.

ALEXANDROWICZ, J. S. (1954) Notes on the nervous system in Stomatopoda. IV. Muscle receptor organs. *Pubbl. Staz. Zool. Napoli*, 25, 94–111.

ALEXANDROWICZ, J. S. (1956) Receptor elements in the muscles of *Leander serratus. J. Mar. Biol. Assoc. U.K.*, **35**, 129–44.

ALVAREZ-BUYLLA, R., and DE ARELLANO, J. R. (1953) Local responses in Pacinian corpuscles. *Am. J. Physiol.*, **127**, 237–50.

AMOURIQ, L. (1957) Optimum vital et rôle des scolopidies du scape et du pédicelle antennaires dans la recherche du preferendum hygrométrique de Gryllus bimaculatus L. *Bull. Soc. Hist. Nat. Afr. Nord.*, **48**, 137–47.

AMOURIQ, L. (1959) Histologie et rôle des organes chordotonaux de l'antenne dans le comportement hygropathique de Gryllus. Thesis, 163 pp. Alger.

ANDERSEN, L. W., and BALL, H. J. (1959) Antennal hygroreceptors of the milkweed bug, Oncopeltus fasciatus (Dallas) (Hemiptera, Lygaeidae). *Ann. Ent. Soc. Amer.*, **52**, 279–84.

ANDERSON, A. L. (1932) The sensitivity of the legs of common butterflies to sugars. *J. Exp. Zool.*, **63**, 253–9.

ANDERSON, D. B. (1936) Relative humidity of vapor pressure deficit. *Ecology*, **17**, 277–82.

ARAB, Y. M. (1958) Behavioural response to electrical stimulation of chemoreceptors in the blowfly. *J. Ins. Physiol.*, **2**, 324–9.

ARAB, Y. M. (1959) Some chemosensory mechanisms in the blowfly *Phormia regina* Meigen. *Bull. College Sci, Univ. Baghdad*, **4**, 77–85.

AUGER, D., and FESSARD, A. (1928) Observations sur l'excitabilité de l'organe tympanique. *C.R. Soc. Biol. Paris*, **99**, 400–1.

AUTRUM, H. (1936) Über Lautäusserungen und Schallwahrnehmung bei Arthropoden. I. Untersuchungen an Ameisen Eine allgemeine Theorie der Schallwahrnehmung bei Arthropoden. *Zeit. vergl. Physiol.*, **23**, 332–73.

AUTRUM, H. (1940) Über Lautäusserungen und Schallwahrnehmung bei Arthropoden. II. Das Richtungshören von Locusta und Versuche einer Hörtheorie für Tympanalorgane vom Locustidentyp. *Zeit. vergl. Physiol.*, **28**, 326–52.

AUTRUM, H. (1941) Über Gehör und Erschütterungssinn bei Locustiden. *Zeit. vergl. Physiol.*, **28**, 580–637.

AUTRUM, H. (1942) Schallempfang bei Tier und Mensch. *Naturwiss.*, **30**, 69–85.

AUTRUM, H. (1943) Über kleinste Reize bei Sinnesorganen. *Biol. Zbl.*, **63**, 209–36.

AUTRUM, H. (1948 a) Über das zeitliche Auflösungsvermögen des Insektenauges. *Nachr. Akad. Wiss. Göttingen, Math.-Phys.*, 1948, 8–12.

AUTRUM, H. (1948 b) Zur Analyse des zeitlichen Auflösungsvermögens des Insektenauges. *Nachr. Akad. Wiss. Göttingen, Math.-Phys.*, 1948, 13–18.

AUTRUM, H. (1948 c) Über Energie-und Zeitgrenzen der Sinnesempfindungen. *Naturwiss.*, **35**, 361–9.

AUTRUM, H. (1949) Neue Versuche zum optischen Auflösungsvermögen fliegender Insekten. *Experientia*, **7**, 271–7.

AUTRUM, H. (1950) Die Belichtungspotentiale und das Sehen der Insekten (Untersuchungen an Calliphora und Dixippus). *Zeit. vergl. Physiol.*, **32**, 176–7.

AUTRUM, H. (1951) Erregungsvorgänge und Leistungen des Insektenauges. *Verhandlungen Deutschen Zool. Gesellschaft Wilhelmshaven*, 1951, 133–43.

AUTRUM, H. (1952) Über zeitliches Auflösungsvermögen und Primärvorgänge im Insektenauge. *Naturwiss.*, **39**, 290–7.

AUTRUM, H. (1953) Elektrobiologie des Auges. *Klinische Wochenschrift*, **31**, 241–5.

AUTRUM, H. (1954 a) Die Sehvorgänge in den Augen der Insekten. *Zeit. Umschau Wiss. Tech.*, 54.

AUTRUM, H. (1954 b) Formensehen im menschlichen und tierischen Auge. *Zeit. Umschau Wiss. Tech.*, 1954.

AUTRUM, H. (1955 a) Die spektrale Empfindlichkeit der Augenmutation white-apricot von Calliphora erythrocephala. *Biol. Zbl.*, **74**, 515–24.

AUTRUM, H. (1955 b) Die Zeit als physiologische Grundlage des Formensehens. *Studium Generale*, **8**, 526–30.

AUTRUM, H. (1955 c) Analyse physiologique de la réception des sons chez les orthoptères. In *Colloque sur L'acoustique des Orthoptères*, ed. R. G. Busnel. Fascicule Hors Série des Ann. Épiphytès, pp. 338–55.

AUTRUM, H. (1958) Electrophysiological analysis of the visual systems in insects. *Exp. Cell Res.* (*Suppl.*), **5**, 426–39.

AUTRUM, H. (1959) Non-photic receptors in lower forms. In *Handbook of Physiology*, ed. J. Field. Am. Physiol. Soc., Washington, D.C.

AUTRUM, H. (1961) Die Sehschärfe pigmentfreier Fazettenaugen von *Calliphora erythrocephala. Biol. Zbl.*, **80**, 1–4.

AUTRUM, H., and BURKHARDT, D. (1961) Spectral sensitivity of single visual cells. *Nature*, **190**, 639.

AUTRUM, H., and GALLWITZ, U. (1951) Zur Analyse der Belichtungspotentiale des Insektenauges. *Zeit. vergl. Physiol.*, **33**, 407–35.

AUTRUM, H., and HOFFMANN, C. (1960) Diphasic and monophasic responses in the compound eye of *Calliphora. J. Ins. Physiol.*, **4**, 122–7.

AUTRUM, H., and HOFFMANN, E. (1957) Die Wirkung von Pikrotoxin und Nikotin auf das Retinogramm von Insekten. *Z. Naturf.*, **126**, 752–7.

AUTRUM, H., and SCHNEIDER, W. (1948) Vergleichende Untersuchungen über den Erschütterungssinn der Insekten. *Zeit. vergl. Physiol.*, **31**, 77–88.

AUTRUM, H., and STÖCKER, M. (1952) Über optische Verschmelzungsfrequenzen und stroboskopisches Sehen bei Insekten. *Biol. Zbl.*, **71**, 129–52.

AUTRUM, H., and STOECKER, M. (1950) Die Verschmelzungsfrequenzen des Bienenauges. *Zeit Naturf.*, **5b**, 38–43.

AUTRUM, H., and STUMPF, H. (1950) Das Bienenauge als Analysator für polarisiertes Licht. *Zeit. Naturf.*, **5b**, 116–22.

AUTRUM, H., and STUMPF, H. (1953) Electrophysiologische Untersuchungen über das Farbensehen von *Calliphora. Zeit. vergl. Physiol.*, **35**, 71–104.

AZIZ, S. A. (1957 a). The reactions of the Desert Locust, Schistocerca gregaria (Forsk.), (Orthoptera, Acrididae) to physical factors, with special reference to relative humidity. *Bull. Entomol. Res.*, **48**, 515–32.

AZIZ, S. A. (1957 b) Probable hygroreceptors in the Desert Locust, Schistocerca gregaria (Forsk.) (Orthoptera, Acrididae). *Indian J. Entomol.*, **19**, 164–70.

BAINBRIDGE, R., and WATERMAN, T. H. (1957) Polarized light and the orientation of two marine Crustacea. *J. Exp. Biol.*, **34**, 342–64.

BÁRÁNY, E. (1946 a) A theory of binocular visual acuity and an analysis of the variability of visual acuity. *Acta. Opthal. Kbh.*, **24**, 63–92.

BÁRÁNY, E. (1946 b) Some statistical observations on the methods in threshold determinations in general with particular regard to determination of visual acuity and subliminal addition. *Acta Opthal. Kbh.*, **24**, 113–27.

BARLOW, H. B. (1952) The size of the ommatidia in apposition eyes. *J. Exp. Biol.*, **29**, 667–74.

BARROWS, W. M. (1907) The reactions of the pomace fly, *Drosophila ampelophila* Loew, to odorous substances. *J. Exp. Zool.*, **4**, 515–37.

BÄSSLER, U. (1957) Zur Funktion des Johnston-Organes bei der Orientierung der Stechmücken. *Naturwiss.*, **44**, 336–7.

BÄSSLER, U. (1958) Versuche zur Orientierung der Stechmücken: Die Schwarmbildung und die Bedentung des Johnstonschen Organs. *Zeit. vergl. Physiol.*, **41**, 300–30.

BAUER, L. (1938) Geschmacksphysiologische Untersuchungen an Wasserkäfern. *Zeit. vergl. Physiol.*, **26**, 107–20.

BAUERS, C. (1953) Der Fixierbereich des Insectenauges. *Zeit. vergl. Physiol.*, **34**, 589–605.

BAUMGÄRTNER, H. (1928) Der Formensinn und die Sehschärfe der Bienen. *Zeit. vergl. Physiol.*, **7**, 56–143.

BAUNACKE, W. (1912) Statische Sinnesorgane bei den Nepiden. *Zool. Jahrb. Abt. Anat. Ontog.*, **34**, 179–346.

BAYLOR, E. R. (1959 a) Polarized light responses in *Limulus*. *Biophysical Soc., Program and Abstracts*, 1959 Meetings.

BAYLOR, E. R. (1959 b) The responses of snails to polarized light. *J. Exp. Biol.*, **36**, 369–76.

BAYLOR, E. R., and KENNEDY, D. (1958) Evidence against a polarizing analyzer in the bee eye. *Anat. Rec.*, **132**, 411.

BAYLOR, E. R., and SMITH, F. E. (1953) The orientation of Cladocera to polarized light. *Amer. Nat.*, **87**, 98–101.

BAYLOR, E. R., and SMITH, F. E. (1957) Diurnal migration of plankton crustaceans. In *Recent Advances in Invertebrate Physiology*. Univ. Oregon Press, pp. 21–35.

BAYLOR, E. R., and SMITH, F. E. (1958) Extra-ocular polarization analysis in the honey bee. *Anat. Rec.*, **132**, 411–12.

BECHT, G. (1959) Studies on insect muscles. *Bijdragen Tot de Dierkunde*, **29**, 5–40.

BEGG, M., and HOGBEN, L. (1946) Chemoreception of *Drosophila melanogaster*. *Proc. Roy. Soc. Lond.* B, **133**, 1–19.

BEIDLER, L. M. (1953) Properties of chemoreceptors of tongue of rat. *J. Neurophysiol.*, **16**, 595–607.

BEIDLER, L. M. (1954) A theory of taste stimulation. *J. Gen. Physiol.*, **38**, 133–9.

BEIDLER, L. M. (1960) Physiology of taste. *The Physiologist*, **3**, 5–12.

BEIDLER, L. M. (1961) The chemical senses. *Ann. Rev. Psychol.*, **12**, 363–88.

BEIDLER, L. M., FISHMAN, I. Y., and HARDIMAN, C. W. (1955) Species differences in taste responses. *Am. J. Physiol.*, **181**, 235–9.

BENTLEY, E. W. (1944) The biology and behaviour of *Ptinus tectus* Boie (Coleoptera, Ptinidae), a pest of stored products. V. Humidity reactions. *J. Exp. Biol.*, **20**, 152–8.

BENZ, G. (1956) Der Trockenheitssinn bei Larven von Drosophila melanogaster. *Experientia*, **12**, 297–8.

BERLESE, A. (1909) *Gli Insetti.* Societa Editrice Libraria, Milano.

BERNHARD, C. G. (1942) Isolation of retinal and optic ganglion response in the eye of *Dytiscus*. *J. Neurophysiol.*, **5**, 32–48.

BERNHARD, C. G., GRANIT, R., and SKOGLAND, C. R. (1942) The breakdown of accommodation-nerve as a model sense-organ. *J. Neurophysiol.*, **5**, 55–68.

BERTHOLF, L. M. (1931 a) Reactions of the honeybee to light. *J. Agr. Res.*, **42**, 379–419.

BERTHOLF, L. M. (1931 b) The distribution of stimulative efficiency in the ultraviolet spectrum for the honeybee. *J. Agr. Res.*, **43**, 703–13.

BERTHOLF, L. M. (1932) The extent of the spectrum for *Drosophila* and the distribution of stimulative efficiency in it. *Zeit. vergl. Physiol.*, **98**, 32–64.

BIRUKOW, G. (1953) Menotaxis im polarisierten Licht bei *Geotrupes silvaticus* Panz. *Naturwiss.*, **40**, 611–12.

BIRUKOW, G., and BUSCH, E. (1957) Lichtkompassorientierung beim Wasserläufer *Velia currens* F. (Heteroptera) am Tage und zur Nachtzeit. II. Orientierungsrhythmik in verschiedenen Lichtbedingungen. *Zeit. Tierpyschol.*, **14**, 184–203.

BOISTEL, J. (1953) Étude functionelle des terminaisons sensorielles des antennes d' Hyménoptères. *C.R. Soc. Biol. Paris*, **147**, 1683–8.

BOISTEL, J., and CORABOEUF, E. (1953) L'activité électrique dans l'antenne isolée de Lépidoptère au cours de l'étude de l'olfaction. *C.R. Soc. Biol. Paris*, **147**, 1172–5.

BOISTEL, J., LECOMPTE, J., and CORABOEUF, E. (1956) Quelques aspects de l'étude électrophysiologique des récepteurs sensoriels des antennes d'hymenoptères. *Insectes Sociaux*, **3**, 25–31.

BOLWIG, N. (1946) Senses and sense organs of the anterior end of the house fly larvae. *Videns. Medd. Dansk Natur. Forening.*, **109**, 82–217.

BORROR, D. J. (1954) Audio-spectographic analysis of the song of the cone-headed grasshopper, *Neoconocephalus ensiger* (Harris) (Orthoptera: Tettigoniidae). *Ohio. J. Sci.*, 54, 297–303.

BOWNESS, J. M., and WOLKEN, J. J. (1959) A light-sensitive yellow pigment from the house-fly. *J. Gen. Physiol.*, **42**, 779–92.

BOZLER, E. (1926) Experimentelle Untersuchungen über die Funktion der Stirnaugen der Insekten. *Zeit. vergl. Physiol.*, **3**, 145–82.

BRAUNS, A. (1939) Morphologische und physiologische Untersuchungen zum Halterenproblem. *Zool. Jahrb.*, **59**, 245–390.

BRETSCHNEIDER, F. (1921) Über das Gehirn des Wolfsmilchschwärmers (Deilephila Euphorbiae). *Jena. Zeit. Naturwiss.*, **57**, 423–62.

BRINK, F., and POSTERNAK, J. M. (1948) Thermodynamic analysis of the relative effectiveness of narcotics. *J. Cell. Comp. Physiol.*, **32**, 211–33.

BUCK, J. B. (1937) Studies on the firefly. II. The signal system and color vision in Photinus pyralis. *Physiol. Zool.*, **10**, 412–19.

BÜCKMANN, D. (1954) Die Leistungen der Schwereorientierung bei dem im Meeressande grabenden Käfer *Bledius bicornis* Grm. (Staphylinidae). *Zeit. vergl. Physiol.*, **36**, 488–507.

BÜCKMANN, D. (1955a) Zur Leistung des Schweresinnes bei Insekten. *Naturwiss.*, **42**, 78–79.

BÜCKMANN, D. (1955b) Zur Frage der Funktion der Insektenfühler als Schweresinnesorgan. *Naturwiss.*, **42**, 79.

VON BUDDENBROCK, W. (1935) Eine neue Methode zur Erforschung des Formensehens der Insekten. *Naturwiss.*, **23**, 98–100.

VON BUDDENBROCK, W. (1952) Vergleichende Physiologie. *Sinnesphysiologie* (Vol. I). Birkhäuser, Basil.

VON BUDDENBROCK, W., and SCHULZ, E. (1933) Beiträge zur Kenntnis der Lichtkompassbewegung und der Adaptation des Insektenauges. *Zool. Jahrb. Zool. Physiol.*, **52**, 513–36.

BULLOCK, T. H. (1953) Comparative aspects of some biological transducers. *Fed. Proc.*, **12** (3), 666–72.

BULLOCK, T. H. (1957) Neuronal integrative mechanisms. In *Recent Advances in Invertebrate Physiology*. Univ. Oregon Publications, pp. 1–20.

BULLOCK, T. H. (1958) Parameters of integrative action of the nervous system at the neuronal level. *Exp. Cell Res.*, **5**, 323–37.

BULLOCK, T. H. (1959) Initiation of nerve impulses in receptor and central neurons. *Rev. Modern Physics*, **31** (2), 504–14.

BURKHARDT, D. (1954) Rhythmische Erregungen in ben optischen Zentren von *Calliphora erythrocephala. Zeit. vergl. Physiol.*, **36**, 595–630.

BURKHARDT, D. (1960) Action potentials in the antennae of the blowfly (*Calliphora erythrocephala*) during mechanical stimulation. *J. Ins. Physiol.*, **4**, 138–45.

BURKHARDT, D., and AUTRUM, H. (1960) Die Belichtungspotentiale einzelner Sehzellen von Calliphora erythrocephala Meig. *Zeit. Naturf.*, **15b**, 612–16.

BURKHARDT, D., and SCHNEIDER, G. (1957) Die Antennen von *Calliphora* als Anzeiger der Fluggeschwindigkeit. *Z. Naturf.*, **12b**, 139–43.

BURKHARDT, D., and WENDLER, L. (1960) Ein direkter Beiveis für die Fähigkeit einzelner Sehzellen des Insektenauges, die Schwingungsrichtung polarisierten Lichtes zu analysieren. *Zeit. vergl. Physiol.*, **43**, 687–92.

BURSELL, E. (1957) The effect of humidity on the activity of tsetse flies. *J. Exp. Biol.*, **34**, 42–51.

BURSELL, E., and EWER, O. W. (1950) On the reactions to humidity of Peripatopsis moseleyi (Wood-Mason). *J. Exp. Biol.*, **26**, 335–53.

BURTT, E. T., and CATTON, W. T. (1952) Nerve impulses originating from the compound eye of the locust. *Nature*, **170**, 285.

BURTT, E. T., and CATTON, W. T. (1954) Visual perception of movement in the locust. *J. Physiol.*, **125**, 566–80.

BURTT, E. T., and CATTON, W. T. (1958) Visual acuity of the compound eye in three species of insects. *XV Internat. Congr. Zool., London.*

BUSNEL, M. C. (1953) Contributions a l'étude des émissions acoustiques des Orthoptères. *Ann. Inst. Nat. Recherche Agron., Ser. C, Ann. Épiphyties*, **4**, 333–421.

BUSNEL, M. C., and BUSNEL, R. G. (1956) Sur une phonocinèse de certains Acridiens à des signaux acoustiques synthétiques. *C.R. Acad. Sci. Paris*, **242**, 292–5.

BUSNEL, R. G. (ed.) (1955a) *Colloque sur L'acoustique des Orthoptères.* Fascicule Hors Série des Ann. Épiphyties, 448 pp.

BUSNEL, R. G. (1955 b) Mise en évidence d'un caractère physique réactogène essentiel de signaux acoustiques synthétiques déclenchant les phonotropismes dans le règne animal. *C.R. Acad. Sci., Paris*, **240**, 1477–9.

BUSNEL, R. G., and CHAVASSE, P. (1950) Recherches sur les émissions sonores et ultrasonores d'Orthopterès nuisibles à l'agriculture. Étude des fréquences. *Nuovo Cimento*, Suppl. 7 (Series IX), 470–86.

BUSNEL, R. G., and LOHER, W. (1953) Recherches sur le comportement de divers Acridoidea mâles seumis à des stimuli acoustiques artificiels. *C.R. Acad. Sci., Paris*, **237**, 1557–9.

BUSNEL, R. G., and LOHER, W. (1954) Recherches sur le comportement de divers males d'acridiens a des signaux acoustiques artificiels. *Ann. Sci. Nat. Zool.*, Ser. 11, 16, 271–81.

BUSNEL, R. G., LOHER, W., and PASQUINELLY, F. (1954) Recherches sur les signaux acoustiques synthétiques réactogènes pour divers Acrididae ♂. *C.R. Soc. Biol. Paris*, **148**, 1987–91.

BUTENANDT, A., BECHMANN, R., STAMM, D., and HECKER, E. (1959) Über den Sexuallockstoff des Seidenspinners *Bombyx mori*. Reindarstellung und Konstitution. *Zeit. Naturf.*, **14b**, 283–4.

CAJAL, S. R. (1909) Nota sobre la estructura de la retina de la Mosca (*Musca vomitoria* L.). *Trabajos deb Lab. de investig. biologicas Univ. Madrid*, **7**, 217–57.

CAJAL, S. R. (1918) Observaciones sobre la estructura de los ocelos y vias nerviosas ocelares de algunos insectos. *Trabajos del Lab. de investig. biologicas Univ. Madrid*, **16**, 109–39.

CAJAL, S. R., and SANCHEZ, D. (1915) Contribucion al conocimiento de los centros nerviosos de los insectos. *Trabajas del Lab. de investig. biologicas Univ. Madrid*, **13**, 1–167.

CAMERON, J. W. M. (1938) The reactions of the housefly, *Musca domestica* Linn., to light of different wave-lengths. *Canad. J. Res.*, D, **16**, 307–42.

CHADWICK, L. E. (1939) Some factors which affect the rate of movement of the wings in Drosophila. *Physiol. Zool.*, **12**, 151–60.

CHADWICK, L. E. (1947) The respiratory quotient of Drosophila in flight. *Biol. Bull.*, **93**, 229–39.

CHADWICK, L. E., and DETHIER, V. G. (1947) The relationship between chemical structure and the response of blowflies to tarsal stimulation by aliphatic acids. *J. Gen. Physiol.*, **30**, 255–62.

CHADWICK, L. E., and DETHIER, V. G. (1949) Stimulation of tarsal receptors of the blowfly by aliphatic aldehydes and ketones. *J. Gen. Physiol.*, **32**, 445–52.

CHILD, C. M. (1894) Ein bisher wenig beachtetes antennales Sinnesorgan der Insekten, mit besonderer Berucksichtigung der Culiciden und Chironomiden. *Zeit. wiss. Zool.*, **58**, 475–528.

COOK, W. C. (1926) The effectiveness of certain paraffin derivatives in attracting flies. *J. Agr. Res.*, **32**, 347–58.

CORNWELL, P. P. (1955) The functions of the ocelli of *Calliphora* (Diptera) and *Locusta* (Orthoptera). *J. Exp. Biol.*, **32**, 217–37.

CRAGG, J. B., and COLE, P. (1956) Laboratory studies on the chemosensory reactions of blowflies. *Ann. Appl. Biol.*, **44**, 478–91.

CRESCITELLI, F., and JAHN, T. L. (1939) The electrical response of the dark-adapted grasshopper eye to various intensities of illumination and to different qualities of light. *J. Cell. Comp. Physiol.*, **19**, 105–12.

CRESCITELLI, F., and JAHN, T. L. (1942) Oscillatory electrical activity from the insect compound eye. *J. Cell. Comp. Physiol.*, **19**, 47–66.

CROMBIE, A. C. (1944) On the measurement and modification of the olfactory responses of blowflies. *J. Exp. Biol.*, **20**, 159–66.

CROZIER, W. J., WOLF, E., and ZERRAHN-WOLF, G. (1937) Critical illumination and critical frequency for response to flickered light, in dragonfly larvae. *J. Gen. Physiol.*, **20**, 363–92.

DAHLBERG, A. C., and PENCZEK, E. S. (1941) The relative sweetness of sugars as affected by concentration. *N.Y. State Ag. Exp. Sta. Tech. Bull.*, **258**, 3–12.

DANNEEL, R., and ZEUTZSCHEL, B. (1957) Über den Feinbau der Retinula bei *Drosophila melanogaster*. *Zeit. Naturforsch.*, **126**, 580–3.

DAUMER, K. (1956) Reizmetrische Untersuchungen des Farbensehens der Bienen. *Zeit. vergl. Physiol.*, **38**, 413–78.

DAUMER, K. (1958) Blumenfarben, wie sie die Bienen sehen. *Zeit. vergl. Physiol.*, **41**, 49–110.

DAVIES, J. T. (1953 a) Olfactory stimulation; some ideas and possible model systems. *Inter. Perfumer*, **3**, 17–22.

DAVIES, J. T. (1953 b) L'odeur et la morphologie des molecules. *Industrie de la Parfumerie*, **8**, 74.

DAVIES, J. T., and TAYLOR, F. H. (1959) The role of adsorption and molecular morphology in olfaction: the calculation of olfactory thresholds. *Biol. Bull.*, **117**, 222–38.

DAVIS, H. (1961) Some principles of sensory receptor action. *Physiol. Rev.*, **41**, 391–416.

DAY, M. F. (1950) The histology of a very large insect, *Macropanesthia rhinocerus* Sauss. (Blattidae). *Australian J. Sci. Res, Ser. B, Biol. Sci.*, **3**, 61–75.

DEBAISIEUX, P. (1935) Organes scolopidiaux des pattes d'insectes. I. Lépidopterès et Trichoptères. *La Cellule*, **44**, 273–314.

DEBAISIEUX, P. (1938) Organes scolopidiaux des pattes d'insectes. II. *La Cellule*, **47**, 77–102.

DEBAUCHE, H. (1935) Recherches sur les organes sensoriels antennaires de *Hydropsyche longipennis* Curt (Trichoptera-Hydropsychidae). *La Cellule*, **44**, 46–84.

DEBAUCHE, H. (1936) Étude cytologique et comparée de l'organe de Johnston des insectes. *La Cellule*, **45**, 77–148.

DEEGENER, P. (1909) Über ein neues Sinnesorgan am Abdomen der Noctuiden. *Zool. Jahrb. Anat.*, **27**, 631–50.

DEMOLL, R. (1917) *Die Sinnesorgane der Arthropoden ihr Bau und ihre Funktion.* Frieder. Vieweg & Sohn, Braunschweig, 243 pp.

DEONIER, C. C. (1938) Effects of some common poisons in sucrose solutions on the chemoreceptors of the housefly, *Musca domestica* L. *J. Econ. Ent.*, **31**, 742–45.

DEONIER, C. C. (1939) Responses of the blowflies Cochliomyia americana C. & P. and Phormia regina Meigen, to stimulation of the tarsal receptors. *Ann. Ent. Soc. Amer.*, **32**, 526–32.

DETHIER, V. G. (1941) The function of the antennal receptors in lepidopterous larvae. *Biol. Bull.*, **80**, 403–14.

DETHIER, V. G. (1942) The dioptric apparatus of lateral ocelli. I. The corneal lens. *J. Cell. Comp. Physiol.*, **19**, 301–13.

DETHIER, V. G. (1943) The dipotric apparatus of lateral ocelli. II. Visual capacities of the ocellus. *J. Cell. Comp. Physiol.*, **22**, 115–26.

DETHIER, V. G. (1947 a) The role of the antennae in the orientation of carrion beetles to odor. *J.N.Y. Ent. Soc.*, **55**, 285–93.

DETHIER, V. G. (1947 b) *Chemical Insect Attractants and Repellents.* Blakiston, Philadelphia.

DETHIER, V. G. (1947 c). The response of hymenopterous parasites to chemical stimulation of the ovipositor. *J. Exp. Zool.*, **105**, 199–208.

DETHIER, V. G. (1951) The limiting mechanism in tarsal chemoreception. *J. Gen. Physiol.*, **35**, 55–65.

DETHIER, V. G. (1952 a) Taste sensitivity to homologous alcohols in oil. *Fed. Proc.*, **11**, 34.

DETHIER, V. G. (1952 b) The relation between olfactory response and receptor population in the blowfly. *Biol. Bull.*, **102**, 111–17.

DETHIER, V. G. (1953 a) Chemoreception. In *Insect Physiology*, ed. K. D. Roeder. John Wiley, New York, pp. 544–76.

DETHIER, V. G. (1953 b) Summation and inhibition following contralateral stimulation of the tarsal chemoreceptors of the blowfly. *Biol. Bull.*, **105**, 257–68.

DETHIER, V. G. (1953 c) Vision. In *Insect Physiology*, ed. K. D. Roeder, John Wiley, New York, pp. 488–522.

DETHIER, V. G. (1954 a) Olfactory responses of blowflies to aliphatic aldehydes. *J. Gen. Physiol.*, **37**, 743–51.

DETHIER, V. G. (1954 b) The physiology of olfaction in insects. *Ann. N. Y. Acad. Sci.*, **58**, 139–57.

DETHIER, V. G. (1955 a) The physiology and histology of the contact chemoreceptors of the blowfly. *Quart. Rev. Biol.*, **30**, 348–71.

DETHIER, V. G. (1955 b) Tarsal chemoreceptors of the housefly. *Proc. Roy. Ent. Soc. Lond.*, **(A)3**, 87–90.

DETHIER, V. G. (1956) Chemoreceptor Mechanisms. In *Molecular Structure and Functional Activity of Nerve Cells*. A.I.B.S., Washington, D.C., pp. 1–30.

DETHIER, V. G. (1957) Chemoreception and the behavior of insects. In *Survey of Biological Progress*, Vol. III, ed. B. Glass. Academic Press, New York, pp. 149–83.

DETHIER, V. G. (1961) Behavioral aspects of protein ingestion by the blowfly Phormia regina Meigen. *Biol. Bull.*, **121**, 456–70.

DETHIER, V. G. (1962) Chemoreceptor mechanisms in insects. *Symp. Soc. Exp. Biol.* **16**, 180–96.

DETHIER, V. G., and ARAB, Y. (1958) Effect of temperature on the contact chemoreceptors of the blowfly. *J. Ins. Physiol.*, **2**, 153–61.

DETHIER, V. G., and CHADWICK, L. E. (1947) Rejection thresholds of the blowfly for a series of aliphatic alcohols. *J. Gen. Physiol.*, **30**, 247–53.

DETHIER, V. G., and CHADWICK, L. E. (1948 a) Chemoreception in insects. *Physiol. Rev.*, **28**, 220–54.

DETHIER, V. G., and CHADWICK, L. E. (1948 b) The stimulating effect of glycols and their polymers on the tarsal receptors of blowflies. *J. Gen. Physiol.*, **32**, 139–51.

DETHIER, V. G., and CHADWICK, L. E. (1950) An analysis of the relationship between solubility and stimulating effect in tarsal chemoreception. *J. Gen. Physiol.*, **33**, 589–99.

DETHIER, V. G., and EVANS, D. R. (1961) The physiological control of water ingestion in the blowfly. *Biol. Bull.*, **121**, 108–16.

DETHIER, V. G., EVANS, D. R., and RHOADES, M. V. (1956) Some factors controlling the ingestion of carbohydrates by the blowfly. *Biol Bull.*, **111**, 204–22.

DETHIER, V. G., HACKLEY, B. E., and WAGNER-JAUREGG, T. (1952) Attraction of flies by iso-valeraldehyde. *Science*, **115**, 141–2.

DETHIER, V. G., and RHOADES, M. V. (1954) Sugar preference-aversion functions for the blowfly. *J. Exp. Zool.*, **126**, 177–203.

DETHIER, V. G., and WOLBARSHT, M. L. (1956) The electronmicroscopy of chemosensory hairs. *Experientia*, **12**, 335.

DETHIER, V. G., and YOST, M. T. (1952) Olfactory stimulation of blowflies by homologous alcohols. *J. Gen. Physiol.*, **35**, 823–39.

DIAKONOFF, A. (1936) Contributions to the knowledge of the fly reflexes and the static sense in *Periplaneta americana* L. *Arch. Neerl. Physiol.*, **21**, 104–29.

DINGLE, H. (1961) Flight and swimming reflexes in giant water bugs. *Biol. Bull.*, **121**, 117–28.

DODDS, S. E., and EWER, D. W. (1952) Effect of desiccation on the humidity response of Tenebrio. *Nature*, **170**, 758.

DONNER, K. O., and KRISZAT, G. (1950) Die electrophysiologisch bestimmte Sensitivitätsverteilung des Fliegenauges im sichtbaren Spektrum. *Arkiv. Zool.*, **42A**, 1–7.

DOSTAL, B. (1958) Riechfähigkeit und Zahe der Riechsinneselemente bei der Honigbiene. *Zeit. vergl. Physiol.*, **41**, 179–203.

DRESDEN, D., and NIJENHUIS, E. D. (1958) Fibre analysis of the nerves of the second thoracic leg in Periplaneta americana. *Proc. Kon. Nederl. Akad. Wetensch. Amsterdam*, C, **61**, 213–23.

EDNEY, E. B. (1957) *The Water Relations of Terrestrial Arthropods.* Cambridge Univ. Press, 109 pp.

EGER, H. (1937) Über den Geschmackssinn von Schmetterlingsraupen. *Biol. Zbl.*, **57**, 293–308.

EGGERS, F. (1911) Über des thoracale Tympanal-Organ der Noctuiden. *Sitzber. Naturf. Ges. Univ. Jurjew (Dorpat.)*, **20**, 138–45.

EGGERS, F. (1919) Das thoracale bitympanale Organ einer Gruppe der Lepidoptera Heterocera. *Zool. Jahrb. Anat.*, **41**, 273–376.

EGGERS, F. (1923) Ergebnisse von Untersuchungen am Johnstonschen Organ der Insekten und ihre Bedeutung für die allgemeine Beurteilung der stiftführenden Sinnesorgane. *Zool. Anz.*, **57**, 224–40.

EGGERS, F. (1924) Zur Kenntnis der antennalen stiftführenden Sinnesorgane der Insekten. *Zeit. Morph. Ökol. Tiere*, **2**, 259–349.

EGGERS, F. (1925) Versuche über das Gehör der Noctuiden. *Zeit. vergl. Physiol.*, **2**, 297–314.

EGGERS, F. (1926a) Beobachtungen über die Verknüpfung von Gehör und Fluchtinstinkt bei Eulenschmetterlingen. *Schriften Naturw. Vereins Schleswig-Holstein*, **17**, 325–33.

EGGERS, F. (1926b) Die mutmassliche Funktion des Johnstonschen Sinnesorgans bei Gyrinus. *Zool. Anz.*, **68**, 184–92.

EGGERS, F. (1927) Nähere Mitteilungen über Johnstonsche Sinnesorgane und über das Ausweichmermögen der Taumelköfer. *Zool. Anz.*, **71**, 136–56.

EGGERS, F. (1928) Die stiftführenden Sinnesorgane. *Zool. Bausteine*, **2**, 1–353.

EGUCHI, E., NAKA, K.-I., and KUWABARA, M. (1962) The development of the rhabdom and the appearance of the electrical response in the insect eye. *J. Gen. Physiol.*, **46**, 143–57.

EHRENSVÄRD, G. (1942) Über die Primärvorgänge bei Chemozeptorenbeeinflussung. *Acta Physiol. Scand.*, **3** (Suppl. 9), 1–151.

ERHARDT, E. (1916) Zur kenntnis der Innervierung und Sinnesorgane der Flügel von Insekten. *Zool. Jahrb. Anat. Ontog.*, **39**, 293–334.

ERNST, E. (1957) Der Einfluss der Luftfeuchtigkeit auf Lebensdauer und Verhalten verschiedener Termitenarten. *Acta Tropica (Basel)*, **14**, 97–156.

EVANS, D. R. (1958) The differential sensitivity of the two neurons in the contact chemoreceptors of the blowfly. *Anat. Rec.*, 132, 433–4.

EVANS, D. R. (1961 a) Control of the responsiveness of the blowfly to water. *Nature*, **190**, 1132–3.

EVANS, D. R. (1961 b) Depression of taste sensitivity to specific sugars by their presence during development. *Science*, **133**, 327–8.

EVANS, D. R., and MELLON, DeF. (1962 a) Electrophysiological studies of a water receptor associated with the taste sensilla of the blowfly. *J. Gen. Physiol.*, **45**, 487–500.

EVANS, D. R., and MELLON, DeF. (1962 b) Stimulation of a primary taste receptor by salts. *J. Gen. Physiol.*, **45**, 651–61.

EXNER, S. (1891) *Die Physiologie der Facetierten Augen von Krebsen und Insecten.* Franz Deuticke, Leipzig and Wien, 206 pp.

EYER, J. R., and MEDLER, J. T. (1940) Attractiveness to codling moth of substances related to those elaborated by heterofermentative bacteria in baits. *J. Econ. Ent.*, **33**, 933–40.

EYZAGUIRRE, C., and KUFFLER, S. W. (1955) Process of excitation in the dendrites and in the soma of single isolated sensory nerve cells of the lobster and crayfish. *J. Gen. Physiol.*, **39**, 87–119.

FAUST, R. (1952) Untersuchungen zum Halterenproblem. *Zool. Jahrb. Allg. Zool. Physiol.*, **63**, 325–66.

FERGUSON, J. (1951) Relations between thermodynamic indices of narcotic potency and the molecular structure of narcotics. In *Mecanisme de la Narcose*. Coll. Internat. Centre Nat. Rech. Sci., **26**, 25–39.

FERNÁNDEZ-MORÁN, H. (1956) Fine structure of the insect retinula as revealed by electron microscopy. *Nature*, **177**, 742–3.

FERNÁNDEZ-MORÁN, H. (1958) Fine structure of the light receptors in the compound eye of insects. *Exp. Cell. Res.*, Suppl. 5, 586–644.

FINGERMAN, M. (1952) The role of the eye-pigments of *Drosophila melanogaster* in photic orientation. *J. Exp. Zool.*, **120**, 131–64.

FINGERMAN, M., and BROWN, F. A. (1952) A 'Purkinje shift' in insect vision. *Science*, **116**, 171–2.

FINGERMAN, M., and BROWN, F. A. (1953) Color discrimination and physiological duplicity of Drosophila vision. *Physiol. Zool.*, **26**, 59–67.

FINLAYSON, L. H., and LOWENSTEIN, O. (1955) A proprioceptor in the body musculature of Lepidoptera. *Nature*, **176**, 1031.

FINLAYSON, L. H., and LOWENSTEIN, O. (1958) The structure and function of abdominal stretch receptors in insects. *Proc. Roy. Soc.*, B, **148**, 433–49.

FISCHER, W. (1957) Untersuchungen über die Riechschärfe der Honigbiene. *Zeit. vergl. Physiol.*, **39**, 634–59.

FOLSOM, J. W. (1931) A chemotropometer. *J. Econ. Ent.*, **24**, 827–33.

FOLSOM, J. W., and WARDLE, R. A. (1943) *Entomology with Special Reference to Its Ecological Aspects*, 4th Ed. Blakiston, Phila., p. 30.

FOREL, A. (1908) *The Senses of Insects*. Methuen, London.

FRAENKEL, G. (1932) Untersuchungen über die Koordination von Reflexen und automatischnervösen Rhythmen bei Insekten. I. die Flugreflexe der Insekten und ihre Koordination. *Zeit. vergl. Physiol.*, **16**, 371–93.

FRIEDMAN, S. (1959) Sustained flight in Phormia (by a new method) and its effect on blood pH. *J. Ins. Physiol*, **3**, 118–19.

FRIEDRICH, H. (1929) Vergleichende Untersuchungen über die tibialen Scolopalorgane einiger Orthopteren. *Zeit. wiss. Zool.*, **134**, 84–148.

FRINGS, H. (1941) The loci of olfactory end-organs in the blowfly, Cynomyia cadaverina Desvoidy. *J. Exp. Zool.*, **88**, 65–93.

FRINGS, H. (1944) The loci of olfactory end-organs in the honey-bee, Apis mellifera Linn. *J. Exp. Zool.*, **97**, 123–34.

FRINGS, H. (1945) Gustatory rejection thresholds for the larvae of the cecropia moth, Samia cecropia (Linn.). *Biol. Bull.*, **88**, 37–43.

FRINGS, H. (1946) Gustatory thresholds for sucrose and electrolytes for the cockroach, *Periplaneta americana* (Linn.). *J. Exp. Zool.*, **102**, 23–50.

FRINGS, H. (1948) A contribution to the comparative physiology of contact chemoreception. *J. Comp. Physiol. Psychol.*, **41**, 25–34.

FRINGS, H., and FRINGS, M. (1949) The loci of contact chemoreceptors in insects. *Am. Midl. Nat.*, **41**, 602–58.

FRINGS, H., and FRINGS, M. (1956) Reactions to sounds by the wood nymph butterfly, Cercyonis pegala. *Ann. Ent. Soc. Amer.*, **49**, 611–17.

FRINGS, H., and FRINGS, M. (1957) Duplex nature of reception of simple sounds in the scape moth, Ctenucha virginica. *Science*, **126**, 24.

FRINGS, H., and FRINGS, M. (1958) Uses of sounds by insects. *Ann. Rev. Ent.*, **3**, 87–106.

FRINGS, H., and O'NEAL, B. R. (1946) The loci and thresholds of contact chemoreceptors in females of the horsefly, Tabanus sulcifrons Macq. *J. Exp. Zool.*, **103**, 61–80.

VON FRISCH, K. (1914) Der Farbensinn und Formensinn der Biene. *Zool. Jahrb. Physiol.*, **37**, 1–238.

VON FRISCH, K. (1919) Über den Geruchsinn der Biene und seine blutenbiologische Bedeutung. *Zool. Jahrb. Zool. Physiol.*, **37**, 1–238.

VON FRISCH, K. (1921) Über den Sitz des Geruchsinnes bei Insekten. *Zool. Jahrb. Zool. Physiol.*, **38**, 449–516.

VON FRISCH, K. (1930) Versuche über den Geschmackssin der Bienen. *Naturwiss.*, **18**, 169–74.

VON FRISCH, K. (1935) Über den Geschmackssinn der Biene. *Zeit. vergl. Physiol.*, **21**, 1–156.

VON FRISCH, K. (1948) Gelöste und ungelöste Rätsel der Bienensprache. *Naturwiss.*, **35**, 38–43.

VON FRISCH, K. (1949) Die Polarisation des Himmelslichtes als orientierender Faktor bei den Tänzen der Bienen. *Experientia*, **5**, 142–8.

VON FRISCH, K. (1950 a) Die Sonne als Kompass im Leben der Bienen. *Experientia*, **6**, 210–21.

VON FRISCH, K. (1950 b) *Bees. Their Vision, Chemical Senses, and Language*. Cornell Univ. Press.

VON FRISCH, K. (1960) Wahrnehmung der Schwingungsrichtung polarisierten Lichtes bei Bienen. *Bayerische Akad. Wiss., Math. Naturwiss. Kl.*, Sitz. 3 Juni 1960, 1–3.

VON FRISCH, K., and LINDAUER, M. (1956) The 'language' and orientation of the honey bee. *Ann. Rev. Ent.*, **1**, 45–58.

VON FRISCH, K., LINDAUER, M., and DAUMER, K. (1960) Über die Wahrnehmung polarsierten Lichtes durch das Bienenauge. *Experientia*, **16**, 289–301.

FRY, W. J., WULFF, V. J., and BRUST, M. (1955) Retinal action potential-effect of temperature on magnitude and latency in the grasshopper. *J. Cell. Comp. Physiol.*, **45**, 265–72.

FULTON, B. B. (1928) Sound perception by insects. *Sci. Monthly*, **27**, 552–6.

FYG, W. (1960) Über die Kristallkegel in den Komplexaugen der Honigbiene. *Mitteilungen Schweiz. Ent. Ges.*, **33**, 185–94.

GAFFRON, M. (1934) Untersuchungen über das Bewegungssehen bei Libellenlarve, Fliegen und Fischen. *Zeit. vergl. Physiol.*, **20**, 299–337.

GETTRUP, E. (1962) Thoracic proprioceptors in the flight system of Locusts. *Nature*, **193**, 498–9.

GOLDSMITH, T. H. (1958 a) The visual system of the honeybee. *Proc. Nat. Acad. Sci.*, **44**, 123–6.

GOLDSMITH, T. H. (1958 b) On the visual system of the bee (*Apis mellifera*). *Ann. N.Y. Acad. Sci.*, **74**, 223–9.

GOLDSMITH, T. H. (1960) The nature of the retinal action potential, and the spectral sensitivities of the ultra violet and green receptor systems of the compound eye of the worker honeybee. *J. Gen. Physiol.*, **43**, 775–99.

GOLDSMITH, T. H. (1961) The color vision of insects. In *Light and Life*, eds. W. D. McElroy and B. Glass. The Johns Hopkins Press, Baltimore, pp. 771–94.

GOLDSMITH, T. H., and PHILPOTT, D. C. (1957) The microstructure of the compound eye of insects. *J. Biophys. Biochem. Cytol.*, **3**, 429–40.

GOLDSMITH, T. H., and RUCK, P. R. (1958) The spectral sensitivities of the dorsal ocelli of cockroaches and honeybees. *J. Gen. Physiol.*, **41**, 1171–85.

GOODWIN, T. W., and SRISUKH, S. (1949) The carotenoids of the integument of two locust species (*Locusta migratoria migratorioides* R. & F. and *Schistocerca gregaria* Forsk.). *Biochem. J.*, **45**, 263–7.

GÖRNER, P. (1957) Die optische und kinästhetische Orientierung der Trichterspinne *Agelena labyrinthica* (Cl.). *Zeit vergl. Physiol.*, **41**, 111–53.

GOTTSCHE, C. M. (1852) Beitrag zur Anatomie und Physiologie des Auges der Krebse und Fliegen. *Archiv. für Anatomie und Physiologie*, 1852, 483–92.

GÖTZE, G. (1927) Untersuchungen an Hymenopteren über das Vorkommen und die Bedeutung der Stirnaugen. *Zool. Jahrb. Zool. Physiol.*, **44**, 211–68.

GRABER, V. (1882 a) Die chordotonalen Sinnesorgane und das Gehör der Insecten. *Archiv. f. mikroskopische Anatomie*, **20**, 506–640.

GRABER, V. (1882 b) Die chordotonalen Sinnesorgane und das Gehör der Insecten. *Archiv. f. mikroskopische Anatomie*, **21**, 65–145.

GRABOWSKI, C. T., and DETHIER, V. G. (1954) The structure of the tarsal chemoreceptors of the blowfly, *Phormia regina* Meigen. *J. Morph.*, **94**, 1–20.

GRAHAM, C. H., and HARTLINE, H. K. (1935) The response of single visual sense cells to lights of different wavelengths. *J. Gen. Physiol.*, **13**, 105–12.

GRANIT, R. (1947) *Sensory Mechanisms of the Retina.* Oxford Univ. Press.

GRANIT, R. (1955) *Receptors and Sensory Perception.* Yale Univ. Press, New Haven, 369 pp.

GRAY, E. G. (1960) The fine structure of the insect ear. *Phil. Trans. Roy. Soc. Lond.*, B, **243**, 75–94.

GRAY, E. G., and PUMPHREY, R. J. (1958) Ultra-structure of the insect ear. *Nature*, **181**, 618.

GRAY, J. A. B., and SATO, M. (1953) Properties of the receptor potential in Pacinian corpuscles. *J. Physiol.*, **122**, 610–36.

GREEN, G. W. (1954) Humidity reactions and water balance of larvae of *Neodiprion americanus banksianae* Rob. and *N. lecontei* (Fitch) (Hymenoptera: Diprionidae). *Canad. Ent.*, **86**, 261–74.

GRENACHER, H. (1879) *Untersuchungen über die Sehorgan der Arthropoden.* Göttingen, pp. 1–188.

GRIFFIN, D. R. (1950) Measurements of the ultrasonic cries of bats. *J. Acoust. Soc. Amer.*, **22**, 247–55.

GRIFFIN, D. R. (1953) Bat sounds under natural conditions, with evidence for echolocation of insect prey. *J. Exp. Zool.*, **123**, 435–66.

GUNN, D. L., and COSWAY, C. A. (1938) The temperature and humidity relations of the cockroach. V. Humidity preference. *J. Exp. Biol.*, **15**, 555–63.

GUNN, D. L., and PIELOU, D. P. (1940) The humidity behaviour of the mealworm beetle, Tenebrio molitor L. III. The mechanism of the reaction. *J. Exp. Biol.*, **17**, 307–16.

GÜNTHER, K. (1912) Die Sehorgane der Larve und Imago von Dytiscus marginalis. *Zeit. wiss. Zool.*, **100**, 60–115.

HAFEZ, M. (1950) On the behaviour and sensory physiology of the house-fly larva, Musca domestica L. I. Feeding stage. *Parasitol.*, **40**, 215–36.

HAFEZ, M. (1953) On the behaviour and sensory physiology of the house-fly larva, Musca domestica L. II. Prepupating stage. *J. Exp. Zool.*, **124**, 199–225.

HAFFER, O. (1921) Bau und Funktion der Sternwarzen von *Saturnia pyri* Schiff. und die Haarentwicklung der Saturnidenraupen. Ein Beitrag zu dem Thema: Das Arthropodenhaar. *Arch. Natg. Berlin*, A, **87** (2), 110–66.

HAGEMANN, J. (1910) Beiträge zur Kenntnis von *Corixa*. *Zool. Jahrb. Anat. Ontog.*, **30**, 373–426.

HAMILTON, M. A. (1931) The morphology of the water-scorpion, *Nepa cinerea* Linn. (Rhymchota, Heteroptera). *Proc. Zool. Soc. Lond.*, 1067–136.

HAMILTON, W. F. (1922) A direct method of testing color vision in lower animals. *Proc. Nat. Acad. Sci.*, **8**, 350–3.

HANSON, F. E., and WOLBARSHT, M. L. (1962) Dendritic action potentials in insect chemoreceptors. *Amer. Zool.*, **2**, 528.

HANSTRÖM, B. (1927) Über die Frage, ob funktionell verschiedene, Zapfen-und Stäbchenartige Sehzellen im Komplexauge der Arthropoden vorkommen. *Zeit. vergl. Physiol.*, **6**, 566–97.

HANSTRÖM, B. (1928) *Vergleichende Anatomie des Nervensystems der wirbellosen Tiere unter Berüchsichtigung seiner Funktion.* J. Springer, Berlin.

HARKER, J. E. (1956) Factors controlling the diurnal rhythm of activity of *Periplaneta americana* L. *J. Exp. Biol.*, **33**, 224–234.

HARTLINE, H. K. (1928) A quantitative and descriptive study of the electric response to illumination of the arthropod eye. *Amer. J. Physiol.*, **83**, 466–83.

HARTLINE, H. K. (1930) The dark adaptation of the eye of Limulus, as manifested by its electrical response to illumination. *J. Gen. Physiol.*, **13**, 379–89.

HARTLINE, H. K. (1934) Intensity and duration in the excitation of single photoreceptor units. *J. Cell. Comp. Physiol.*, **5**, 229–47.

HARTLINE, H. K. (1935) The discharge of nerve impulses from the single visual sense cell. *Cold Spring Harbor Symp. Quant. Biol.*, **3**, 245–9.

HARTLINE, H. K., and GRAHAM, C. H. (1934) The spectral sensitivity of single visual sense cells. *Amer. J. Physiol.*, **109**, 49–50.

HARTLINE, H. K., and McDONALD, P. R. (1947) Light and dark adaptation of single photoreceptor elements in the eye of Limulus. *J. Cell. Comp. Physiol.*, **30**, 225–53.

HARTLINE, H. K., WAGNER, H. G., and MACNICHOL, E. F. (1952) The peripheral origin of nervous activity in the visual system. *Cold Spring Harbor Symp. Quant. Biol.*, **17**, 125–41.

HASKELL, P. T. (1955) Intensité sonore des stridulations de quelques Orthopterès Britannique. In *Colloque sur L'acoustique des Orthopterès*, ed R. G. Busnel. Fascicule Hors Série des Ann. Épiphyties, pp. 154–67.

HASKELL, P. T. (1956 a) Hearing in certain Orthoptera. I. Physiology of sound receptors. *J. Exp. Biol.*, **33**, 756–66.

HASKELL, P. T. (1956 b) Hearing in certain Orthoptera. II. The nature of the response of certain receptors to natural and imitation stridulation. *J. Exp. Biol.*, **33**, 767–76.

HASKELL, P. T. (1957) The influence of flight noise on behaviour in the desert locust *Schistocerca gregaria* (Forsk). *J. Ins. Physiol.*, **1**, 52–75.

HASKELL, P. T., and BELTON, P. (1956) Electrical responses of certain lepidopterous tympanal organs. *Nature*, **177**, 139–40.

HASLINGER, F. (1935) Über den Geschmackssinn von *Calliphora erythrocephala* Meigen und die Verwertung von Zuckern und Zuckeralkoholen durch diese Fliege. *Zeit. vergl. Physiol.*, **22**, 614–40.

HASSENSTEIN, B. (1951) Ommatidienraster und afferente Bewegungsintegration. *Zeit. vergl. Physiol.*, **33**, 301–26.

HASSENSTEIN, B. (1957) Uber Belichtungspotentiale in den Augen der Fliegen *Sarcophaga* und *Eristalis*. *J. Ins. Physiol.*, **1**, 124–30.

HASSENSTEIN, B. (1958) Über die Wahrnehmung der Bewegung von Figueren und unregelmässigen Helligkeitsmustern. *Zeit. vergl. Physiol.*, **40**, 556–92.

HASSENSTEIN, B. (1959) Optokinetische Wirksamkeit bewegter periodischer Muster (Nach Messungen am Rüsselkäfer *Chlorophanus viridis*). *Zeit. Naturf.*, **14B**, 659–74.

HASSENSTEIN, B., and REICHARDT, W. (1956) Analyse der Zeit-, Reihenfolgen- und Systemtheoretische bei der Bewegungsperzeption des Vorzeichenauswertung Rüsselkäfers *Chlorophanus*. *Zeit. Naturf.*, **11B**, 513–24.

HASSETT, C. C., DETHIER, V. G., and GANS, J. (1950) A comparison of nutritive values and taste thresholds of carbohydrates for the blowfly. *Biol. Bull.*, **99**, 446–53.

HAUSER, G. (1880) Physiologische und histologische Untersuchungen über das Geruchsorgan der Insekten. *Zeit. wiss. Zool.*, **34**, 367–403.

HECHT, S., and WALD, G. (1934) The visual acuity and intensity descrimination of Drosophila. *J. Gen. Physiol.*, **17**, 517–47.

HECHT, S., and WOLF, E. (1929) The visual acuity of the honey-bee. *J. Gen. Physiol.*, **12**, 727–60.

HEINTZ, E. (1959) La question de la sensibilité des abeilles à l'ultraviolet. *Insectes Sociaux*, **6**, 223–9.

HENKE, K., and RÖNSCH, G. (1951) Über Bildungsgleichheiten in der Entwicklung epidermaler Organe und die Entstehung des Nervensystems im Flügel der Insekten. *Naturwiss.*, **38**, 335–6.

HERAN, H. (1957) Die Bienenantenne als Messorgan der Flugeigengeschwindigkeit. *Naturwiss.*, **44**, 475.

HERAN, H. (1959) Wahrnehmung und Regelung der Flugeigengeschwindigkeit bei *Apis mellifica* L. *Zeit. vergl. Physiol.*, **42**, 103–63.

HERS, J. (1938) Organe tympanal du *Schistocerca gregaria* Forsk. *Proc. 5th Internat. Locust Conference, Brussels*, 434–45.

HERTWICK, M. (1931) Anatomie und Variabilität des Nervensystems und der Sinnesorgane von *Drosophila melanogaster* (Meigen). *Z. wiss Zool.*, **139**, 559–663.

HERTZ, M. (1929 a) Die Organisation des optischen Feldes bei der Biene. I. *Zeit. vergl. Physiol.*, **8**, 693–748.

HERTZ, M. (1929 b) Die organisation des optischen Feldes bei der Biene. II. *Zeit. vergl. Physiol.*, **11**, 107–45.

HERTZ, M. (1931) Die organisation des optischen Feldes bei der Biene. III. *Zeit. vergl. Physiol.*, **14**, 629–74.

HERTZ, M. (1933) Über figurale Intensitäten und Qualitäten in der optischen Wahrnehmung der Biene. *Biol. Zbl.*, **53**, 10–40.

HERTZ, M. (1934) Zu Physiologie des Formen-und Bewegungssehens. I. Optomotorische Versuche an Fliegen. *Zeit. vergl. Physiol.*, **20**, 430–49.

HERTZ, M. (1935 a) Zur Physiologie des Formen-und Bewegungssehens. II. Auflösungsvermögen des Bienenauges und optomotorische Reaktion. *Zeit. vergl. Physiol.*, **21**, 579–603.

HERTZ, M. (1935 b) Zur Physiologie des Formen-und Bewegungssehens. III. Figurale Unterscheidung und reziproke Dressuren bei der Biene. *Zeit. vergl. Physiol.*, **21**, 604–15.

HERTZ, M. (1935 c) Die Untersuchungen über den Formensinn der Honigbiene. *Naturwiss.*, **23**, 618–24.

HERTZ, M. (1937 a) Beitrag zum Farbensinn und Formensinn der Biene. *Zeit. vergl. Physiol.*, **24**, 413–21.

HERTZ, M. (1937 b) Zur Technik und Methode der Bienenversuche mit Farbpapieren und Glasfiltern. *Zeit. vergl. Physiol.*, **25**, 239–50.

HERTZ, M. (1939) New experiments on colour vision in bees. *J. Exp. Biol.*, **16**, 1–18.

HESS, C. (1920) Neues zur Frage nach einem Farbensinne bei Bienen. *Naturwiss.*, **8**, 927–9.

HESS, W. N. (1917) The chordotonal organs and pleural discs of cerambycid larvae. *Ann. Ent. Soc. Amer.*, **10**, 63–78.

HESSE, R. (1901) Untersuchungen über die Organe der Lichtempfindung bei niedere Tieren. VII. Von den Arthropoden-Augen. *Zeit. wiss. Zool.*, **70**, 347–473.

HICKS, J. B. (1857) On a new organ in insects. *J. Proc. Linn. Soc. (Zool.)*, **1**, 136–40.

HINTON H. E. (1955) Sound producing organs in the Lepidoptera. *Proc. Roy. Ent. Soc. Lond.*, C, **20**, 5–6.

HODGSON, E. S. (1951) Rejection thresholds of an aquatic beetle, *Laccophilus maculosus* Germ., to salts and alcohols. *Physiol. Zool.*, **24**, 131–140.

HODGSON, E. S. (1953) Chemoreception in aqueous and gas phases. *Biol. Bull.*, **105**, 115–27.

HODGSON, E. S. (1956 a) Physiology of the labellar sugar receptors of flies. *Anat. Rec.*, **125**, 555.

HODGSON, E. S. (1956 b) Temperature sensitivity of primary chemoreceptors of insects. *Anat. Rec.*, **125**, 560–1.

HODGSON, E. S. (1957) Electrophysiological studies of arthropod chemoreception. II. Responses of labellar chemoreceptors of the blowfly to stimulation by carbohydrates. *J. Ins. Physiol.*, **1**, 240–7.

HODGSON, E. S. (1958 a) Chemoreception in arthropods. *Ann. Rev. Ent.*, **3**, 19–36.

HODGSON, E. S. (1958 b) Electrophysiological studies of arthropod chemoreception. III. Chemoreceptors of terrestrial and fresh water arthropods. *Biol. Bull.*, **115**, 114–25.

HODGSON, E. S., and BARTON BROWNE, L. (1960) Electrophysiology of blowfly taste receptors. *Anat. Rec.*, **137**, 365.

HODGSON, E. S., LETTVIN, J. Y., and ROEDER, K. D. (1955) Physiology of a primary chemoreceptor unit. *Science*, **122**, 417–18.

HODGSON, E. S., and ROEDER, K. D. (1956) Electrophysiological studies of arthropod chemoreception. I. General properties of the labellar chemoreceptors of Diptera. *J. Cell. Comp. Physiol.*, **48**, 51–76.

HOLLICK, F. S. J. (1940) The flight of the dipterous fly *Muscina stabulans* Fallen. *Phil. Trans. Roy. Soc. Lond.*, B, **230**, 357–90.

HOLSTE, G. (1923) Das Gehirn von Dytiscus marginalis L. *Zeit. wiss. Zool.*, **120**, 251–80.

HOMANN, H. (1924) Zum Problem der Ocellenfunktion bei den Insekten. *Zeit. vergl. Physiol.*, **1**, 541–78.

HOYLE, G. (1955) Functioning of the insect ocellar nerve. *J. Exp. Biol.*, **32**, 397–407.

HOYLE, G. (1957) Nervous control of insect muscles. In *Recent Advances in Invertebrate Physiology*. Univ. of Oregon Pub., 1957, pp. 73–78.

HSÜ F. (1938) Étude cytologique et comparée sur les sensilla des insectes. *La Cellule*, **47**, 1–60.

HUGHES, G. M. (1952) Abdominal mechano-receptors in *Dytiscus* and *Locusta*. *Nature*, **170**, 531–32.

HUGHES, G. M. (1957) The co-ordination of insect movements. II. The effect of limb amputation and the cutting of commissures in the cockroach (*Blatta orientalis*). *J. Exp. Biol.*, **34**, 306–33.

HUGHES, G. M. (1958) The co-ordination of insect movements. III. Swimming in *Dytiscus*. *Hydrophilus*, and a dragonfly nymph. *J. Exp. Biol.*, **35**, 567–83.

HUMPHREYS, W. J. (1940) *Physics of the Air*, 3rd ed. McGraw-Hill, New York, 676 pp.

HUNDERTMARK, A. (1936) Helligkeits-und Farbenunterscheidungsvermögen der Eiraupen der Nonne (Lymantria monacha). *Zeit. vergl. Physiol.*, **24**, 42–57.

HUNDERTMARK, A. (1937) Das Formunterscheidungsvermögen der Eiraupen der Nonne (Lymantria monacha). *Zeit. vergl. Physiol.*, **24**, 563–82.

ILSE, D. (1928) Über den Farbensinn der Tagfalter. *Zeit. vergl. Physiol.*, **8**, 658–92.

ILSE, D. (1937) New observations on responses to colours in egg-laying butterflies. *Nature*, **140**, 544–5.

ILSE, D. (1949) Colour discrimination in the dronefly, *Eristalis tenax*. *Nature*, **163**, 255–6.

IMAMURA, S. (1938) Studies on the chemical susceptibility of the Kyôsofly, *Sturmia sericariae* Cornalia. *Bull. Imp. Seri. Exp. Sta.* (Tokyo), **9**, 219–69.

ISHIKAWA, S. (1962) Visual response patterns of single ganglion cells in the optic lobes of the silkworm moth, *Bombyx mori* L. *J. Ins. Physiol.* **8**, 485–92.

ISHIKAWA, S., and HIRAO, T. (1960 a) Electrophysiological studies on vision of the silkworm, *Bombyx mori*. (I) Electroretinogram of stemmata, *J. Sericultural Sci. Japan*, **29**, 8–14. (In Japanese.)

ISHIKAWA, S., and HIRAO, T. (1960 b) Electrophysiological studies on vision of silkworm, *Bombyx mori.* (II) Analyses of ERG in stemmata with special reference to dark- and light-adaptation. *J. Sericultural Sci. Japan*, **29**, 211–17. (In Japanese.)

ISHIKAWA, S., and HIRAO, T. (1960 c) Electrophysiological studies on vision of silkworm, *Bombyx mori.* (III) The effects of temperature on the ERG of the compound eye. *J. Sericultural Sci. Japan*, **24**, 334–6. (In Japanese.)

JACOBS-JESSEN, U. (1959) Zur Orientierung der Hummeln und einiger anderer Hymenopteren. *Zeit. vergl. Physiol.*, **41**, 597–641.

JAHN, T. L. (1946) The electroretinogram as a measure of wave-length sensitivity to light. *J. N.Y. Ent. Soc.*, **54**, 1–8.

JAHN, T. L., and CRESCITELLI, F. (1938) The electrical response of the grasshopper eye under conditions of light and dark adaptation. *J. Cell. Comp. Physiol.*, **12**, 39–55.

JAHN, T. L., and CRESCITELLI, F. (1939) The electrical response of the Cecropia moth eye. *J. Cell. Comp. Physiol.*, **13**, 113–19.

JAHN, T. L., and CRESCITELLI, F. (1940) Diurnal changes in the electrical responses of the compound eye. *Biol. Bull.*, **78**, 42–52.

JAHN, T. L., and WULFF, V. J. (1941 a) Influence of a visual diurnal rhythm on flicker response contours of *Dytiscus. Proc. Soc. Exp. Biol. and Med.*, **48**, 660–5.

JAHN, T. L., and WULFF, V. J. (1941b) Retinal pigment distribution in relation to a diurnal rhythm in the compound eye of Dytiscus. *Proc. Soc. Exp. Biol. Med.*, **48**, 656–60.

JAHN, T. L., and WULFF, V. J. (1942) Allocation of electrical responses from the compound eye of grasshoppers. *J. Gen. Physiol.*, **26**, 75–88.

JAHN, T. L., and WULFF, V. J. (1943) Electrical aspects of a diurnal rhythm in the eye of Dytiscus fasciventris. *Physiol. Zool.*, **16**, 101–9.

JAHN, T. L., and WULFF, V. J. (1948) The spectral sensitivity of Dytiscus fasciventris. *J. N.Y. Ent. Soc.*, **56**, 109–16.

JANDER, R. (1957) Die optische Richtungsorientierung der Roten Waldameise (Formica rufa L.). *Zeit. vergl. Physiol.*, **40**, 162–238.

JANDER, R., and WATERMAN, T. H. (1960) Sensory discrimination between polarized light and light intensity patterns by arthropods. *J. Cell. Comp. Physiol.*, **56**, 137–60.

JOHNSON, B. (1956) Function of the antennae of aphids during flight. *Austral. J. Sci.*, **18**, 199–200.

JOHNSTON, C. (1855) Auditory apparatus of the Culex mosquito. *Quart. J. Micr. Sci.*, Old Series, **3**, 97–102.

JORDAN, K. (1905) Note on a peculiar secondary sexual character found among Geometridae at the sensory organ situated at the base of the abdomen. *Nov. Zool.*, **12**, 506–8.

KALMUS, H. (1958) Responses of insects to polarized light in the presence of dark reflecting surfaces. *Nature*, **182**, 1526–7.

KALMUS, H. (1959) Orientation of animals to polarized light. *Nature*, **184**, 228–30.

KATSUKI, Y., and SUGA, N. (1960) Neural mechanism of hearing in insects. *J. Exp. Biol.*, **37**, 279–90.

KATZ, B. (1950) Depolarization of sensory terminals and the initiation of impulses in the muscle spindle. *J. Physiol.*, **11**, 261–82.

KENNEDY, J. S. (1937) The humidity reactions of the African migratory locust, *Locusta migratoria migratorioides* R. & F., gregarious phase. *J. Exp. Biol.*, **14**, 187–97.

VON KENNEL, J. (1912) Über Tympanalorgane im Abdomen der Spanner und Zünsler. *Zool. Anz.*, **39**, 163–70.

VON KENNEL, J., and EGGERS, F. (1933) Die abdominalen Tympanalorgane der Lepidopteren. *Zool. Jahrb. Anat. Ontog.*, **57**, 1–104.

KEPPLER, E. (1958) Über des Richtungshören von Stechmücken. *Zeit. Naturf.*, **13b**, 285–6.

KIM, C.-W. (1961) Development of the chordotonal organ, olfactory organ and their nerves in the labial palp in *Pieris rapae* L. *Bull. Dept. Biol. Korea Univ.*, **3** (4), 23–30.

KIRSCHFELD, K. (1959) Quantitative Beziehungen zwischen Lichtreiz und Reaktion beim diphasischen Elektroretinogramm. *Zeit. Naturf.*, **14b**, 212–13.

KOEHLER, O. (1924) Sinnesphysiologische Untersuchungen an Libellenlarven. *Verhandl. deut. Zool. Ges. Berlin*, **29**, 83–91.

KRAEPELIN, K. (1833) Über die Geruchsorgane der Gliedertiere. *Osterprogramm*. Realschule Johanneum, Hamburg.

KRUMIŅŠ, R. (1952) Die Borstenewicklung bei der Wachmotte Galleria mellonella L. *Biol. Zbl.*, 183–210.

KÜHN, A. (1927) Über den Farbensinn der Bienen. *Zeit. vergl. Physiol.*, **5**, 762–800.

KÜHN, A., and POHL, R. (1921) Dressurfähigkeit der Bienen auf Spektrallinien. *Naturwiss.*, **9**, 738–40.

KUNZE, G. (1933) Einige Versuche über den Antennengeschmackssinn der Honigbiene. *Zool. Jahrb. Zool. Physiol.*, **52**, 465–512.

KUWABARA, M. (1951) Effects of inorganic ions on the tarsal chemoreceptor of the butterfly, *Vanessa indica*. *Zool. Mag.*, **60**, 9. (In Japanese.)

KUWABARA, M. (1952a) Effects of inorganic salts on the tarsal chemoreceptor of the butterfly, *Vanessa indica* II. *Zool. Mag.*, **61**, 121.

KUWABARA, M. (1952b) Über die Funktion der Antenne der Honigbiene in bezug auf die Raumorientierung. *Mem. Fac. Sci. Kuyshu Univ.*, Ser. E, **1**, 13–64.

KUWABARA, M. (1953) Effects of successive stimulation on the tarsal chemoreceptor of *Vanessa indica. Zool. Mag.*, **62**, 154. (In Japanese.)

KUWABARA, M. (1957) Bildung des bedingten Reflexes von Pavlove Typus bei der Honigbiene, *Apis mellifica. J. Fac. Sci. Hokkaido Univ.*, Ser. VI, **13**, 458–64.

KUWABARA, M. and NAKA, K. (1957) ERG from the compound eye of the honeybee. *Zool. Mag., Tokoyo*, **66**, 112. (In Japanese.)

KUWABARA, M., and TAKEDA, K. (1956) On the hygroceptor of the honeybee, *Apis mellifica. Physiology and Ecology*, **7**, 1–6. (In Japanese.)

LARSEN, J. R. (1962) The fine structure of the labellar chemosensory hairs of the blowfly, *Phormia regina* Meigen. *J. Ins. Physiol.*, **8**, 683–91.

LARSEN, O. (1955) Spezifische Mechanorezeptoren bei Aphelocheirus aestivalis Fabr. nebst. Bemerkungen über die Respiration dieser Wanze. *Lunds Univ. Årsskrift N. F. Avd.* 2, **51** (11), 1–58.

LEES, A. D. (1942) Homology of the campaniform organs on the wing of Drosophila melanogaster. *Nature*, **150**, 375.

LEES, A. D. (1943) On the behaviour of wireworms of the genus *Agriotes* Esch. (Coleoptera, Elateridae). I. Reactions to humidity. *J. Exp. Biol.*, **20**, 43–53.

LEES, A. D. (1948) The sensory physiology of the sheep tick, *Ixodes ricinus* L. *J. Exp. Biol.*, **25**, 145–207.

LEHR, R. (1914) Die Sinnesorgane der Beiden Flügelpaare von *Dytiscus marginalis. Z. wiss. Zool.*, **110**, 87–150.

LEIGHLY, J. (1937) A note on evaporation. *Ecology*, **18**, 180–98.

LEMBERGER, F. (1908) Psychophysische Untersuchungen über den Geschmack von Zucker und Saccharin (Saccharose und Krystallose). *Arch. f. ges. Physiol.*, **123**, 293–311.

LEYDIG, F. (1851) Anatomisches und Histologisches über die Larvae von Corethra plumicornis. *Zeschr. wiss. Zool.*, **3**, 435–51.

LIEBERMANN, A. (1926) Correlation zwischen den antennalen Geruchorganen und der Biologie der Musciden. *Zeit. Morph. Ökol. Tiere*, **4**, 1–97.

LINDAUER, M. (1961) *Communication Among Social Bees.* Harvard Univ. Press, Cambridge, Mass.

LINDAUER, M., and NEDEL, J. O. (1959) Ein Schweresinnesorgan der Honigbiene. *Zeit. vergl. Physiol.*, **42**, 334–64.

LISSMANN, H. W. (1950) Proprioceptors. In *Physiological Mechanisms in Animal Behaviour.* Academic Press, New York, pp. 34–59.

LOHER, W., and BROUGHTON, W. B. (1955) Études sur le comportement acoustique de Chorthippus bicolor (Charp) avec quelques notes comparatives sur les espèces voisines (Acrididae). In

Colloque sur L'acoustique des Orthoptères, ed. R. B. Busnel. Fasciules Hors Série les Ann. Épiphyties, pp. 248–77.

LOTMAR, R. (1933) Neue Untersuchungen über den Farbensinn der Bienen, mit besonderer Berücksichtigung des Ultraviolettes. *Zeit. vergl. Physiol.*, **19**, 673–723.

LOWENSTEIN, O., and FINLAYSON, L. H. (1960) The response of the abdominal stretch receptor of an insect to phasic stimulation. *Comp. Biochem. Physiol.*, **1**, 56–61.

LOWENSTEIN, W. R. (1956) Excitation and changes in adaptation by stretch of mechanoreceptors. *J. Physiol.*, **133**, 588–602.

LOWNE, B. T. (1890) *The Blow-fly*. London.

LUBBOCK, J. (1886) *Ants, Bees, and Wasps*. Pp. 152–68.

LÜDTKE, H. (1953) Retinomotorik und Adaptationsvorgänge im Auge des Rückenschwimmers (Notonecta glauca L.). *Zeit. vergl. Physiol.*, **35**, 129–52.

LÜDTKE, H. (1957) Beziehungen des Feinbaues im Ruckenschwimmerauge zu seiner Fähigkeit, polarisiertes Licht zu analysieren. *Zeit. vergl. Physiol.*, **40**, 329–44.

LUTZ, F. E. (1924) Apparently non-selective characters and combinations of characters, including a study of ultraviolet in relation to the flower-visiting habits of insects. *Ann. N.Y. Acad. Sci.*, **29**, 181–283.

LUTZ, F. E., and GRISEWOOD, E. N. (1934) Reactions of *Drosophila* to 2537 Å radiation. *Am. Mus. Novit.*, **706**, 1–14.

MACHATSCHKE, J. W. (1936) Der cuticuläre Aufban des Rhabdoms im Arthropodenauge. *Vest. Ceskoslov. Zool. Spol.*, **4**, 90–109.

MacNICHOL, E. F., WAGNER, H. G., and HARTLINE, H. K. (1953) Electrical activity recorded within single ommatidia of eye of *Limulus*. *XIX Internat. Physiol. Congress, Montreal*, p. 582.

MARKL, H. (1962) Borstenfelder an den Gelenken als Schweresinnesorgane bei Ameisen und anderen Hymenopteren. *Zeit. vergl. Physiol.*, **45**, 475–569.

MARSHALL, J. (1935) The location of olfactory receptors in insects: a review of experimental evidence. *Trans. Roy. Ent. Soc. Lond.*, **88**, 49–72.

MASSERA, M. G. (1952) Osservazioni preliminari sur potenziali elettrici delle libellule per stimoli luminosi. *Experientia*, **8**, 271–3.

MAYER, A. M. (1874) Experiments on the supposed auditory apparatus of the mosquito. *Am. Nat.*, **8**, 577–92.

McINDOO, N. E. (1914 a) The olfactory sense of insects. *Smithson. Misc. Pub.*, **63**, 1–63.

McINDOO, N. E. (1914 b) The olfactory sense of the honeybee. *J. Exp. Zool.*, **16**, 265–346.

McINDOO, N. E. (1916) The sense organs on the mouthparts of the honey bee. *Smithson. Misc. Coll.*, **65** (14), 1–55.

MELIN, D. (1941) The function of the pore-plates in Hymenoptera. *Zool. Bidr. Uppsala*, **20**, 303–344.

MELLON, D., and EVANS, D. R. (1961) Electrophysiological evidence that water stimulates a fourth sensory cell in the blowfly taste receptor. *Amer. Zoologist*, **1**, 372.

MENZER, G., and STOCKHAMMER, K. (1951) Zur Polarisationsoptik der Fazettenaugen von Insekten. *Naturwiss.*, **38**, 190–1.

MERKER, E. (1929) Die Fluoreszenz im Insektenauge, die Fluoreszenz des Chitins der Insekten und seine Durchlässigkeit für ultraviolettes Licht. *Zool. Jahrb. Zool. Physiol.*, **46**, 483–574.

MILLER, W. H. (1957) Morphology of the ommatidia of the compound eye of Limulus. *J. Biophys. Biochem. Cytol.*, **3**, 421–8.

MILNE, L. J., and MILNE, M. J. (1945) Selection of colored lights by night-flying insects. *Ent. Americana*, **24**, 21–86.

MINNICH, D. E. (1922) The chemical sensitivity of the tarsi of the red admiral butterfly, Pyrameis atalanta Linn. *J. Exp. Zool.*, **35**, 57–81.

MINNICH, D. E. (1925) The reactions of the larvae of Vanessa antiopa Linn. to sounds. *J. Exp. Zool.*, **42**, 443–69.

MINNICH, D. E. (1929 a) The chemical senses of insects. *Quart. Rev. Biol.*, **4**, 100–12.

MINNICH, D. E. (1929 b) The chemical sensitivity of the legs of the blowfly, Calliphora vomitoria Linn., to various sugars. *Zeit. vergl. Physiol.*, **11**, 1–55.

MINNICH, D. E. (1931) The sensitivity of the oral lobes of the proboscis of the blowfly, Calliphora vomitoria Linn., to various sugars. *J. Exp. Zool.*, **60**, 121–39.

MINNICH, D. E. (1932) The contact chemoreceptors of the honey bee, Apis mellifera Linn. *J. Exp. Zool.*, **61**, 375–93.

MINNICH, D. E. (1936) The responses of caterpillars to sounds. *J. Exp. Zool.*, **72**, 439–53.

MINNICH, D. E. (1937) The reactions of fragments of the larvae of *Aglais antiopa* Linn. to sounds. *Bull. Mount Desert Biol. Lab.* 1937, 19–20.

MITTELSTAEDT, H. (1950) Physiologie des Gleichgewichtssinnes bei Fliegenden Libellen. *Zeit. vergl. Physiol.*, **32**, 422–63.

MITTELSTAEDT, H. (1952) Über den Beutefangmechanismus der Mantiden. *Verh. Dtsch. Zool. Ges.*, 1952, 102–6.

MITTELSTAEDT, H. (1954) Regelung und Steuerung bei der Orientierung der Lebewesen. *Regelungstechnik*, 2. Jahrg. 1954 (10), 226–32.

MITTELSTAEDT, H. (1957) Prey capture in mantids. In *Recent Advances in Invertebrate Physiology*. Univ. Oregon Pub., pp. 51–71.

MITTELSTAEDT, H. (1961) Control systems of orientation in insects. *Ann. Rev. Ent.*, **7**, 177–98.

MÖLLER, H. (1921) Über Lethocerus uhleri Mont. *Zool. Jahrb. Abt. Ont. Tiere*, **42**, 43–90.

MOLLER-RACKE, I. (1952) Farbensinn und Farbenblindheit bei Insekten. *Zool. Jb., Jena Allg. Zool.*, **63**, 237–74.

MONCRIEFF, R. W. (1944) *The Chemical Senses.* Leonard Hill, London.

MORITA, H. (1959) Initiation of spike potentials in contact chemosensory hairs of insects. III. D. C. stimulation and generator potential of labellar chemoreceptor of Calliphora. *J. Cell. Comp. Physiol.*, **54**, 189–204.

MORITA, H., DOIRA, S., TAKEDA, K., and KUWABARA, M. (1957) Electrical response of contact chemoreceptor on tarsus of the butterfly, *Vanessa indica. Mem. Fac. Sci. Kyushu Univ.*, Ser. E (Biol.), **2**, 119–39.

MORITA, H., and TAKEDA, K. (1957) The electrical resistance of the tarsal chemosensory hair of the butterfly, *Vanessa indica. J. Fac. Sci. Hokkaido Univ.*, Ser. VI, Zool, **13**, 465–69.

MORITA, H., and TAKEDA, K. (1959) Initiation of spike potentials in contact chemosensory hairs of insects. II. The effect of electric current on tarsal chemosensory hairs of Vanessa. *J. Cell. Comp. Physiol.*, **54**, 177–87.

MORITA, H., and YAMASHITA, S. (1959 a) Generator potential of insect chemoreceptor. *Science*, **130**, 922.

MORITA, H., and YAMASHITA, S. (1959 b) The back-firing of impulses in a labellar chemosensory hair of the fly. *Mem. Fac. Sci. Kyushu Univ.*, Ser. E (Biol.), **3**, 81–87.

MORITA, H., and YAMASHITA, S. (1961) Receptor potentials recorded from sensilla basiconica on the antenna of the silkworm larvae, *Bombyx mori. J. Exp. Biol.*, **38**, 851–61.

MÜLLER, E. (1931) Experimentelle Untersuchungen an Bienen und Ameisen über die Funktionweise der Stirnocellen. *Zeit. vergl. Physiol.*, **14**, 348–84.

MÜLLER, J. (1826) *Zur vergleichenden Physiologie des Gesichtssinnes des Menschen und der Tiere.* Leipzig.

MULLINS, L. J. (1954) Some physical mechanisms in narcosis. *Chem. Rev.*, **54**, 289–323.

MULLINS, L. J. (1955 a) Olfactory thresholds for some homologous series of compounds. *Fed. Proc.*, **14**, 105–6.

MULLINS, L. J. (1955 b) Olfaction. *Ann. N. Y. Acad. Sci.*, **62**, 247–76.

NAKA, K., and EGUCHI, E. (1962) Spike potentials recorded from the insect photoreceptor. *J. Gen. Physiol.*, **45**, 663–80.

NAKA, K., and KUWABARA, M. (1959) Electrical response from the compound eye of *Lucilia. J. Ins. Physiol.*, **3**, 41–49.

NEUHAUS, W. (1953 a) Über die Riechscärfe des Hundes für Fettsäuren. *Zeit. vergl. Physiol.*, **35**, 527–52.

NEUHAUS, W. (1953 b) Die Riechschwellen des Hundes für Jonon und Äthyl-Mercaptan und ihr Verhältnis zu anderen Riechschwellen bei Hund und Mensch. *Zeit. Naturf.*, **9b**, 560–7.

NEWTON, H. C. F. (1931) On the so-called 'olfactory pores' in the honeybee. *Quart. J. Micr. Sci.*, **74**, 647–68.

NIJENHUIS, E. D., and DRESDEN, D. (1952) A micro- and morphological study on the sensory supply of the mesothoracic leg of the american cockroach, *Periplaneta americana. Proc. Kon. Nederl. Akad. Wetensch. Amsterdam*, C, **55**, 300–10.

OEVERMANN, H. (1936) Das statische Verhalten einiger Wasserwanzenarten. *Zeit. wiss. Zool.*, **147**, 595–628.

ORLOV, J. (1924) Die Innervation des Darmes der Insekten (Larven von Lamellicorniern). *Z. wiss. Zool.*, **122**, 425–502.

OSBORNE, M. P. (1963) An electron microscope study of an abdominal stretch receptor of the cockroach. *J. Insect, Physiol.*, **9** (in press).

OSBORNE, M. P., and FINLAYSON, L. H. (1962) The structure and topography of stretch receptors in representatives of seven orders of insects. *Quart. J. Micr. Sci.*, **103**, 227–42.

OSTERHOUT, W. J. V., KAMERLING, S. E., and STANLEY, W. M. (1934) Kinetics of penetration. VII. Molecular versus ionic transport. *J. Gen. Physical.*, **17**, 469–80.

OWEN, W. B. (1962) The contact chemoreceptor organs of the mosquito and their function in feeding behaviour. *J. Insect Physiol.*, **8** (in press).

PAPI, F. (1955) Richerche sull 'orientamento astronomico di Arctosa perita (Latr.) (Araneae-Lycosidae). *Pubbl. Staz. Zool. Napoli*, **27**, 80–107.

PARRY, D. A. (1947) The function of the insect ocellus. *J. Exp. Biol.*, **24**, 211–19.

PASQUINELLY, F., and BUSNEL, M. C. (1955) Études préliminaires sur les mécanismes de la production des sons par les Orthoptères. In *Colloque sur L'acoustique des Orthoptères*, ed. R. B. Busnel. Fascicules Hors Série Ann. Épiphyties, pp. 145–53.

PERTTUNEN, V. (1951) The humidity preferences of various Carabid species (Col., Carabidae) of wet and dry habitats. *Ann. Ent Finnica*, **17**, 72–84.

PERTTUNEN, V. (1953) Reactions of diplopods to the relative humidity of the air. Investigations on Orthomorpha gracilis, Iulus terrestris, and Schizophyllum sabulosum. *Ann. Zool. Soc. 'Vanamo'*, **16**, 1–69.

PERTTUNEN, V. (1955 a) The reversal of the humidity reaction at the onset of the egg-laying period in the diplopod Schizophyllum sabulosum. *Arch. Soc. 'Vanamo'*, **9**, 231–34.

PERTTUNEN, V. (1955 b) The effect of antennectomy on the humidity reactions of normal and desiccated specimens of Schizophyllum sabulosum L. (Diplopoda, Iulidae). *Ann. Ent. Fenn.*, **21**, 157–62.

PERTTUNEN, V., and AHONEN, U. (1956) The effect of age on the humidity reaction of Drosophila melanogaster (Dipt. Drosophilidae). *Ann. Ent. Fennica*, **22**, 63–71.

PERTTUNEN, V., and ERKKILÄ, H. (1952) Humidity reactions in *Drosophila melanogaster*. *Nature*, **169**, 78.

PERTTUNEN, V., and SALMI, H. (1956) The responses of *Drosophila melanogaster* (Dipt. Drosophilidae) to the relative humidity of air. *Ann. Ent. Fennica*, **22**, 36–45.

PERTTUNEN, V., and SYRJÄMÄKI, J. (1958) The effect of antennectomy on the humidity reactions of Drosophila melanogaster (Dipt., Drosophilidae). *Ann. Ent. Fennica*, **24**, 78–83.

PETERS, W. (1961a) Morphologische Untersuchungen an chemischen Sinnesorganen der Schmeissfliege Calliphora erythrocephala Mg. (Diptera). XI Internat. Congress Entomology Vienna 1960, **1**., 407–9.

PETERS, W. (1961b) Die Zahl der Sinneszellen von Marginalborsten und das Vorkommen multipolarer Nervenzellen in den Labellen von Calliphora erythrocephala Mg. (Diptera). *Naturwiss.*, **48** (10), 412–13.

PETERS, W. (1962) Die propiorezeptiven Organe am Prosternum und an den Labellen von *Calliphora erythrocephala* Mg. (Diptera). *Zeit. Morph. Ökol. Tiere*, **51**, 211–26.

PETERSON, A., and HAEUSSLER, G. J. (1928) Response of the oriental peach moth and codling moth to coloured lights. *Ann. Ent. Soc. Amer.*, **21**, 353–79.

PFLUGSTAEDT, H. (1912) Die Halteren der Dipteren. *Zeit. wiss. Zool.*, **100**, 1–59.

PIELEMEIER, W. H. (1946 a) Supersonic insects. *J. Acous. Soc. Amer.*, **17**, 337–8.

PIELEMEIER, W. H. (1946 b) Seeing summer sounds. *Sci. Monthly*, **62**, 450–2.

PIELOU, D. P. (1940) The humidity behaviour of the mealworm beetle, *Tenebrio molitor* L. II. The humidity receptors. *J. Exp. Biol.*, **17**, 295–306.

PIELOU, D. P., and GUNN, D. L. (1940) The humidity behaviour of the mealworm beetle, *Tenebrio molitor* L. I. The reaction to differences of humidity. *J. Exp. Biol.*, **17**, 286–94.

PIERCE, G. W. (1948) *The Songs of Insects*. Harvard Univ. Press.

PIRENNE, M. H. (1943) Binocular and monocular threshold of vision. *Nature*, **152**, 698–9.

PLATEAU, F. (1888) Recherches expérimentales sur la vision chez arthropodes. *Bull. Acad. Roy. Belg.*, Ser. 3, **15**, 28–46.

DEL PORTILLO, J. (1936) Beziehungen zwischen den Öffnungswinkeln der Ommatidien, Krümung und Gestalt der Insektenaugen und ihrer Funktionellen Aufgabe. *Zeit. vergl. Physiol.*, **23**, 100–45.

POWER, M. E. (1943) The brain of Drosophila melanogaster. *J. Morph.*, **72**, 517–60.

PRINGLE, J. W. S. (1938 a) Proprioception in insects. I. A new type of mechanical receptor from the palps of the cockroach. *J. Exp. Biol.*, **15**, 101–13.

PRINGLE, J. W. S. (1938 b) Proprioception in insects. II. The action of the campaniform sensilla on the legs. *J. Exp. Biol.*, **15**, 114–31.

PRINGLE, J. W. S. (1938 c) Proprioception in insects. III. The function of the hair sensilla at the joints. *J. Exp. Biol.*, **15**, 467–73.

PRINGLE, J. W. S. (1940) The reflex mechanism of the insect leg. *J. Exp. Biol.*, **17**, 8–17.

PRINGLE, J. W. S. (1948) The gyroscopic mechanism of the halteres of Diptera. *Phil. Trans. Roy. Soc. London*, **233**, 347–84.

PRINGLE, J. W. S. (1950) The flight of insects. *School Sci. Rev.*, **31**, 364–9.

PRINGLE, J. W. S. (1957) *Insect Flight.* Cambridge Monographs in Experimental Biology, Cambridge Univ. Press, 132 pp.

PRINGLE, J. W. S., and WILSON, V. J. (1952) The response of a sense organ to a harmonic stimulus. *J. Exp. Biol.*, **29**, 220–34.

PUMPHREY, R. J. (1936) Slow adaptation of a tactile receptor in the leg of the common cockroach. *J. Physiol.*, **87**, 6P–7P.

PUMPHREY, R. J. (1940) Hearing in insects. *Biol. Rev.*, **15**, 107–32.

PUMPHREY, R. J. (1950) Hearing. In *Physiological Mechanisms in Animal Behaviour.* Academic Press, New York, pp. 1–18.

PUMPHREY, R. J., and RAWDON-SMITH, A. F. (1936 a) Synchronized action potentials in the cercal nerve of the cockroach (*Periplaneta americana*) in response to auditory stimuli. *J. Physiol.*, **87**, 4P–5P.

PUMPHREY, R. J., and RAWDON-SMITH, A. F. (1936 b) Sensitivity of insects to sound. *Nature*, **137**, 990.

PUMPHREY, R. J., and RAWDON-SMITH, A. F. (1936 c) Hearing in insects: The nature of the response of certain receptors to auditory stimuli. *Proc. Roy. Soc. Lond.*, B, **121**, 18–27.

PUMPHREY, R. J., and RAWDON-SMITH, A. F. (1939) Frequency discrimination in insects: A new theory. *Nature*, **143**, 806–7.

RABE, W. (1953) Beiträge zum Orientierungsproblem der Wasserwanzen. *Zeit. vergl. Physiol.*, **35**, 300–25.

RADL, E. (1905) Über das Gehor der Insekten. *Biol. Zbl.*, **25**, 1–5.

RAMSAY, J. A. (1935) Methods of measuring the evaporation of water from animals. *J. Exp. Biol.*, **12**, 355–72.

VOM RATH, O. (1888) Über die Hautsinnesorgane der Insekten. *Z. wiss. Zool.*, **46**, 413–54.

VOM RATH, O. (1895) Über die Nervenendigungen der Hautsinnesorgane der Arthropoden nach Behandlung mit der Methylenblau-u. Chromsilbermethode. *Berichte Naturforsch. Gesellschaft Freiburg. I. B.*, **9**, 137–64.

VOM RATH, O. (1896) Zur Kenntnis der Hautsinnesorgane und des sensiblen Nervensystems der Arthropoden. *Z. wiss. Zool.*, **61**, 499–539.

RAU, P. (1940) Auditory perception in insects, with special reference to the cockroach. *Quart. Rev. Biol.*, **15**, 121–55.

REDIKORZEW, W. (1900) Untersuchungen über den Bau der Ocellen der Insekten. *Zeit. wiss. Zool.*, **68**, 581–624.

REED, M. R. (1938) The olfactory responses of *Drosophila melanogaster* Meigen to the products of fermenting banana. *Physiol. Zool.*, **11**, 317–25.

REGEN, J. (1908) Das tympanale Sinnesorgan von Thamnotrizon apterus Fab. ♂ als Gehörapparat experimentelle nachgewiesen. *S. B. Math. Naturwiss. Akad. Wiss. Wien.*, **117**, 487–90.

REGEN, J. (1912) Experimentelle Untersuchungen über das Gehör von Liogryllus campestris L. *Zool. Anz.*, **40**, 305–16.

REGEN, J. (1913) Über die Anlockung des Weibchens von Gryllus campestris L. durch telephonisch übertragene Stridulationslaute des Männchens. *Pflüg. Arch. ges. Physiol.* (*Arkiv. ges. Physiol.*), **155**, 193–200.

REGEN, J. (1914 a) Untersuchungen über die Stridulation und das Gehör von Thamnotrizon apterus Fab. ♂. *Sitzungsberichte Math. -Naturwiss. Akad. Wiss. Wien.*, **123** (1), 853–92.

REGEN, J. (1914 b) Haben die Antennen für die alternierende Stridulation von Thamnotrizon apterus Fab. ♂ eine Bedeutung? *Pflüg. Archiv. ges. Physiol.*, **155**, 245–50.

REGEN, J. (1924) Über die Orientierung des Weibschens von *Liogryllus campestris* L. nach dem Stridulationsschall des Männchens. *Sitzber. Akad. Wiss. Wien.*, Abt. 1, **132**, 81–88.

REGEN, J. (1926) Über die Beeinflüssung der Stridulation von *Thamnotrizon apterus* Fab. ♂ durch künstlich erzeute Töne und verschiedenartige Gerärsche. *Sitzber. Akad. Wiss. Wien.*, Abt. 1, **135**, 329–68.

RESCH, B. (1954) Untersuchungen über das Farbensehen von *Notonecta glauca* L. *Zeit. vergl. Physiol.*, **36**, 27–40.

RICHARD, G. (1951) L'innervation et les organes sensoriels des pieces buccales du termite a cou jaune (*Calotermes flavicollis* Fab). *Ann. Des Sc. Nat. Zool.*, **13**, 397-412.

RICHARD, G. (1952) L'innervation sensorielle pendant des mues chez les insectes. *Bull. Soc. Zool. France*, **77**, 99–106.

RICHARD, G. (1956) Ontogénèse de l'Organe de Johnston chez divers insectes. *Tenth Internat. Congr. Ent.*, **1**, 523–4.

RICHARD, G. (1957) L'ontogénèse des organes chordotonaux antennaires de *Calotermes flavicollis* (Fab.). *Insectes Sociaux*, **4**, 107–11.

RICHARDS, A. G. (1951) *The Integument of Arthropods.* Univ. Minn. Press, Minneapolis, Minn.

RIEGERT, P. W. (1958) Humidity reactions of *Melanoplus bivittatus* (Say) and *Camnula pellucida* (Scudd.) (Orthoptera, Acrididae): Reactions of starved and of moulting grasshoppers. *Canad. Entomol.*, **90**, 680–4.

RIEGERT, P. W. (1959) Humidity reactions of Melanoplus bivittatus (Say) and Camnula pellucida (Scudd.) (Orthoptera, Acrididae): Reactions of normal grasshoppers. *Canad. Entomol.*, **91**, 35–40.

RIEGERT, P. W. (1960) The humidity reactions of Melanoplus bivittatus (Say) (Orthoptera, Acrididae): Antennal sensilla and hygroception. *Canad. Entomol.*, **92**, 561–70.

RITTER, E. (1936) Untersuchungen über chemischen Sinn beim schwarzen Kolbenwasserkäfer *Hydrous piceus. Zeit. vergl. Physiol.*, **23**, 543–70.

ROEDER, K. D. (1939) Synchronized activity in the optic and protocerebral ganglion of the grasshopper, Melanoplus femur-rubrum. *J. Cell. Comp. Physiol.*, **14**, 299–307.

ROEDER, K. D. (1940) The origin of visual rhythms in the grasshopper, Melanoplus femur-rubrum. *J. Cell. Comp. Physiol.*, **16**, 399–401.

ROEDER, K. D. (1948) Organization of the ascending giant fiber system in the cockroach (*Periplaneta americana*). *J. Exp. Zool.*, **108**, 342–62.

ROEDER, K. D. (1959) A physiological approach to the relation between prey and predator. *Smithson. Misc. Coll.*, **137**, 287–306.

ROEDER, K. D., and TREAT, A. E. (1957) Ultrasonic reception by the tympanic organ of noctuid moths. *J. Exp. Zool.*, **134**, 127–57.

ROEDER, K. D., and TREAT, A. E. (1961 a) The reception of bat cries by the tympanic organ of noctuid moths. In *Sensory Communication*, ed. W. Rosenblith, M. I. T. Technology Press.

ROEDER, K. D., and TREAT, A. E. (1961b) The detection and evasion of bats by moths. *Amer. Sci.*, **49**, 135–48.

ROGOSINA, M. (1928) Über das periphere Nervensystem der Aeschna-Larve. *Z. Zellforsch.*, **6**, 732–58.

RÖHLER, E. (1906) Beiträge zur Kenntnis der Sinnesorgane der Insekten. *Zool. Jahrb. Anat. Physiol.*, **22**, 225–88.

ROKOHL, R. (1942) Über die regionale Verschiedenheit der Farbentüchtigkeit in Zusammengesetzten Auge von Notonecta glauca *Zeit. vergl. Physiol.*, **29**, 538–76.

ROTH, L. M. (1948) A study of mosquito behavior. An experimental laboratory study of sexual behavior of Aedes aegypti (Linnaeus). *Amer. Midl. Nat.*, **40**, 265–352.

ROTH, L. M., and WILLIS, E. R. (1951a) Hygroreceptors in adults of Tribolium (Coleoptera, Tenebrionidae). *J. Exp. Zool.*, **116**, 527–70.

ROTH, L. M., and WILLIS, E. R. (1951b) Hygroreceptors in Coleoptera. *J. Exp. Zool.*, **117**, 451–88.

ROTH, L. M., and WILLIS, E. R. (1951c) The effects of desiccation and starvation on the humidity behavior and water balance of Tribolium confusum and Tribolium castaneum. *J. Exp. Zool.*, **118**, 337–62.

ROTH, L. M., and WILLIS, E. R. (1952) Possible hygroreceptors in Aedes aegypti (L.) and Blatella germanica L. *J. Morph.*, **91**, 1–14.

ROYS, C. (1954) Olfactory nerve potentials a direct measure of chemoreception in insects. *Ann. N.Y. Acad. Sci.*, **58**, 250–5.

RUCK, P. (1957) The electrical responses of dorsal ocelli in cockroaches and grasshoppers. *J. Ins. Physiol.*, **1**, 109–23.

RUCK, P. (1958 a) Dark adaptation of the ocellus in *Periplaneta americana*: A study of the electrical response to illumination. *J. Ins. Physiol.*, **2**, 189–98.

RUCK, P. (1958 b) A comparison of the electrical responses of compound eyes and dorsal ocelli in four insect species. *J. Ins. Physiol.*, **2**, 261–74.

RUCK, P. (1961a) Electrophysiology of the insect dorsal ocellus I.. Origin of the components of the electroretinogram. *J. Gen. Physiol.*, **44**, 605–27.

RUCK, P. (1961b) Electrophysiology of the insect dorsal ocellus. II. Mechanisms of generation and inhibition of impulses in the ocellar nerve of dragonflies. *J. Gen. Physiol.*, **44**, 629–39.

RUCK, P. (1961c) Electrophysiology of the insect dorsal ocellus. III. Responses to flickering light of the dragonfly ocellus. *J. Gen. Physiol.*, **44**, 641–57.

RUCK, P., and JAHN, T. L. (1954) Electrical studies on the compound eye of Ligia occidentalis dana (Crustacea: Isopoda). *J. Gen. Physiol.*, **37**, 825–49.

RUDERMAN, M. A., and ROSENFELD, A. H. (1960) An explanatory statement of elementary particle physics. *Am. Sci.*, **48** (2), 209–17.

SÄLZLE, K. (1932) Untersuchungen an Libellenlarven über das Sehen bewegter Objekte. *Zeit. vergl. Physiol.*, **18**, 345–68.

SANDER, W. (1933) Phototaktische Reaktionen der Bienen auf Lichter verschiedener Wellenlänge. *Zeit. vergl. Physiol.*, **20**, 267–86.

SATIJA, R. C. (1958 a) A histological and experimental study of nervous pathways in the brain and thoracic nerve cord of *Locusta migratoria migratorioides* (R. & F.). *Res. Bull. Panjab Univ.*, **138**, 13–32.

SATIJA, R. C. (1958 b) A histological study of the brain and thoracic cord of *Calliphora erythrocephala* with special reference to the descending nervous pathways. *Res. Bull. Panjab Univ.*, **142**, 81–98.

SCHALLER, A. (1926) Sinnesphysiologische und psychologische Untersuchungen an Wasserkäfern und Fischen. *Zeit. vergl. Physiol.*, **4**, 370–464.

SCHALLER, F. (1951) Lauterzeugung und Hörvermögen von Corixa (Callicorixa) striata L. *Zeit. vergl. Physiol.*, **33**, 476–86.

SCHALLER, F. (1960) Die optomotorische Komponente bei der Flugsteuerung der Insekten. *Zool. Beiträge* (*Neue Folge*) **5**, 483–96.

SCHALLER, F., and TIMM, C. (1950) Das Hörvermögen der Nachtschmetterlinge. *Zeit. vergl. Physiol.*, **32**, 468–81.

SCHANZ, M. (1953) Der Geruchssinn des Kartoffelkäfers. *Zeit. vergl. Physiol.*, **35**, 353–79.

SCHENK, O. (1903) Die antennalen Hautsinnesorgane einiger Lepidopteren und Hymenopteren mit besonderer Berücksichtigung der sexuellen Unterschiede. *Zool. Jahrb. Anat. Ontog.*, **17**, 573–618.

SCHLEGTENDAL, A. (1934) Beitrag zum Farbensinn der Arthropoden. *Zeit. vergl. Physiol.*, **20**, 545–81.

SCHLIEPER, C. (1927) Farbensinn der Tiere und optomotorische Reaktionen. *Zeit. vergl. Physiol.*, **6**, 453–72.

SCHMIDT, A. (1938) Geschmacksphysiologische Untersuchungen an Ameisen. *Zeit. vergl. Physiol.*, **25**, 351–78.

SCHNEIDER, D. (1955) Mikro-Elektroden registrieren die elektrischen Impulse einzelner Sinnesnervenzellen der Schmetterlingsantenne. *Industrie-Elektronik* (*Elektro-Spezial, Hamburg*), **3**, 3–7.

SCHNEIDER, D. (1957 a) Electrophysiological investigation on the antennal receptors of the Silk Moth during chemical and mechanical stimulation. *Experientia*, **13**, 89–91.

SCHNEIDER, D. (1957 b) Elektrophysiologische Untersuchungen von Chemo und Mechanorezeptoren der Antenne des Seidenspinners *Bombyx mori* L. *Zeit. vergl. Physiol.*, **40**, 8–41.

SCHNEIDER, D. (1961) The olfactory sense of insects. *Dragoco Report, Monthly Information Service, Gerberding & Co., Holzminden, West Germany*, **6**, 135–51.

SCHNEIDER, D. (1962) Electrophysiological investigation on the olfactory specificity of sexual attracting substances in different species of moths. *J. Ins. Physiol.*, **8**, 15–30.

SCHNEIDER, D., and HECKER, E. (1956) Elektrophysiologie der Antenne des Seidenspinners *Bombyx mori* bei Reizung mit angereicherten Extrakten des Sexuallockstoffes. *Zeit. Naturf.*, **11b**, 121–4.

SCHNEIDER, G. (1953) Die Halteren der Schmeissfliege (*Calliphora*) als Sinnesorgane und als mechanische Flugstabilisatoren. *Z. vergl. Physiol.*, **35**, 416–58.

SCHNEIDER, G. (1955) Die spektrale Empfindlichkeit des Rezeptors für das 'Dämmerungssehen' bei Calliphora. *Verhandl. Deut. Zool. Gesellschaft*, 1954, 346–51.

SCHNEIDER, G. (1956) Zur spektralen Empfindlichkeit des Komplexauges von Calliphora. *Zeit. vergl. Physiol.*, **39**, 1–20.

SCHNEIDER, W. (1950) Über den Erschütterungssinn von Käfern und Fliegen. *Zeit. vergl. Physiol.*, **32**, 287–302.

SCHÖN, A. (1911) Bau und Entwicklung des tibialen Chordotonalorgane bei der Honigbiene und bei Ameisen. *Zool. Jahrb. Anat.*, **31**, 439–72.

SCHÖNE, H. (1950) Die Augen als Gleichgewichtsorgane bei Wasserkäferlarven. *Naturwiss.*, **10**, 235–6.

SCHÖNE, H. (1953) Farbhelligkeit und Farbunterscheidung bei den Wasserkäfern *Dytiscus marginalis*, *Acilius sulcatus* und ihren larven. *Zeit. vergl. Physiol.*, **35**, 27–35.

SCHULTZE, M. (1868) *Untersuchungen über die Zusammenengesetzten Augen der Krebse und Insekten*. Bonn.

SCHUTZ, H. G., and PILGRIM, F. J. (1957) Differential sensitivity in gustation. *J. Exp. Psychol.*, **54**, 41–48.

SCHWABE, J. (1906) Beiträge zur Morphologie und Histologie der tympanalen Sinnesapparate der Orthoptera. *Zoologica, Stuttgart*, **20**, 1–154.

SCHWARZ, R. (1955) Über die Riechschärfe der Honigbiene. *Zeit. vergl. Physiol.*, **37**, 180–210.

SIEBOLD, T. (1844) Über das Stimm-und Gehörorgan der Orthoptera. *Wiegmanns Arch. Naturg.*, *Jahrg.*, **10**, 52–81.

SIHLER, H. (1924) Die Sinnesorgane an den Cerci der Insekten. *Zool. Jahrb. Anat.*, **45**, 519–80.

SLIFER, E. H. (1935) Morphology and development of the femoral chordotonal organs of Melanoplus differentialis (Orthoptera, Acrididae). *J. Morph.*, **58**, 615–37.

SLIFER, E. H. (1961) The fine structure of insect sense organs. *International Review of Cytology*, **2**, 125–59.

SLIFER, E. H., and FINLAYSON, L. H. (1956) Muscle receptor organs in grasshoppers and locusts (Orthoptera, Acrididae). *Quart. J. Micr. Sci.*, **97**, 617–20.

SLIFER, E. H., PRESTAGE, J. J., and BEAMS, H. W. (1957) The fine structure of the long basiconic sensory pegs of the grasshopper (Orthoptera, Acrididae) with special reference to those on the antenna. *J. Morph.*, **101**, 359–96.

SLIFER, E. H., PRESTAGE, J. J., and BEAMS, H. W. (1959) The chemoreceptors and other sense organs on the antennal flagellum of the grasshopper (Orthoptera; Acrididae). *J. Morph.*, **105**, 145–91.

SMITH, F. E., and BAYLOR, E. R. (1960) Bees, *Daphnia* and polarized light. *Ecology*, **41**, 360–3.

SMITH, M. H., and LICKLIDER, J. C. R. (1949) Statistical bias in comparisons of monaural and binaural thresholds: binaural summation or binaural supplementation. *Psychol. Bull.*, **46**, 278–84.

SMYTH, T., and ROYS, C. C. (1954) Chemoreception in insects and the action of DDT. *Biol. Bull.*, **108**, 66–76.

SNODGRASS, R. E. (1926) The morphology of insect sense organs and the sensory nervous system. *Smithson. Misc. Coll.*, **77** (8), 1–80.

SNODGRASS, R. E. (1935) *Principles of Insect Morphology*. McGraw-Hill, N.Y.

SNODGRASS, R. E. (1956) *Anatomy of the Honey Bee*. Cornell Univ. Press, Ithaca, N.Y.

SOTAVALTA, O. (1954) Preliminary observations on sensory impulses from insect wing nerves. *Suomen Hyonteistieteellinen Aikakaus Kirja* (*Ann. Ent. Fenn.*), **20**, 148–50.

SPEYER, E. R. (1920) Notes on the chemotropism in the house-fly. *Ann. Applied Biol.*, **7**, 124–40.

STEINER, G. (1942) Behaviour of the red-legged earth mite, Halotydens destructor, in relation to environmental conditions. *J. Anim. Ecol.*, **6**, 340–61.

STEPHENS, G. C., FINGERMAN, M., and BROWN, F. A. (1953) The orientation of *Drosophila melanogaster* to plane polarized light. *Ann. Ent. Soc. Amer.*, **46**, 75–83.

STOBBE, R. (1911) Ueber das abdominale Sinnesorgan und über den Gehörsinn der Lepidopteren mit besonderer Berücksichtigung der Noctuiden. *S. B. Ges. naturf. Fr. Berl.*, 93–105.

STOCKHAMMER, K. (1956) Zur Wahrnehmung der Schwingungsrichtung linear polarisierten Lichtes bei Insekten. *Zeit. vergl. Physiol.*, **38**, 30–83.

STOCKHAMMER, K. (1959) Die Orientierung nach der Schwingungsrichtung linear polarisierten Lichtes und ihre sinnesphysiologischen Grundlagen. *Ergeb. Biol.*, **21**, 23–56.

STUDNITZ, G. (1932) Die statische Funktion der sog. 'pelotaktischen' Organe ('Schlammisinnesorgane') der Limnobiidenlarven. *Zool. Jahrb. abt. Zool. Physiol. Tiere*, **50**, 419–46.

STÜRCKOW, B. (1959) Über den Geschmackssin und den Tastsinn von *Leptinotarsa decemlineata* Say (Chrysomelidae). *Zeit. vergl. Physiol.*, **42**, 255–302.

STÜRCKOW, B. (1960) Elektrophysiologische Untersuchungen am Chemoreceptors von *Calliphora erythrocephala*. *Zeit. vergl. Physiol.*, **43**, 141–8.

SUGA, N., and KATSUKI, Y. (1961) Central mechanism of hearing in insects. *J. Exp. Biol.*, **38**, 545–58.

SWINTON, A. (1877) On an organ of hearing in insects, with special reference to the Lepidoptera. *Ent. Monthly Mag.*, **14**, 121–6.

SYRJÄMÄKI, J. (1962) Humidity perception in Drosophila melanogaster. *Ann. Zool. Soc. 'Vanamo'*, **23**, 1–72.

TAKEDA, K. (1961) The nature of impulses of single tarsal chemoreceptors in the butterfly, *Vanessa indica*. *J. Cell. Comp. Physiol.*, **58**, 233–44.

TATEDA, H., and MORITA, H. (1959) Initiation of spike potentials in contact chemosensory hairs of insects. I. Generating site of the recorded spike potentials. *J. Cell. Comp. Physiol.*, **54**, 171–6.

TAYLOR, I. R., and CRESCITELLI, F. (1944) The electrical changes in response to illumination of the dark- and light-adapted eye of Dissosteira carolina. *Physiol. Zool.*, **17**, 193–9.

TAYLOR, I. R., and NICKERSON, M. (1943) Features of the electrical responses of the bee-moth eye. *Physiol. Zool.*, **16**, 213–22.

TAYLOR, N. W., FARTHING, F. R., and BERMAN, R. (1930) Quantitative measurements on the acid taste and their bearing on the nature of the nerve receptor. *Protoplasma*, **10**, 84–97.

THOMPSON, D. W. (1943) *On Growth and Form*. Cambridge University Press, Cambridge, p. 52.

THOMSON, R. C. M. (1938) The reactions of mosquitoes to temperature and humidity. *Bull. Ent. Res.*, **29**, 125–40.

THORNTHWAITE, C. W. (1940) Atmospheric moisture in relation to ecological problems. *Ecology*, **21**, 17–28.

THORPE, W. H., and CRISP, D. J. (1947) Studies on plastron respiration. III. The orientation responses of *Aphelocheirus* [Hemiptera, Aphelocheiridae (Naucoridae)] in relation to plastron respiration; together with an account of specialized pressure receptors in aquatic insects. *J. Exp. Biol.*, **24**, 310–28.

THORPE, W. H., CROMBIE, A. C., HILL, R., and DARRAH, J. H. (1947) The behaviour of wireworms in response to chemical stimulation. *J. Exp. Biol.*, **23**, 234–66.

TISCHNER, H. (1953) Über den Gehörsinn der Stechmücken. *Acustica*, **3**, 335–43.

TONNER, F. (1938) Halsreflexe und Bewegungssehen bei Arthropoden. *Zeit. vergl. Physiol.*, **25**, 427–54.

TREAT, A. E. (1955) The response to sound in certain Lepidoptera. *Ann. Ent. Soc. Amer.*, **48**, 272–84.

TREAT, A. E. (1959) The metathoracic musculature of Crymodes devastator (Brace) (Noctuidae) with special reference to the tympanic organ. *Smithson. Misc. Coll.*, **137**, 365–78.

TREAT, A. E., and ROEDER, K. D. (1959) A nervous element of unknown function in the tympanic organs of moths. *J. Ins. Physiol.*, **3**, 262–70.

TURNER, C. H. (1914) An experimental study of the auditory powers of the giant silkworm moths (Saturniidae). *Biol. Bull.*, **27**, 325–32.

TURNER, C. H., and SCHWARZ, E. (1914) Auditory powers of the Catocala moths; an experimental field study. *Biol. Bull.*, **27**, 275–93.

UCHIYAMA, H., and KATSUKI, Y. (1956) Recording of action potentials from the antenneal nerve of locusts by means of microelectrodes. *Physiol. Comp. Oecol.*, **4**, 154–63.

URVOY, J. (1958) Ontogenese de l'organe de Johnston chez les phasmides. *Ann. Sci. Nat., Zool.*, **11**, 183–95.

VERLAINE, L. (1927) Le determinisme du deroulement de la trompe et la physiologie du gout chez les lepidopteres (Pieris rapae Linn.). *Ann. Bull. Soc. Ent. Belg.*, **67**, 147–82.

VIALLANES, H. (1884) Le ganglion optique de la Libellule (Aeschna maculatissima). *Ann. Sci. Nat. Zool., Paris*, **18**, 1–34.

VOGEL, B. (1931) Über die Beziehungen zwischen Süssgeschmack und Nährwert von Zuckern und Zuckeralkoholen bei der honigbiene. *Zeit. vergl. Physiol.*, **14**, 273–347.

VOGEL, R. (1911) Über die Innervierung der Schmetterlingsflügel und über den Bau und die Verbreitung der Sinnesorgane auf denselben. *Z. wiss. Zool.*, **98**, 68–134.

VOGEL, R. (1912) Über die Chordotonalorgane in der Wurzel der Schmetterlingsflügel. *Zeit. wiss. Zool.*, **100**, 210–44.

VOGEL, R. (1921) Zur Kenntnis der Geruchsorgane der Wespen und Bienen. *Zool. Anz.*, **53**, 20–28.

VOGEL, R. (1923 a) Über ein tympanales Sinnesorgan, das mutmassliche Hörorgan der Singzikaden. *Zeit. Anat. Entwicklungsg.*, **67**, 190–231.

VOGEL, R. (1923 b) Zur Kenntnis des feineren Baues der Geruchsorgane der Wespen und Bienen. *Zeit. wiss. Zool.*, **120**, 281–324.

VOWLES, D. M. (1950) Sensitivity of ants to polarized light. *Nature*, **165**, 282–3.

VOWLES, D. M. (1954) The orientation of ants. II. Orientation to light, gravity and polarized light. *J. Exp. Biol.*, **31**, 365–75.

DE VRIES, H. (1956) Physical aspects of the sense organs. *Progress in Biophysics and Biophysical Chemistry*, **6**, 207–64.

DE VRIES, H., and KUIPER, J. W. (1958) Optics of the insect eye. *Ann. N.Y. Acad. Sci.*, **74**, 196–203.

DE VRIES, H. L., SPOOR, A., and JIELOF, R. (1953) Properties of the eye with respect to polarized light. *Physica*, **19**, 419–32.

WALD, G., and BURG, S. P. (1957) The vitamin A of the lobster. *J. Gen. Physiol.*, **40**, 609–25.

WALTHER, J. B. (1958 a) Untersuchungen am Belichtungspotential des Komplexauges von *Periplaneta* mit farbigen Reizen und selektive Adaptation. *Biol. Zbl.*, **77**, 63–104.

WALTHER, J. B. (1958 b) Changes induced in spectral sensitivity and form of retinal action potential of the cockroach eye by selective adaptation. *J. Ins. Physiol.*, **2**, 142–51.

WALTHER, J. B., and DODT, E. (1957) Elektrophysiologische Untersuchungen über die Ultraviolettempfindlichkeit von Insektenaugen. *Experientia*, **13**, 333.

WALTHER, J. B., and DODT, E. (1959) Die Spektralsensitivität von Insekten-Komplexaugen im Ultraviolett bis 290 mμ. *Zeit. Naturf.*, **14b**, 273–8.

WARNKE, G. (1931) Experimentelle Untersuchungen über den Geruchssinn von *Geotrupes sylvaticus* Panz. und *Geotrupes vernalis* Lin. *Zeit. vergl. Physiol.*, **14**, 121–99.

WARNKE, G. (1934) Die Geruchsorgane der Lamellikornier. *Zool. Anz.*, **108**, 217–24.

WATERMAN, T. H. (1954 a) Directional sensitivity of single ommatidia in the compound eye of Limulus. *Proc. Nat. Acad. Sci.*, **40**, 252–7.

WATERMAN, T. H. (1954 b) Polarized light and angle of stimulus incidence in the compound eye of Limulus. *Proc. Nat. Acad. Sci.*, **40**, 258–62.

WATERMAN, T. H. (1960) Light sensitivity and vision. In *Physiology of Crustacea*, ed. T. H. Waterman. Academic Press, New York, vol 2, 1–64.

WEBB, C. S. (1953) *A Wanderer in the Wind.* Hutchinson, London, p. 125.

WEFELSCHEID, H. (1912) Über die Biologie und Anatomie von Plea minutissima Leach. *Zool. Jahr. Syst.*, **32**, 389–474.

WEIS, I. (1930) Versuche über die Geschmackrezeption durch die Tarsen die Admirals, *Pyrameis atalanta* L. *Zeit. vergl. Physiol.*, **12**, 206–46.

WEIS-FOGH, T. (1949) An aerodynamic sense-organ stimulating and regulating flight in locusts. *Nature*, **164**, 873–4.

WEIS-FOGH, T. (1950) An aerodynamic sense organ in locusts. *8th Internat. Congress, Entomol.*, pp. 1–5.

WEIS-FOGH, T. (1956) Biology and physics of locust flight. IV. Notes on sensory mechanisms in locust flight. *Phil. Trans. Roy. Soc. Lond.*, B, **239**, 553–84.

WEISS, H. B. (1943 a) Color perception in insects. *J. Econ. Ent.*, **36**, 1–17.

WEISS, H. B. (1934 b) The group behavior of 14,000 insects to colors. *Ent. News*, **54**, 152–6.

WEISS, H. B. (1944) Insect responses to colors. *J. N.Y. Ent. Soc.*, **52**, 267–71.

WEISS, H. B. (1946) Insects and the spectrum. *J. N.Y. Ent. Soc.*, **54**, 17–30.

WEISS, H. B., McCOY, E. E., and BOYD, W. M. (1944) Group motor responses of adult and larval forms of insects to different wave-lengths of light. *J. N.Y. Ent. Soc.*, **52**, 27–43.

WEISS, H. B., SORACI, F. A., and McCOY, E. E. (1941) Notes on the reactions of certain insects to different wave-lengths of light. *J. N. Y. Ent. Soc.*, **49**, 1–20.

WEISS, H. B., SORACI, F. A., and McCOY, E. E. (1942) The behavior of certain insects to various wave-lengths of light. *J. N.Y. Ent. Soc.*, **50**, 1–35.

WEISS, H. B., SORACI, F. A., and McCOY, E. E. (1943) Insect behavior to various wave-lengths of lights. *J. N.Y. Ent. Soc.*, **50**, 117–31.

WELLINGTON, W. G. (1949) The effects of temperature and moisture upon the behaviour of the spruce bidworm, *Choristoneura fumiferana* Clemens (Lepidoptera: Tortricidae). *Sci. Agric.*, **29**, 201–29.

WELLINGTON, W. G. (1953) Motor responses evoked by the dorsal ocelli of *Sarcophaga aldrichi* Parker, and the orientation of the fly to plane polarized light. *Nature*, **172**, 1177–9.

WELLINGTON, W. G., SULLIVAN, C. R., and GREEN, G. W. (1957) Polarized light and body temperature level as orientation factors in the light reactions of some hymenopterous and lepidopterous larvae. *Canad. J. Zool.*, **29**, 339–51.

WEVER, E. G. (1935) A study of hearing in the sulphur-winged grasshopper (*Arphia sulphurea*). *J. Comp. Psychol.*, **20**, 17–20.

WEVER, E. G., and BRAY, C. W. (1933) A new method for the study of hearing in insects. *J. Cell. Comp. Physiol.*, **4**, 79–93.

WHITE, F. B. (1877) (Untitled communications.) *Nature*, **15**, 293.

WIERSMA, C. A. G. (1952) The neuron soma. Neurons of Arthropods. *Cold Spring Harbor Symposia in Quantitative Biology*, **17**, 155–63.

WIETING, J. O. G., and HOSKINS, W. M. (1939) The olfactory responses of flies in a new type of insect olfactometer. *J. Econ. Ent.*, **32**, 24–29.

WIGGLESWORTH, V. B. (1933) The physiology of the cuticle and of ecdysis in *Rhodnius prolixus* (Triatomidae, Hemiptera); with special reference to the function of the oenocytes and of the dermal glands. *Quart. J. Micr. Sci.*, **76**, 269–318.

WIGGLESWORTH, V. B. (1941) The sensory physiology of the human louse *Pediculus humanis corporis* De Geer (Anoplura). *Parasitol*, **33**, 67–109.

WIGGLESWORTH, V. B. (1949) The utilization of reserve substances in *Drosophila* during flight. *J. Exp. Biol.*, **26**, 150–163.

WIGGLESWORTH, V. B. (1953) The origin of sensory neurones in an insect, *Rhodnius prolixus* (Hemiptera). *Quart. J. Micr. Sci.*, **94**, 93–112.

WIGGLESWORTH, V. B. (1959) The histology of the nervous system of an insect, *Rhodnius prolixus* (Hemiptera). I. The peripheral nervous system. *Quart. J. Micr. Sci.*, **100**, 285–98.

WILLIS, E. R., and ROTH, L. M. (1950) Humidity reactions of Tribolium cartaneum (Herbst). *J. Exp. Zool.*, **115**, 561–88.

WILSON, D. M. (1961) The central nervous control of flight in a locust. *J. Exp. Biol.*, **38**, 471–90.

WIRTH, W. (1928) Untersuchungen über Reizschwellenwerte von Geruchsstoffen bei Insekten. *Biol. Zbl.*, **48**, 567–76.

WOLBARSHT, M. L. (1957) Water taste in Phormia. *Science*, **125**, 1248.

WOLBARSHT, M. L. (1958) Electrical activity in the chemoreceptors of the blowfly. II. Responses to electrical stimulation. *J. Gen. Physiol.*, **42**, 413–28.

WOLBARSHT, M. L. (1960) Electrical characteristics of insect mechanoreceptors. *J. Gen. Physiol.*, **44**, 105–22.

WOLBARSHT, M. L., and DETHIER, V. G. (1958) Electrical activity in the chemoreceptors of the blowfly. I. Responses to chemical and mechanical stimulation. *J. Gen. Physiol.*, **42**, 393–412.

WOLF, E. (1933 a) The visual intensity discrimination of the honey bee. *J. Gen. Physiol.*, **16**, 407–22.

WOLF, E. (1933 b) On the relation between measurements of intensity discrimination and of visual acuity in the honey bee. *J. Gen. Physiol.*, **16**, 773–86.

WOLF, E. (1933 c) Das Verhalten der Bienen gegenüber flimmernden Feldern und bewegten Objeckten. *Zeit. vergl. Physiol.*, **20**, 151–61.

WOLF, E. (1933 e) Critical frequency of flicker as a function of intensity of illumination for the eye of the bee. *J. Gen. Physiol.*, **17**, 7–19.

WOLF, E. (1935) An analysis of the visual capacity of the bee's eye. *Cold Spring Harbor Symposia on Quantitative Biol.*, **2**, 255–60.

WOLF, E. (1942) Spatial relations of ommatidia in insects and differential sensitivity to moving visual stimuli. *Anat. Rec.*, **84**, 469–70.

WOLF, E., and ZERRAHN-WOLF, G. (1935 a) The dark adaptation of the eye of the honey bee. *J. Gen. Physiol.*, **19**, 299–337.

WOLF, E., and ZERRAHN-WOLF, G. (1935 b) The effect of light intensity, area, and flicker frequency on the visual reactions of the honey bee. *J. Gen. Physiol.*, **18**, 853–64.

WOLF, E., and ZERRAHN-WOLF, G. (1935 c) The validity of Talbot's law for the eye of the honey bee. *J. Gen. Physiol.*, **20**, 865–8.

WOLF, E., and ZERRAHN-WOLF, G. (1937) Flicker and the reactions of bees to flowers. *J. Gen. Physiol.*, **20**, 511–17.

WOLFF, B. (1922) Schlammsinnesorgane (pelotaktische Organe) bei Limnobiinenlarven. *Jena. Z. Naturw.*, **58**, 77–144.

WOLKEN, J. J. (1957) A comparative study of photoreceptors. *Trans. N.Y. Acad. Sci.*, **19**, 315–27.

WOLKEN, J. J., CAPENOS, J., and TURANO, A. (1957) Photoreceptor structures. III. Drosophila melanogaster. *J. Biophys. Biochem. Cytol.*, **3**, 441–8.

WOLKEN, J. J., MELLON, A. D., and CONTIS, G. (1957) Photoreceptor structures. II. Drosophila melanogaster. *J. Exp. Zool.*, **134**, 383–410.

WOLSKY, A. (1930) Optische Untersuchungen über die Bedeutung und Funktion der Insektenocellen. *Zeit. vergl. Physiol.*, **12**, 783–7.

WOLSKY, A. (1931) Weitere Beiträge zum Ocellenproblem. Die optischen Verhaltniesse der Ocellen der Honigbiene (*Apis mellifica* L.). *Zeit. vergl. Physiol.*, **14**, 385–91.

WOLSKY, A. (1933) Stimulationsorgane. *Biol. Rev.*, **8**, 370–417.

WULFF, V. J. (1943) Correlation of photochemical events with the action potential of the retina. *J. Cell. Comp. Physiol.*, **21**, 319–26.

WULFF, V. J. (1950) Duality in the electrical response of the lateral eye of Limulus polyphemus. *Biol. Bull.*, **98**, 258–65.

WULFF, V. J. (1956) Physiology of the compound eye. *Physiol. Rev.*, **36**, 145–63.

WULFF, V. J., FRY, W. L., and LINDE, F. A. (1955) Retinal action potential-theory and experimental results for grasshopper eyes. *J. Cell. Comp. Physiol.*, **45**, 247–63.

WULFF, V. J., and JAHN, T. L. (1943) Intensity–EMF relationships of the electroretinogram of beetles possessing a visual diurnal rhythm. *J. Cell. Comp. Physiol.*, **22**, 89–94.

YAGI, N., and TAGUTI, R. (1941) Note on the reactions of *Culex pipiens* Coquillet to the sound of 217 cycles. *Proc. Imperial Acad. Tokyo*, **17**, 160–1.

ZÁCWILICHOWSKI, J. (1936) Über die Innervierung und Sinnesorgane der Flügel der Aflerfrühlingsfliege *Isopteryx tripunctata* Scop. (Plecoptera). *Bull. Inst. Acad. Cracevie* (*Acad. Pol. Sci.*), **BII**, 267–84 (and earlier papers in this series).

ZAWARZIN, A. (1912 a) Histologische Studien über Insekten. II. Des sensible Nervensystem der Aeschnalarven. *Z. wiss. Zool.*, **100**, 245–86.

ZAWARZIN, A. (1912 b) Histologische Studien über Insekten. III. Über das sensible Nervensystem der Larven von Melolontha vulgaris. *Z. wiss. Zool.*, **100**, 447–58.

ZAWARZIN, A. (1914) Histologische Studien uber Insekten. IV. Die optischen Ganglion der Aeschna-Larven. *Zeit. wiss. Zool.*, **108**, 175–257.

ZERRAHN, B. (1933) Formdressur und Formunterscheidung bei der Honigbiene. *Zeit. vergl. Physiol.*, **20**, 117–50.

Author Index

Subject Index

26